11·9.9

Basic Mathematics Skills:

Revision and Practice

A. Ledsham and M. E. Wardle

OXFORD

OXFORD
UNIVERSITY PRESS

Great Clarendon Street, Oxford OX2 6DP

Oxford University Press is a department of the University of Oxford.
It furthers the University's objective of excellence in research, scholarship,
and education by publishing worldwide in

Oxford   New York

Auckland   Bangkok   Buenos Aires   Cape Town   Chennai
Dar es Salaam   Delhi   Hong Kong   Istanbul   Karachi   Kolkata
Kuala Lumpur   Madrid   Melbourne   Mexico City   Mumbai   Nairobi
São Paulo   Shanghai   Taipei   Tokyo   Toronto

Oxford is a registered trade mark of Oxford University Press
in the UK and in certain other countries

© Oxford University Press
First published 1998
Reprinted 2003 (with corrections)

ISBN 0 19 914704 3   School and College edition
ISBN 0 19 914725 6   Bookshop edition

A CIP catalogue record for this book is available from the
British Library.

Typeset and illustrated by Moondisks Ltd, Cambridge.
Printed and bound in Great Britain by
Butler & Tanner Ltd, Frome and London

Preface

Basic Mathematics Skills has been written to provide a sound foundation in the basic mathematical skills of number, measures and data handling. It is specifically aimed at those students who wish to develop the numeracy skills that are particularly applicable to everyday life.

The book will be especially useful for students who are working towards the City and Guilds Numeracy (Numberpower) Certificates, the RSA Basic Numerical Skills and Numeracy Examinations, or any of the other basic certificates for achievement in numeracy.

Each topic is introduced with a mixture of teaching and worked examples. The exercises which follow are carefully structured to enable students to work through at their own pace and develop confidence. These exercises will also be useful for revision.

The final section of the book relates the mathematical skills learnt earlier to everday situations. The topics covered include such things as household bills, leisure, personal finance and DIY.

We are both experienced teachers, writers and textbook authors. The essence of our approach is, as ever, simplicity and directness.

Alf Ledsham and Michael Wardle
January 1998

CONTENTS

List of mathematical abbreviations and symbols

C	Celsius	kg	kilogram	mph	miles per hour	+	plus; add
cl	centilitre	km	kilometre	O	origin; centre of circle	−	minus; subtract
cm	centimetre	kph	kilometres per hour	p	penny	×	times; multiply
cwt	hundredweight	kpl	kilometres per litre	pt	pint	÷ or /	share; divide
F	Fahrenheit	l	litre	qt	quart	a/b or $\frac{a}{b}$	fraction
ft	foot	lb	pound	rpm	revolutions per minute	:	ratio
g	gram	m	metre	s	second	%	percentage
h	hour	ml	millilitre	sec	second	=	equals
ha	hectare	mm	millimetre	sq	square	(,)	coordinates
hr	hour	min	minute	VAT	value-added tax	'	foot
in	inch	mpg	miles per gallon	yd	yard	"	inch

Table of common imperial and metric units of measure and conversions

	Imperial measures	**Metric measures**
Length	1 mile = 1760 yards = 5280 feet	1 kilometre = 1000 metres = 1 000 000 millimetres
	1 yard = 3 feet = 36 inches	1 metre = 100 centimetres = 1000 millimetres
	1 foot = 12 inches	1 centimetre = 10 millimetres
	1 mile = 1.6093 kilometres	1 kilometre = 0.6214 miles (8 kilometres ≈ 5 miles)
	1 yard = 0.9144 metres	1 metre = 1.0904 yards (1 metre ≈ 39 inches)
	1 foot = 30.48 centimetres	1 metre = 3.281 ft
	1 inch = 2.54 centimetres	1 centimetre = 0.3937 inches (10 centimetres ≈ 4 inches)
Area	1 square mile = 640 acres	1 square kilometre = 100 hectares = 1 000 000 square metres
	1 acre = 4840 square yards	1 hectare = 10 000 square metres
	1 square yard = 9 square feet	1 square metre = 10 000 square centimetres
	1 square foot = 144 square inches	1 square centimetre = 100 square millimetres
	1 square mile = 2.59 square kilometres	1 square kilometre = 0.386 square miles
	1 acre = 0.405 hectares	1 hectare = 2.457 acres
	1 square yard = 0.836 square metres	1 square metre = 1.189 square yards
	1 square inch = 6.452 square centimetres	1 square centimetre = 0.155 square inches
Volume	1 cubic yard = 27 cubic feet	1 cubic metre = 1 000 000 cubic centimetres
	1 cubic foot = 1728 cubic inches	1 cubic centimetre = 1000 cubic millimetres
	1 cubic yard = 0.765 cubic metres	1 cubic metre = 1.308 cubic yards
Capacity	1 gallon = 4 quarts = 8 pints	1 litre = 1000 millilitres = 1000 cubic centimetres
	1 quart = 2 pints	1 millilitre = 1 cubic centimetre
	1 gallon = 4.546 litres	1 litre = 0.220 gallons (4.5 litres ≈ 1 gallon)
	1 pint = 0.568 litres	1 litre = 1.761 pints (1 litre ≈ 1.75 pints)
Mass	1 ton = 20 hundredweight = 2240 pounds	1 tonne = 1000 kilograms = 1 000 000 grams
		1 kilogram = 1000 grams
	1 hundredweight = 112 pounds	
	1 stone = 14 pounds	1 cubic centimetre of water has a mass of 1 gram
	1 pound = 16 ounces	1 litre of water has a mass of 1 kilogram
	1 ton = 1.0159 tonnes	1 tonne = 2205 pounds (1000 kilograms = 1 ton)
	1 pound = 0.4536 kilograms	1 kilogram = 2.205 pounds (1 kilogram ≈ 2.2 pounds)
	1 ounce = 28.35 grams	1 gram = 0.0353 ounces (100 grams ≈ 4 ounces)
	1 gallon of water has a mass of about 10 pounds or 4.5 kilograms	

1 UNDERSTANDING NUMBERS

1.1 Counting and recording numbers

From the earliest of times people wanted to count and record how many possessions they had. Shepherds used a very crude method to record the number of sheep that they had. They simply cut a notch in their sticks to represent each sheep.

One sheep   Two sheep   Three sheep

This method was fine for small numbers of sheep, but it had to be improved on for larger numbers.

Later, words, and then symbols, were used to describe each of the numbers and as a result most countries in the world (except for China) use the Arabic system; this system has the symbol 0 for nought, and combinations of the ten symbols 0, 1, 2, 3, 4, 5, 6, 7, 8 and 9 can be used to record any number.

We actually use different names for each of the numbers up to twenty, and thereafter combinations of the names previously used. These are shown in the table on the next page.

Number	Mark on a stick	Arabic symbol	Name
•		1	One
••		2	Two
•••		3	Three
•• ••		4	Four
•• • ••		5	Five
••• •••		6	Six
••• • •••		7	Seven
••• •• •••		8	Eight
••• ••• •••		9	Nine

Number	Number name	Arabic symbol	Notes
	Ten	10	Ten
	Eleven	11	Ten plus one
	Twelve	12	Ten plus two
	Thirteen	13	Ten plus three
	Fourteen	14	Ten plus four
	Fifteen	15	Ten plus five
	Sixteen	16	Ten plus six
	Seventeen	17	Ten plus seven
	Eighteen	18	Ten plus eight
	Nineteen	19	Ten plus nine
	Twenty	20	Two tens
	Twenty-one	21	Two tens plus one

Then we use twenty-two (22), twenty-three (23), and so on.

We can use 30, 40, 50 etc., to represent three tens (thirty), four tens (forty), five tens (fifty), and so on until we get to ten tens, which we call one hundred and represent as 100.

Example 1

Write each of these numbers in: **a** words   **b** the Arabic system.

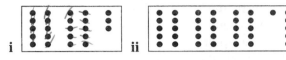

i   **a** two tens and three, i.e. twenty-three   **b** 23
ii **a** three tens and six, i.e. thirty-six   **b** 36
iii **a** six tens and nine, i.e. sixty-nine   **b** 69

Exercise 1A

Write each of these numbers in: **a** words,   **b** the Arabic system.

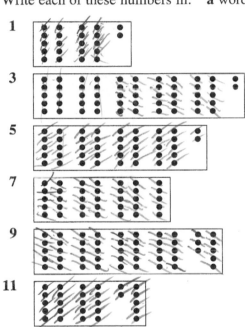

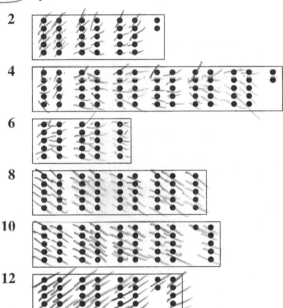

Example 2

Record each of the following numbers using the Arabic system.

a two hundred   **b** three hundred and fifty   **c** six hundred and eighty-seven
d forty-four   **e** one hundred and ninety

a 200   **b** 350   **c** 687   **d** 44   **e** 190

Exercise 1B

Record each of the following numbers using the Arabic system.

1	three hundred	**2**	three hundred and thirty
3	three hundred and thirty-two	**4**	two hundred and twenty
5	two hundred and twenty-eight	**6**	five hundred
7	five hundred and ten	**8**	five hundred and fifteen
9	seven hundred	**10**	seven hundred and ninety

1.2   Reading, writing and ordering whole numbers

Our number system uses the idea of **place value** where the actual value of the number symbol depends on its place in the number.

The number 152 is made up like this:

1	5	2
number of hundreds	number of tens	number of units

This means one hundred and five tens and two units. Five tens is called 'fifty' so the number is written in words as one hundred and fifty-two.

The number represented by 215 is:

2	1	5
number of hundreds	number of tens	number of units

This means two hundreds and one ten and five units. One ten and five units is fifteen, so the number is written as two hundred and fifteen.

Further examples are:
- 235, which is two hundreds, three tens and five units. This is written as two hundred and thirty-five.
- 205, which is two hundreds, no tens and five units. This is written as two hundred and five. (The zero is not mentioned in words.)
- 230, two hundreds, three tens and no units. This is written as two hundred and thirty. (Again, the zero is not mentioned in words.)

Exercise 1C

Write each of the following numbers in words.

	a	**b**	**c**	**d**	**e**	**f**
1	18	13	15	19	12	
2	24	28	34	38	45	49
3	68	62	77	92	90	60
4	540	590	593	750	759	
5	800	810	815	803	808	
6	230	238	538	508		

7   The River Severn is 334 km long.   **8**   Loch Lomond is 189 m deep.

Exercise 1D

Write each of the following numbers in figures.

1 **a** seventeen **b** fifteen **c** sixteen **d** fourteen **e** eleven
2 **a** twenty-six **b** twenty-five **c** twenty-nine **d** thirty-two **e** thirty-seven
3 **a** eighty **b** seventy **c** forty
4 three hundred and fifty-seven   5 three hundred and sixty-five
6 seven hundred and thirty-six   7 seven hundred and ninety-two
8 six hundred and fifty   9 six hundred and thirty
10 four hundred and eight
11 The distance from London to Dundee is seven hundred and twenty-six kilometres.
12 The planet Venus takes two hundred and twenty-five days to orbit around the Sun.

Place value

The place value of any figure in a number can easily be found.

The place value of each figure in the number 453 is worked out as:

Hundreds	Tens	Units
4	5	3

The place value of the four is four hundreds or 400.
The place value of the five is five tens or 50.
The place value of the three is three units or 3.

Exercise 1E

Give the place value of the underlined figure.

1 1<u>4</u>   2 1<u>5</u>   3 1<u>9</u>   4 28<u>3</u>
5 <u>5</u>32   6 3<u>5</u>6   7 3<u>9</u>4   8 43<u>5</u>
9 5<u>6</u>0   10 51<u>8</u>   11 <u>8</u>00   12 <u>9</u>03
13 <u>5</u>70   14 <u>8</u>08   15 1<u>9</u>   16 <u>3</u>6

The place value of figures can be used to arrange numbers in order of size.
The example below shows how this is done.

Example 3

Arrange these numbers in order of size, starting with the largest:

302   203   230   320

Put the largest figure first, followed by the next largest, and so on.
Work down through the hundreds, then down through the tens and units, and so on.

The order is:

320   (three hundreds, two tens and no units)
302   (three hundreds, no tens and two units)
230   (two hundreds, three tens and no units)
203   (two hundreds, no tens and three units)

Exercise 1F

Arrange these numbers in order of size starting with the largest.

1 890   809   980   908   **2**   760   607   706   670
3 675   567   765   657   756   576   **4**   435   534   345   354   543   453

Arrange these numbers in order of size starting with the smallest.

5 456   466   465   455   **6**   867   876   866   877
7 233   332   223   322   323   232   **8**   998   889   899   898   988   989

It is well known that more than one number can be made up from the same
set of figures.
For example, the figures 5, 3 and 2 can be used to make up these six numbers:

532 five hundred and thirty-two   523 five hundred and twenty-three
352 three hundred and fifty-two   325 three hundred and twenty-five
253 two hundred and fifty-three   235 two hundred and thirty-five

The six numbers have different values because the place value of at least
one figure has changed.

Exercise 1G

For each of the following find all the three-figure numbers that can be
made from the figures and arrange them in descending order.

1 2, 5 and 8   **2** 3, 4 and 7   **3** 5, 7 and 9   **4** 1, 2 and 4   **5** 8, 4 and 0
6 7, 6 and 0   **7** 3, 3 and 5   **8** 8, 8 and 2   **9** 2, 2 and 7   **10** 7, 7 and 0

For each of the following find all the three-figure numbers that can be
made from the figures and arrange them in ascending order.

11 2, 3 and 9   **12** 3, 6 and 8   **13** 1, 3 and 5   **14** 1, 4 and 8   **15** 6, 5 and 0
16 4, 2 and 0   **17** 5, 5 and 3   **18** 4, 4 and 7   **19** 1, 1 and 6   **20** 4, 4 and 0

Reading, writing and recording large numbers

When we write a number such as seventeen thousand it is easier to read if a space is used between the
17 and the 000, i.e. 17 000. (In some countries a comma is used instead of a space, i.e. 17,000.) In the
same way a number such as two hundred and fifty-three thousand is written as 253 000.

For numbers larger than a thousand thousand we use two spaces, one before each set of three figures
working from the right, so seventeen thousand thousand is written as 17 000 000.

The word million is used to describe one thousand thousand. This is written as 1 000 000. The word
billion is used to describe one thousand thousand thousand. This is written as 1 000 000 000.

Example 4

a Write these numbers using figures: **i** twenty-three thousand **ii** ninety-six million
  iii eighty-five billion

b Write these numbers in words: **i** 61 000 **ii** 29 000 000 **iii** 70 000 000 000

a i 23 000 **ii** 96 000 000 **iii** 85 000 000 000
b i sixty-one thousand **ii** twenty-nine million **iii** seventy billion

---

Exercise 1H

In questions 1–4 write each number using figures.

1   The distance around the earth is about twenty-four thousand miles.
2   In 1997 the nil rate band for inheritance tax was two hundred and fifteen thousand pounds.
3   The prize money available in the roll-over lottery was nineteen million pounds.
4   In 1997 the Government's projected borrowing requirement was thirteen billion pounds.

In questions 5–10 write each number using words.

5   49 000   6   973 000   7   12 000 000
8   200 000 000   9   53 000 000 000   10 777 000 000 000

Using powers of ten to write large numbers

When a figure has a large number of zeros scientists use a shorthand to make the reading easier.
10 000 is written as 10^4, 100 000 000 is written as 10^8, 1 000 000 000 000 is written as 10^{12}.
10^4 is read as ten to the power four. 10^8 is read as ten to the power eight, etc.
One million is written as 10^6 since there are six zeros. 10^9 is one billion since there are nine zeros.

Exercise 1J

1   Write each power of ten as a number:
    a 10^3 b 10^2 c 10^5 d 10^{10} e 10^7 f 10^{11}

2   Write each number using a power of ten:
    a 100 000   b 10 000 000   c 1000   d 100   e 1 000 000 000 000 000

1.3   Counting in 2s, 5s and 10s

It is very helpful when counting coins to be able to count in 2s, 5s and 10s.

Example 5

a Count the number of dots altogether in each of the following and record your answer in words.
b Record your answer in symbols.

i

ii

iii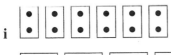

Working from the left:
i   a Counting in twos: two, four, six, eight, ten, twelve   b 12
ii a Counting in fives: five, ten, fifteen, twenty, twenty-five   b 25
iii a Counting in tens: ten, twenty, thirty, forty   b 40

Exercise 1K

a Count the number of dots altogether in each of the following and record your answer in words.
b Record your answer in symbols.

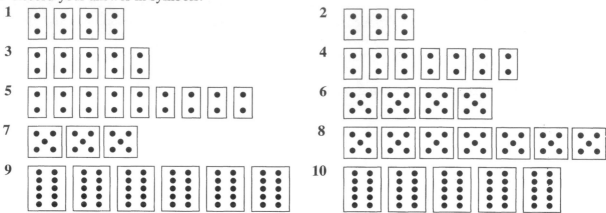

Using number lines

Each of the numbers can be represented on a number line, which has markings rather like a ruler. Counting in ones would look like this:

Counting in twos would look like this:

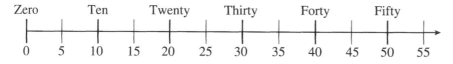

Counting in fives would look like this:

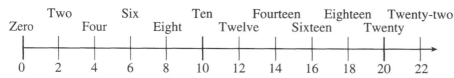

Example 6

Write down in words and symbols the number represented on each of the following number lines.

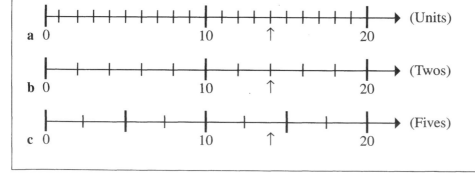

a   fourteen, 14
b   eighteen, 18
c   thirty-five, 35

Exercise 1L

Write down in words and symbols the numbers represented on each of the following number lines.

1

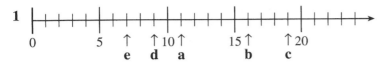

2

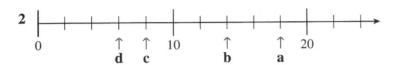

3

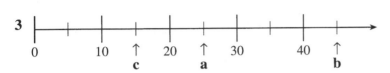

1.4   Understanding place value

The place value of a figure usually means more than one thing. The figure 5 in the number 500 can mean :

   500 is **five** hundreds   or   500 is **fifty** tens   or   500 is **five hundred** units

---

Example 7

State the number of: **a** thousands   **b** hundreds   **c** tens   **d** units in the number 3000.

a The number of thousands is **three** $(3000 = \quad 3 \times 1000)$
b The number of hundreds is **thirty** $(3000 = \quad 30 \times \ 100)$
c The number of tens is **three hundred** $(3000 = \ 300 \times \quad 10)$
d The number of units is **three thousand** $(3000 = 3000 \times \quad 1)$

Exercise 1M

For questions 1–4 state the number of: **a** thousands,   **b** hundreds,   **c** tens   **d** units in the number.

1   7000   **2**   5000   **3**   8000   **4**   1000

For questions 5–8 state the number of: **a** hundreds,   **b** tens   **c** units in the number.

5   400   **6**   600   **7**   700   **8**   500

For questions 9–12 state the number of: **a** tens   **b** units in the number.

9   90   **10**   40   **11**   20   **12**   60

Example 8

9000 centimetres of dressmaking tape is wound on a reel. If the tape is cut up into 100 centimetre lengths, how many lengths are made?

9000 is **ninety** hundreds (9000 = 90 × 100).

Therefore 90 lengths are made.

Exercise 1N

1   A greengrocer has 5000 grams of nuts. He pours them into 100 gram packets. How many packets will he fill?

2   2000 cars have filled a multi-level car park. If there are 100 cars on each level, how many levels does the car park have?

3   A builders' merchant has 4000 kg of sand.
   a If he packs it into 100 kg bags how many bags will he fill?
   b If, instead, he packs it into 10 kg bags, how many of these bags will he fill?

4   9000 cm of wire is wound on a reel.
   a If the wire is cut into 100 cm lengths, how many lengths will be cut?
   b If, instead, the wire is cut into 10 cm lengths, how many lengths will be cut?

5   800 cm of sticky tape is wound on a reel. If the tape is cut up into 10 cm pieces, how many pieces will be cut?

6   A confectioner has 400 cakes. She packs them into cartons which hold 10 cakes each. How many cartons will she fill?

Example 9

A hardware shop manager has 2000 screws. He distributes them equally into 10 boxes.
a How many screws will there be in each box?
b If, instead, he distributes them equally into 100 small packets, how many screws will there be in each packet?

a 2000 is **two hundred** tens (2000 = 200 × 10).
   Therefore there will be 200 screws in each box.
b 2000 is **twenty** hundreds (2000 = 20 × 100).
   Therefore there will be 20 screws in each packet.

Exercise 1P

1   A grocer has 4000 grams of raisins.
    If they exactly fill 10 bags, how many
    grams does each bag hold?

2   A pet shop manager has 9000 grams of bird
    seed.
    If it exactly fills 10 bags, how many grams
    does each bag hold?

3   There are 3000 bricks on a lorry.
    If 10 bricklayers each take away the same
    number of bricks, how many does each one
    take?

4   8000 away supporters travel to a football
    match.
    a If they exactly fill 10 special trains, how
    many travel on each train?
    b If each train consists of 10 identical
    coaches, how many sit in each coach?

5   A confectioner has 2000 decoration
    cherries.
    a If she stores them equally between 10
    cartons, how many does she place in each
    carton?
    b If she then uses them to decorate 100
    identical cakes, how many does she put
    on each cake?

6   A catering manager has 1000 grams of tea.
    a If he pours it out equally into 10 packets,
    how many grams will there be in each
    packet?
    b If, instead, he puts the tea in equal
    amounts into 100 tea bags, how many
    grams will there be in each tea bag?

7   A brewer has 500 litres of beer.
    a If it exactly fills 10 barrels, how many
    litres does each barrel hold?
    b If it also exactly fills 100 party cans, how
    many litres does each party can hold?

8   A potato merchant has 700 kg of potatoes.
    If they exactly fill 10 sacks, how many
    kilograms does each sack hold?

2 ADDITION

2.1 Addition of whole numbers

(single-figure, two-figure and three-figure)

'Find the sum of' and 'find the total of' are different ways of saying 'add together'. Each of these can be represented by the symbol '+'.

Addition by counting

Example 1
Add together 3 and 5.

3 dots   5 dots   8 dots

Therefore $3 + 5 = 8$.

Example 2
Find the sum of 7 and 8.

7 dots   8 dots   15 dots

10 dots   5 dots

Therefore $7 + 8 = 10 + 5 = 15$.

Exercise 2A

Add together, by counting, each of the following.

1 $6 + 2$	**2** $4 + 3$	**3** $7 + 2$	**4** $5 + 4$	**5** $8 + 2$	**6** $8 + 4$
7 $8 + 6$	**8** $9 + 3$	**9** $7 + 3$	**10** $8 + 3$	**11** $9 + 4$	**12** $6 + 4$

Addition using number facts

The table on the right shows the results of adding pairs of numbers between 0 and 9.

For example:
$5 + 7 = 12$

+	0	1	2	3	4	5	6	⑦	8	9
0	0	1	2	3	4	5	6	7	8	9
1	1	2	3	4	5	6	7	8	9	10
2	2	3	4	5	6	7	8	9	10	11
3	3	4	5	6	7	8	9	10	11	12
4	4	5	6	7	8	9	10	11	12	13
⑤	5	6	7	8	9	10	11	12	13	14
6	6	7	8	9	10	11	12	13	14	15
7	7	8	9	10	11	12	13	14	15	16
8	8	9	10	11	12	13	14	15	16	17
9	9	10	11	12	13	14	15	16	17	18

Example 3

Find the total of: **a** 4, 5 and 8 **b** 6, 4 and 8

a $4 + 5 = 9$, $9 + 8 = 17$ so the total of 4, 5 and 8 is 17
b $6 + 4 = 10$, $10 + 8 = 18$ so the total of 6, 4 and 8 is 18

Example 4

Add together: **a** 4 and 6 **b** 6 and 9 **c** 3, 7 and 8

a $4 + 6 = 10$ **b** $6 + 9 = 15$
c $3 + 7 = 10$ and $10 + 8 = 18$ so $3 + 7 + 8 = 18$

Exercise 2B

Find the total for each of the following.

1	$8 + 5$	**2**	$6 + 5$	**3**	$8 + 7$	**4**	$9 + 7$	**5**	$7 + 4$
6	$9 + 8$	**7**	$9 + 2$	**8**	$5 + 3$	**9**	$4 + 3 + 2$	**10**	$5 + 3 + 1$
11	$6 + 2 + 1$	**12**	$5 + 4 + 6$	**13**	$4 + 6 + 2$	**14**	$4 + 3 + 7$	**15**	$3 + 6 + 7$
16	$4 + 5 + 8$	**17**	$3 + 2 + 9$	**18**	$5 + 3 + 9$	**19**	$5 + 4 + 7$	**20**	$8 + 4 + 7$

Adding two-figure numbers

Reminder The number 27 (twenty-seven) means 2 tens and 7 units, or $20 + 7$.

Example 5

Find $13 + 25$.

	Tens	Units	
We can show this as:	1	3	i.e. one ten and three units
	+ 2	5	i.e. two tens and five units
	3	8	i.e. three tens and eight units

Therefore $13 + 25 = 38$.

Example 6

Find $47 + 25$.

	Tens	Units	
We can show this as:	4	7	i.e. four tens and seven units
	+ 2	5	i.e. two tens and five units
	6	12	i.e. six tens and twelve units
	6 + 1	2	i.e. six tens and one ten and two units
	7	2	i.e. seven tens and two units

Tens	Units
4	7
2₁	5
7	2

Note we need to 'carry' one ten from the units column to the tens column.

Therefore $47 + 25 = 72$.

Exercise 2C

Evaluate each of the following.

1	65 + 13	**2**	75 + 14	**3**	45 + 32	**4**	25 + 71	**5**	56 + 23
6	36 + 62	**7**	31 + 56	**8**	17 + 52	**9**	27 + 61	**10**	43 + 53
11	36 + 54	**12**	27 + 43	**13**	68 + 24	**14**	59 + 23	**15**	32 + 29
16	24 + 67	**17**	19 + 46	**18**	48 + 27	**19**	58 + 36	**20**	29 + 44

Adding three-figure numbers

Reminders i   The number 327 (three hundred and twenty-seven)
means 3 hundreds, 2 tens and 7 units, or 300 + 20 + 7.

ii   10 tens = 1 hundred, and 10 hundreds = 1 thousand.

Example 7

Find   162 + 234.

	Hundreds	Tens	Units	
We can show this as:	1	6	2	i.e. 1 hundred, 6 tens and 2 units
	+ 2	3	4	i.e. 2 hundreds, 3 tens and 4 units
	3	9	6	i.e. 3 hundreds, 9 tens and 6 units

Therefore   162 + 234 = 396.

Example 8

Find   127 + 345.

	Hundreds	Tens	Units	
We can show this as:	1	2	7	i.e. 1 hundred, 2 tens and 7 units
	+ 3	4	5	i.e. 3 hundreds, 4 tens and 5 units
	4	6	12	i.e. 4 hundreds, 6 tens and 12 units
	4	6+1	2	i.e. 4 hundreds, 6 tens and 1 ten and 2 units
	4	7	2	i.e. 4 hundreds, 7 tens and 2 units

Therefore   127 + 345 = 472.

A quick way of showing this would be:

	Hundreds	Tens	Units	
	1	2	7	**Note** we need 'carry' one ten from
	3	4₁	5	the units column to the tens column.
	4	7	2	

Example 9

Find   147 + 395.

	Hundreds	Tens	Units	
We can show this as:	1	4	7	i.e. 1 hundred, 4 tens and 7 units
	+ 3	9	5	i.e. 3 hundreds, 9 tens and 5 units
	4	13	12	i.e. 4 hundreds, 13 tens and 12 units
	4+1	3+1	2	i.e. 4 plus 1 hundreds, 3 plus 1 tens and 2 units
	5	4	2	i.e. 5 hundreds, 4 tens and 2 units

Therefore   147 + 395 = 542.

A quick way of showing this would be:

	Hundreds	Tens	Units
	1	4	7
	3₁	9₁	5
	5	4	2

Note   we need to 'carry' one ten from the units column to the tens column and one hundred from the tens column to the hundreds column.

Exercise 2D

Find the sum for each of the following.

1 743 + 125	**2** 352 + 417	**3** 256 + 542	**4** 435 + 562	**5** 623 + 144
6 452 + 313	**7** 438 + 154	**8** 327 + 546	**9** 469 + 315	**10** 538 + 126
11 395 + 574	**12** 161 + 586	**13** 382 + 276	**14** 579 + 363	**15** 268 + 455
16 645 + 489	**17** 897 + 526	**18** 776 + 465	**19** 898 + 652	**20** 979 + 337

Note in questions 15–20 you will need a thousands column.

2.2   Quick ways of adding numbers

Example 10

Find 3 + 5 + 7 + 6 + 4 + 5.

Look for pairs of numbers which add up to 10.

So,   3 + 5 + 7 + 6 + 4 + 5 = 3 + 7 + 6 + 4 + 5 + 5 = 10 + 10 + 10 = 30

Therefore   3 + 5 + 7 + 6 + 4 + 5 = 3 + 7 + 6 + 4 + 5 + 5 = 30.
(It does not matter in what order we decide to add these numbers.)

Exercise 2E

Find each of the following.

1 9 + 7 + 3 + 8 + 1 + 2	**2** 8 + 5 + 2 + 5 + 3 + 1	**3** 6 + 3 + 5 + 4 + 7 + 1
4 3 + 8 + 9 + 7 + 2 + 6	**5** 4 + 5 + 7 + 9 + 6 + 1	**6** 5 + 9 + 2 + 5 + 7 + 8

Example 11

Find the total of 31, 23, 67, 19 and 42.

Again, look for pairs of numbers whose units digits add up to 10.

$$31 + 23 + 67 + 19 + 42 = 31 + 19 + 23 + 67 + 42$$
$$= 50 + 90 + 42$$
$$= 140 + 42$$
$$= 182$$

Therefore $31 + 23 + 67 + 19 + 42 = 31 + 19 + 23 + 67 + 42 = 182$.

(Again the order doesn't matter.)

Exercise 2F

Evaluate each of the following.

1 $26 + 17 + 24 + 13$
3 $23 + 25 + 17 + 35$
5 $58 + 14 + 40 + 26 + 12$

2 $39 + 28 + 12 + 11$
4 $34 + 20 + 16 + 35 + 25$
6 $36 + 21 + 15 + 19 + 44$

Example 12

Find the sum of 39, 59 and 89.

Each of the numbers is one less than a 'multiple' of 10. The respective multiples are 40, 60 and 90. These three numbers can therefore be added followed by a subtraction of three from the result.

$$39 + 59 + 89 = 40 - 1 + 60 - 1 + 90 - 1$$
$$= 40 + 60 + 90 - 1 - 1 - 1$$
$$= 190 - 3$$
$$= 187$$

Therefore $39 + 59 + 89 = 187$.

Example 13

Find the sum of 38, 79, 49 and 28.

$$38 + 79 + 49 + 28 = 40 - 2 + 80 - 1 + 50 - 1 + 30 - 2$$
$$= 40 + 80 + 50 + 30 - 2 - 1 - 1 - 2$$
$$= 200 - 6$$
$$= 194$$

Therefore $38 + 79 + 49 + 28 = 194$.

Exercise 2G

Find each of the following.

1	29 + 19 + 69	**2**	49 + 39 + 59	**3**	59 + 49 + 18	**4**	78 + 28 + 68
5	19 + 29 + 49 + 39	**6**	19 + 29 + 39 + 58	**7**	68 + 28 + 48 + 18	**8**	49 + 28 + 59 + 50
9	38 + 20 + 18 + 39	**10**	58 + 30 + 40 + 49	**11**	19 + 38 + 49 + 68	**12**	69 + 48 + 27 + 50

2.3   Using addition in simple situations

Example 14

Mrs Jones has 2 pints of milk on Monday, 4 on Tuesday, 2 on
Wednesday, 3 on Thursday, 2 on Friday and 5 on Saturday.
How many pints did she have altogether?

$$2 + 4 + 2 + 3 + 2 + 5 = 2 + 4 + 2 + 2 + 3 + 5$$
$$= 10 + 3 + 5$$
$$= 10 + 8$$
$$= 18$$

So Mrs Jones had 18 pints altogether.

Exercise 2H

1 In Short Street there are only six houses.
The numbers of occupants in these houses
are: 1, 3, 5, 4, 7 and 2. How many people
live in the street altogether?

2 A ferry makes six daily sailings. One day
the numbers of cars on the sailings were as
follows: 5, 4, 3, 1, 2 and 6.
How many cars were carried on that day?

3 A football team wins a trophy after a seven-
round contest. Their goal scoring record
was as follows: 2, 1, 3, 2, 4, 1 and 3.
How many goals did they score in the
tournament altogether?

4 Five children on a trip bought some
sandwiches: David buys 1, Jane buys 3,
Mary buys 2, Susan buys 2 and William
buys 4. How many sandwiches did they
buy altogether?

5 A furniture company has stores in five
large cities:
4 in London, 3 in Birmingham, 1 in Liverpool, 2 in Manchester and 2 in Glasgow.
How many stores do they have altogether?

6 A vending machine sells packets of crisps.
One day the sales were as follows:
Plain 5, Bovril 2, Salt and Vinegar 3,
Cheese and Onion 7.
How many packets were bought altogether?

7 A preparatory school has only four classes.
The numbers of children in each class with
red hair are as follows: Class One 6, Class
Two 3, Class Three 4, Class Four 1. How
many children in the school have red hair?

8 One week Mrs Patel posted the following
numbers of letters on each day: Monday 4,
Tuesday 2, Wednesday 1, Thursday 2,
Friday 1, Saturday 5. How many letters did
Mrs Patel post altogether?

Example 15

Dr Williams bought sweets for her three children costing 22p, 27p and 33p. How much did she spend altogether?

$$22 + 27 + 33 = 27 + 33 + 22$$
$$= 60 + 22$$
$$= 82$$

so Dr Williams spent 82p altogether.

Exercise 2J

1   The numbers of vehicles on a ferry sailing are as follows:
    Cars 27, Vans 13, Lorries 5, Coaches 2. How many vehicles are being carried altogether?

2   A commuter bus is overcrowded. 25 passengers are sitting in the lower deck seats, 29 are sitting in the upper deck seats and 11 are standing. How many passengers are on the bus?

3   A small primary school has five classes. The numbers in each class are as follows:
    Class 1 – 17, Class 2 – 19, Class 3 – 15, Class 4 – 21, Class 5 – 23. How many pupils does the school have altogether?

4   One week a factory canteen served the following numbers of lunches:
    Monday 11, Tuesday 15, Wednesday 15, Thursday 9 and Friday 8. How many lunches did the canteen serve altogether?

5   A snack bar sell four kinds of sandwiches. One day the sales were as follows:
    Cheese 23, Ham 15, Egg 25 and Tomato 27. How may did they sell altogether?

6   A vending machine sells four kinds of hot drinks. One day the sales were as follows:
    Tea 34, Coffee 26, Hot Chocolate 21, Soup 19.
    How many drinks were bought altogether?

Very often in practice more than two large numbers have to be added together. It usually helps if the numbers are arranged in columns.

Example 16

Add together 123, 461 and 272.

First write these numbers in columns:

Hundreds	Tens	Units
1	2	3
4	6	1
2₁	7	2
8	5	6

Then add the columns, starting with the units, taking care of any 'carry' figures.

Therefore $123 + 461 + 272 = 856$.

Exercise 2K

Evaluate each of the following.

1	243 + 331 + 124	**2**	435 + 142 + 321	**3**	322 + 445 + 214	**4**	146 + 235 + 311
5	116 + 248 + 411	**6**	143 + 452 + 332	**7**	261 + 425 + 172	**8**	384 + 212 + 53
9	365 + 121 + 82	**10**	436 + 381 + 40	**11**	565 + 234 + 43	**12**	252 + 443 + 68

Example 17

Mr Ahmed is a travelling salesman. He travelled 153 miles on Monday, 227 miles on Wednesday and 118 miles on Friday. How many miles did he travel altogether?

Using the quick method, since 3 and 7 = 10:
153 + 227 + 118 = 380 + 118 = 498

Alternatively by using columns:

Hundreds	Tens	Units
1	5	3
2	2	7
1	1₁	8
4	9	8

So Mr Ahmed travelled 498 miles altogether.

Exercise 2L

1 Find the distance from London to Bristol (km is short for kilometres).

Bristol ——→ Bath ——→ Swindon ——→ London
20 km   55 km   125 km

2 Over a bank holiday weekend an ice cream van sells the following numbers of cornets: Saturday 215, Sunday 185, Monday 250. How many cornets are sold altogether?

3 Stickee's Sugar is available in boxes of three different sizes:
Small 250 grams, Medium 475 grams, Large 625 grams.
If Anne buys one packet of each kind how many grams of sugar does she buy?

4 A railway station has four platforms. 135 people are waiting at Platform 1, 90 people at Platform 2, 65 people at Platform 3 and 50 people at Platform 4. How many people are waiting for trains altogether?

5 Centreville school has 102 pupils from Centreville, 190 from Northville and 198 from Southville. If all the pupils live in one of the three villages how many pupils attend the school?

6 A man of weight 88 kg is pushing a trolley of weight 120 kg, on which there is a case of weight 112 kg, on to a lift. What is the total weight that will go into the lift cage? (kg is short for kilograms.)

3 SUBTRACTION

3.1 Subtraction of whole numbers

(single-figure, two-figure and three-figure)

'Take away', 'How much bigger than?' and 'Find the difference between', are all different ways of saying 'Subtract'.

Each of these can therefore be represented by the minus symbol '–'.

Subtraction by taking away

Example 1

Work out the value of 8 take away 5.

8 dots   5 dots   3 dots

Therefore $8 - 5 = 3$.

Example 2

How much bigger is 7 than 3?

7 dots   3 dots   4 dots

Therefore $7 - 3 = 4$.

Example 3

Find the difference between 13 and 8.

13 dots   8 dots   5 dots

Therefore $13 - 8 = 5$.

Exercise 3A

Work out:

1 9 take away 5   2 7 take away 5   3 7 take away 2   4 10 take away 2
5 10 take away 3   6 12 take away 3   7 12 take away 5

How many is:

8 9 bigger than 4   **9** 9 bigger than 6   **10** 11 bigger than 8
11 11 bigger than 5   **12** 8 bigger than 4   **13** 8 bigger than 1

Find the difference between:

14 8 and 3   **15** 8 and 6   **16** 9 and 7   **17** 12 and 7   **18** 12 and 2

Example 4

How many more than 5 is 8?

5 dots   ? dots   8 dots

Therefore 8 − 5 = 3.

Example 5

Find 13 − 8.

This can be rewritten as: 'What can be added to 8 to give 13?'

i.e.   8 + ? = 13
but   8 + 5 = 13
Therefore 13 − 8 = 5.

Exercise 3B

How many more than:

1 6 is 10?   **2** 6 is 12?   **3** 8 is 12?   **4** 8 is 15?   **5** 7 is 11?
6 7 is 13?   **7** 9 is 13?   **8** 9 is 15?   **9** 5 is 11?   **10** 3 is 11?

What can be added to:

11 3 to make 9?   **12** 3 to make 6?   **13** 4 to make 10?   **14** 8 to make 11?
15 6 to make 11?   **16** 10 to make 15?   **17** 12 to make 15?   **18** 10 to make 14?

Subtracting two-figure numbers

Example 6

Find 46 − 12.

We can write this as: Tens Units

                            4   6   i.e. 4 tens and 6 units, then take away:
                          − 1   2   1 ten and 2 units
                          ‾‾‾‾‾‾‾‾‾‾‾‾   ‾‾‾‾‾‾‾‾‾‾‾‾‾‾‾‾‾‾
                            3   4   3 tens and 4 units

Therefore 46 − 12 = 34.

Example 7

Find 46 – 19.

We can write this as:

	Tens	Units	
	4	6	i.e. 4 tens and 6 units

This can be thought of as:

	Tens	Units	
	3+1	6	i.e. 3 tens, 1 ten and 6 units
	3	16	or 3 tens and 16 units
			then take away:
–	1	9	1 ten and 9 units
	2	7	2 tens and 7 units

$$\begin{array}{cc} \text{Tens} & \text{Units} \\ 4^{3} & {}^{1}6 \\ -\ 1 & 9 \\ \hline 2 & 7 \end{array}$$

Note we need to 'carry' one ten from the tens column to the units column.

Therefore 46 – 19 = 27.

Exercise 3C

Evaluate each of the following.

1	65 – 23	**2**	47 – 14	**3**	58 – 32	**4**	79 – 25	**5**	86 – 41
6	59 – 17	**7**	68 – 36	**8**	95 – 32	**9**	76 – 35	**10**	75 – 30
11	52 – 29	**12**	73 – 28	**13**	82 – 46	**14**	91 – 37	**15**	70 – 38

Subtracting three-figure numbers

Example 8

Find the value of 746 – 512.

We can show this as:

	Hundreds	Tens	Units	
	7	4	6	i.e. 7 hundreds, 4 tens and 6 units
–	5	1	2	i.e. 5 hundreds, 1 ten and 2 units
	2	3	4	i.e. 2 hundreds, 3 tens and 4 units

Therefore 746 – 512 = 234.

Example 9

Find the value of 746 – 519.   (**Reminder** 1 ten is the same as 10 units)

We can show this as:

	Hundreds	Tens	Units	
	7	4	6	i.e. 7 hundreds, 4 tens and 6 units

This can be thought of as:

	Hundreds	Tens	Units	
	7	3+1	6	i.e. 7 hundreds, 3 tens and 1 ten and 6 units
or:	7	3	16	i.e. 7 hundreds, 3 tens and 16 units.
				Then take away:
–	5	1	9	5 hundreds, 1 ten and 9 units
	2	2	7	i.e. 2 hundreds, 2 tens and 7 units

A quick way of showing this would be:

$$
\begin{array}{ccc}
\text{Hundreds} & \text{Tens} & \text{Units} \\
7 & {}_{}\!\!\not{4}^{3} & {}^{1}6 \\
5 & 1 & 9 \\
\hline
2 & 2 & 7 \\
\end{array}
$$

Note   we need to 'carry' one ten
from the tens column to the units column.

Therefore $746 - 519 = 227$.

Example 10

Find the value of $746 - 599$.   (**Reminder** 1 hundred is the same as 10 tens)

We can show this as: Hundreds Tens Units

$$
\begin{array}{ccc}
7 & 4 & 6
\end{array}
$$ i.e. 7 hundreds, 4 tens and 6 units.

This can be thought of as:

$$
\begin{array}{ccc}
6+1 & 3+1 & 6
\end{array}
$$ i.e. 6 plus 1 hundreds, 3 plus 1 tens and 6 units

or:

$$
\begin{array}{ccc}
6 & 13 & 16
\end{array}
$$ i.e. 6 hundreds, 13 tens and 16 units.

Then take away:

$$
\begin{array}{ccc}
-\,5 & 5 & 9 \\
\hline
1 & 8 & 7 \\
\end{array}
$$

i.e. 5 hundreds, 5 tens and 9 units

i.e. 1 hundred, 8 tens and 7 units

A quick way of showing this would be:

$$
\begin{array}{ccc}
\text{Hundreds} & \text{Tens} & \text{Units} \\
{}^{}\!\not{7}^{6} & {}^{1}\!\not{4}^{3} & {}^{1}6 \\
-\,5 & 5 & 9 \\
\hline
1 & 8 & 7 \\
\end{array}
$$

Note   we need to 'carry' one ten from
the tens column to the units column *and*
one hundred from the hundreds column
to the tens column.

Therefore $746 - 559 = 187$.

Exercise 3D

Evaluate each of the following.

1 $856 - 532$	**2** $975 - 433$	**3** $689 - 426$	**4** $578 - 126$	**5** $757 - 524$
6 $652 - 228$	**7** $881 - 629$	**8** $974 - 238$	**9** $685 - 129$	**10** $870 - 237$
11 $624 - 78$	**12** $412 - 67$	**13** $853 - 85$	**14** $731 - 94$	**15** $1235 - 487$
16 $1312 - 685$	**17** $1529 - 978$	**18** $1107 - 472$	**19** $1252 - 319$	**20** $1491 - 965$

3.2   Alternative ways of subtracting numbers

Example 11

Find: **a** 70 – 39   **b** 90 – 28   **c** 200 – 159

a Taking away 39 is the same as taking away 40 and adding 1,
so 70 – 39 = 70 – 40 + 1 = 30 + 1 = 31.
Therefore 70 – 39 = 31.

b Taking away 28 is the same as taking away 30 and adding 2,
so 90 – 28 = 90 – 30 + 2 = 60 + 2 = 62.
Therefore 90 – 28 = 62.

c Taking away 159 is the same as taking away 160 and adding 1,
so 200 – 159 = 200 – 160 + 1 = 40 + 1 = 41.

Therefore 200 – 159 = 41.

Exercise 3E

Find the value of:

1	90 – 29	**2**	80 – 49	**3**	60 – 19	**4**	70 – 49	**5**	80 – 39
6	50 – 19	**7**	80 – 38	**8**	60 – 28	**9**	70 – 18	**10**	90 – 48
11	200 – 129	**12**	300 – 259	**13**	300 – 239	**14**	400 – 329	**15**	400 – 369
16	500 – 479	**17**	500 – 449	**18**	200 – 49	**19**	200 – 69	**20**	200 – 29

Example 12

Find by adding on: **a** 80 – 59   **b** 70 – 28   **c** 300 – 129.

a We can think of 80 – 59 as what can be added to 59 to make 80? Or 59 + ?? = 80.
As 59 + 1 = 60 and 60 + 20 = 80, it follows that 59 + 1 + 20 = 80, i.e. 59 + 21 = 80.
Therefore 80 – 59 = 21.

b We can think of 70 – 28 as 28 + ?? = 70.
As 28 + 2 = 30 and 30 + 40 = 70 it follows that 28 + 2 + 40 = 70, i.e. 28 + 42 = 70.
Therefore 70 – 28 = 42.

c We can think of 300 – 129 as 129 + ??? = 300.
As 129 + 1 = 130 and 130 + 170 = 300 it follows that 129 + 1 + 170 = 300, i.e. 129 + 171 = 300.

Therefore 300 – 129 = 171.

Exercise 3F

Find each of the following by writing the subtraction as an addition.

1	80 – 29	**2**	70 – 49	**3**	90 – 39	**4**	80 – 59	**5**	70 – 19
6	90 – 58	**7**	50 – 28	**8**	80 – 18	**9**	70 – 38	**10**	60 – 48
11	300 – 149	**12**	300 – 179	**13**	300 – 129	**14**	400 – 259	**15**	400 – 289
16	400 – 298	**17**	500 – 198	**18**	500 – 298	**19**	600 – 199	**20**	500 – 399

3.3   Using subtraction in simple situations

Example 13

David is 5 and his sister Jane is 9. How much older is Jane than David?

The answer is 9 – 5 or 4. This follows from either 'counting on' (i.e. 5 + 4 = 9) or simply 'removing' 5 from 9.

Exercise 3G

1 Shani is 7 and her sister Candace is 12. How much older is Candace than Shani?

2 Robert is 2 and his brother Paul is 11. How much older is Paul than Robert?

3 Marcus has 9 sweets and his sister Trisha has 15. How many more sweets has Trisha than Marcus?

4 Ronnie has 7 nuts and his sister Charmaine has 13. How many more nuts has Charmaine than Ronnie?

5 Anne takes 8 biscuits out of a packet of 15 and puts them on a plate. How many are left in the packet?

6 Laura has 9 marbles. After winning a game she had 16. How many did she win?

7 One day I saw 8 people waiting at the bus stop. By the time the bus arrived, however, 16 people were waiting. How many more people had walked to the bus stop?

8 One day I saw 6 cars waiting at the traffic lights. By the time the lights had changed to green, however, there were 14 cars in the queue. How many more had arrived?

9 An empty lorry weighs 8 tonnes, but when it is loaded it weighs 13 tonnes. What is the weight of its load?

10 A baby mouse was 3 cm long when born but grew to a length of 11 cm. By how many centimetres did it grow?

11 Nicola's pencil is 7 cm long and her pen is 15 cm long. How much longer is her pen than her pencil?

12 A train leaves Waterloo station in London. It arrives at Clapham Junction after 5 minutes and at Wimbledon after 11 minutes. How long did it take to travel from Clapham Junction to Wimbledon?

Example 14

Mrs Brown bought a packet of mints for 22p. How much change did she get if she paid with: **a** a 50p coin   **b** a £1 coin?

a We need to find 50 – 22, so:

$$
\begin{array}{cc}
\text{Tens} & \text{Units} \\
\cancel{5}^4 & {}^1 0 \\
-\;2 & 2 \\
\hline
2 & 8
\end{array}
\qquad \text{i.e. } 50 - 22 = 28
$$

Therefore Mrs Brown received 28p in change.

Alternatively: 22 + ?? = 50.

22 + 8 = 30   30 + 20 = 50   so   22 + 8 + 20 = 50   or   22 + 28 = 50

So again Mrs Brown had 28p in change.

b We need to find 100 – 22, so:

$$
\begin{array}{ccc}
\text{Hundreds} & \text{Tens} & \text{Units} \\
1 & 1\cancel{0}^9 & {}^1 0 \\
- & 2 & 2 \\
\hline
& 7 & 8
\end{array}
\qquad \text{i.e. } 100 - 22 = 78
$$

Note   we need to carry a hundred (10 tens) from the hundreds column to the tens column and then one ten to the units column.

Therefore Mrs Brown received 78p in change.

Alternatively: 22 + ?? = 100.

22 + 8 = 30   30 + 70 = 100   so   22 + 8 + 70 = 100   or   22 + 78 = 100

So again Mrs Brown had 78p in change.

Exercise 3H

1   If I buy a packet of sweets which costs 36p, what is my change if I pay with:
a a 50p coin   **b** a £1 coin?

2   Julie requires 24 cm of string to tie up a small parcel.
How many centimetres will be left if she cuts this length off:
a a 50 cm piece
b a 1 m (i.e. 100 cm) piece of string?

3   Candace is running in a 100 m race.
After she has run 47 m how much further does she have to go?

4   Shani is saving for her holiday and she has £28 so far. If she requires £50, how much more must she save?

5   Mr Khan has 13 litres of petrol in his car's tank. If he stops at a garage to fill up how many litres can he put in if the tank holds 50 litres?

6   A nursery school can only accommodate 72 pupils.
If they receive 100 applications how many pupils are they unable to accept?

7 There are 65 people at a meeting in a village hall. How many empty seats are there if the hall has enough seats for 90 people?

8 Mumbi is reading through a magazine and has read 46 pages.
How many more pages has she still to read if the magazine has 80 pages altogether?

9 Tnisha is holding a party. She gives each of her 21 guests a chocolate out of a box. How many chocolates are left in the box if it originally contained 60 altogether?

10 An empty bus arrives at a bus station and there are 75 people waiting.
If the bus can only carry 48 passengers, how many people must wait for the next bus?

Example 15

Mrs Joshi travelled 327 miles on Monday and 183 miles on Tuesday. How much further did she travel on Monday?

Writing in columns:

	Hundreds	Tens	Units
	$\cancel{3}^{2}$	$^{1}2$	7
−	1	8	3
	1	4	4

As 327 − 183 = 144, Mrs Joshi travelled 144 miles further on Monday.

Exercise 3J

1 Mr Gray travelled 250 km on Saturday and 115 km on Sunday.
How much further did he travel on Saturday than on Sunday?

2 Marlon has collected 360 stamps but his brother Jordan has collected only 245.
How many more stamps has Marlon collected?

3 The stand at a rugby ground can seat 500 people and at one match 324 spectators are sitting in it.
How many empty seats are there?

4 Bernard has saved up £725 towards buying a motor-cycle. If the motor-cycle he wants costs £900, how much more must he save?

5 Hadrian's Wall was completed by the Romans in the year 122. If they left Britain in the year 410 for how long did they man the wall?

6 The Eiffel Tower in Paris is 300 m tall, but Blackpool Tower is only 165 m tall.
How much taller is the Eiffel Tower?

7 Anne is 155 cm tall but her younger sister Nicola is only 98 cm tall.
How much taller is Anne?

8 George is climbing Scafell Pike, the highest mountain in England. The summit is 980 m above sea level and George has reached Sty Head Pass which is 527 m above sea level. Through how many more metres must he ascend?

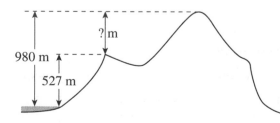

4 MULTIPLICATION

4.1 Multiplication by counting

'Find three lots of five', 'find three times five' and 'find the product of 3 and 5' are different ways of saying 'multiply three by five'.

Each can be represented by 3×5, where the $\times$ is the symbol for multiplication.

Example 1

Find: **a** three lots of five   **b** four times five   **c** 3×4.

a 'Three lots of five' is:

Therefore $3 \times 5 = 15$.

b 'Four times five' is:

Therefore $4 \times 5 = 20$.

c 3×4 can be thought of as '3 lots of 4' or '4 lots of 3':

Therefore $3 \times 4 = 12$.

Exercise 4A

Find the value of each of the following by drawing an array of dots.

1	2×4	**2**	2×5	**3**	2×6	**4**	2×3	**5**	3×3
6	3×6	**7**	3×7	**8**	4×4	**9**	4×6	**10**	5×5

4.2   Multiplying whole numbers by 10 and by 100

If a number is multiplied by 10, the place value of each of the figures is
changed. Look at the two examples below.

$7 \times 10 = 70$ Seven units becomes seven tens.
$51 \times 10 = 510$ Five tens and one unit becomes five hundreds and one ten.

It can easily be seen that if we multiply a number by 10, each figure moves
one place to the left.

Multiplying a number by 100 also changes the place value of each of the
figures. The examples below illustrate how.

$5 \times 100 = 500$ Five units becomes five hundreds.
$10 \times 100 = 1000$ One ten becomes one thousand.

We can therefore quite easily see that if we multiply a number by 100,
each figure moves two places to the left.

Exercise 4B

Multiply each of the following numbers by 10.

1	3	**2**	5	**3**	9	**4**	12	**5**	18
6	36	**7**	72	**8**	50	**9**	10	**10**	30

Multiply each of the following numbers by 100.

11	7	**12**	8	**13**	3	**14**	1	**15**	13
16	19	**17**	25	**18**	60	**19**	20	**20**	90

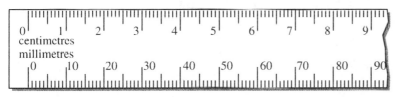

Given that 1 centimetre equals 10 millimetres, change each of the
following distances to millimetres

21	14 cm	**22**	18 cm	**23**	85 cm	**24**	30 cm
25	8 cm	**26**	7 cm	**27**	9 cm	**28**	6 cm

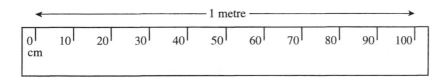

Given that 1 metre = 100 centimetres change each of the following
distances to centimetres.

29	5 m	**30**	2 m	**31**	4 m	**32**	9 m	**33**	30 m	**34**	50 m

35   Mary is 6 years old. Her grandmother is 10 times older. How old is
her grandmother?

4.3   Multiplying by single-figure whole numbers

The result of multiplying any single-figure number by another is shown in the table opposite.

For example:
3×5 (3 times 5) = 15
6×9 (6 times 9) = 54
8×3 (8 times 3) = 24

×	0	1	2	3	4	5	6	7	8	9
0	0	0	0	0	0	0	0	0	0	0
1	0	1	2	3	4	5	6	7	8	9
2	0	2	4	6	8	10	12	14	16	18
3	0	3	6	9	12	(15)	18	21	24	27
4	0	4	8	12	16	20	24	28	32	36
5	0	5	10	15	20	25	30	35	40	45
6	0	6	12	18	24	30	36	42	48	(54)
7	0	7	14	21	28	35	42	49	56	63
8	0	8	16	(24)	32	40	48	56	64	72
9	0	9	18	27	36	45	54	63	72	81

Example 2

a My three sons have five sweets each. How many sweets do they have altogether?

b On each of six days my hen laid nine eggs. How many eggs were laid altogether?

c If I buy eight pots of hyacinths with three in each pot, how many flowers have I bought altogether?

a $3 \times 5 = 15$ so there are 15 sweets altogether.

b $6 \times 9 = 54$ so there are 54 eggs altogether.

c $8 \times 3 = 24$ so there are 24 flowers altogether.

Exercise 4C

1 Six children are playing in a paddling pool, but in the swimming pool nearby there are five times as many children. How many children are there in the swimming pool?

2 At Sanjay's school only nine boys choose needlework as a crafts option, but seven times as many girls do so. How many girls choose needlework?

3 At one end of Tony's village there is a small car park which has room for only nine cars. At the other end of the village, however, there is a larger one which can take four times as many.
How many cars can the larger car park hold?

4 A small screwdriver is 8 cm long. A much larger one is 5 times longer.
How long is the larger one?

5   A mouse who is hiding from a cat is 8 cm long. If the cat is 4 times longer than the mouse, how long is the cat?

6   Barbara has a doll whose shoes are 6 cm long. If her own shoes are 4 times longer, how long are they?

7   A small sweet weighs 7 grams. If a large toffee is 3 times heavier, how heavy is the toffee?

8   A young puppy weighs 7 kg. If its mother is 4 times heavier, how heavy is she?

When a two-figure number is multiplied by a single-figure number the unit figure of the two-figure number is multiplied by the single-figure number first.

Example 3

Work out 73×5.

We can show this as:

Hundreds	Tens	Units		
	7	3		
	×	5		
	1	5		(3×5)
3	5	0		(70×5)
3	6	5		

or

Hundreds	Tens	Units	
	7	3	
	×	5	
3	6	5	
₃	₁		

Note   we need to 'carry' one ten from the units column to the tens column and three tens from tens column to the hundreds column.

Therefore $73 \times 5 = 365$.

Exercise 4D

For questions 1–8 find the answer which is different.

	a	**b**	**c**
1	38×2	18×4	24×3
2	12×7	14×6	22×4
3	23×4	14×7	49×2
4	32×3	47×2	12×8
5	22×6	17×8	33×4
6	16×8	14×9	21×6
7	12×9	13×8	18×6
8	16×9	24×6	22×7

9   A drawer has a height of 12 cm. Find: **a** the width **b** the length if they are respectively 4 and 7 times greater than the height.

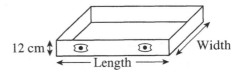

10   Mrs Brown has four children. The youngest is Maria who weighs 13 kg. Find the weight of:
a James   **b** Donna   **c** Paul if they are respectively 3, 5 and 6 times heavier than Maria.

4.4   Long multiplication

Example 4

Work out: 43×14.

$43 \times 14 = 43 \times 10$ add 43×4 But $43 \times 10 = 430$

and $43 \times 4 = 172$

Therefore $43 \times 14 = 430 + 172 = 602$

It is probably more convenient to set out the working as:

$$
\begin{array}{r}
43 \\
\times \quad 14 \\
\hline
430 \\
+ \quad 172 \\
\hline
602 \\
\end{array}
$$

$\leftarrow 43 \times 10$

$\leftarrow 43 \times 4$

$\leftarrow 43 \times 14$

Therefore $43 \times 14 = 602$.

Exercise 4E

Evaluate each of the following.

1 51×15	**2** 22×13	**3** 21×14	**4** 24×12	**5** 44×13	**6** 23×15
7 53×14	**8** 42×16	**9** 32×18	**10** 23×17	**11** 25×15	**12** 34×16
13 53×18	**14** 24×19	**15** 45×17	**16** 44×18	**17** 34×18	**18** 19×15

In Exercise 4E above we multiplied by numbers which had values between 10 and 20, but the same method can be used for multiplying by any two-figure number.

Example 5

Find the answer which is different.

a 88×23 **b** 56×36 **c** 96×21

a
$$
\begin{array}{r}
88 \\
\times \quad 23 \\
\hline
1760 \\
+ \quad 264 \\
\hline
2024 \\
\end{array}
$$
$\leftarrow 88 \times 20$
$\leftarrow 88 \times 3$
$\leftarrow 88 \times 23$

b
$$
\begin{array}{r}
56 \\
\times \quad 36 \\
\hline
1680 \\
+ \quad 336 \\
\hline
2016 \\
\end{array}
$$
$\leftarrow 56 \times 30$
$\leftarrow 56 \times 6$
$\leftarrow 56 \times 36$

c
$$
\begin{array}{r}
96 \\
\times \quad 21 \\
\hline
1920 \\
+ \quad 96 \\
\hline
2016 \\
\end{array}
$$
$\leftarrow 96 \times 20$
$\leftarrow 96 \times 1$
$\leftarrow 96 \times 21$

The answer which is different is **a**.

Exercise 4F

Find the answer which is different.

1 **a** 28×27 **b** 36×21 **c** 32×23		2 **a** 31×22 **b** 32×21 **c** 28×24
3 **a** 42×24 **b** 39×26 **c** 36×28		4 **a** 48×28 **b** 41×34 **c** 42×32
5 **a** 48×41 **b** 51×38 **c** 57×34		6 **a** 63×46 **b** 54×52 **c** 69×42
7 **a** 63×56 **b** 72×49 **c** 68×52		8 **a** 64×59 **b** 68×57 **c** 76×51

So far only numbers which themselves have two figures have been multiplied by two-figure numbers. We will now extend the method to multiply three-figure numbers by two-figure numbers.

Example 6

Find the answer which is different.

a 184×38 b 152×46 c 249×28

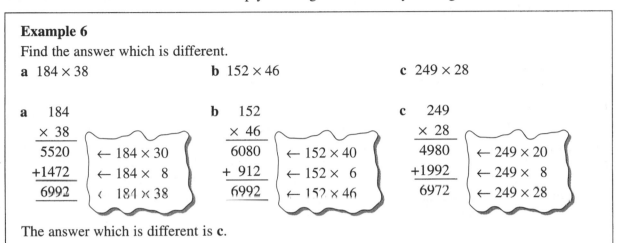

a
```
   184
 × 38
  5520    ← 184 × 30
+1472    ← 184 ×  8
  6992    ← 184 × 38
```

b
```
   152
 × 46
  6080    ← 152 × 40
+ 912    ← 152 ×  6
  6992    ← 152 × 46
```

c
```
   249
 × 28
  4980    ← 249 × 20
+1992    ← 249 ×  8
  6972    ← 249 × 28
```

The answer which is different is **c**.

Exercise 4G

Find the answer which is different.

1 **a** 117×56 **b** 124×53 **c** 182×36		2 **a** 128×63 **b** 183×44 **c** 224×36
3 **a** 252×16 **b** 212×19 **c** 168×24		4 **a** 169×26 **b** 183×24 **c** 244×18
5 **a** 296×14 **b** 259×16 **c** 173×24		6 **a** 144×26 **b** 142×27 **c** 156×24
7 **a** 154×25 **b** 160×24 **c** 256×15		8 **a** 225×16 **b** 136×25 **c** 150×24

Example 7

Find the value of 357×124.

Remember to put the numbers underneath each other in units, tens and hundreds, etc.

```
     357                    or        357
   × 124                            × 124
  35700    (357 × 100)               1428    (357 ×   4)
   7140    (357 ×  20)               7140    (357 ×  20)
   1428    (357 ×   4)              35700    (357 × 100)
  44268    (357 × 124)              44268    (357 × 124)
```

Therefore $357 \times 124 = 44268$.

Exercise 4H

For questions 1–5 evaluate the multiplication.

1 284×132 **2** 253×145 **3** 314×236 **4** 326×213 **5** 412×153

For questions 6–9 find the answer which is different.

6   **a** 198×124 **b** 192×128 **c** 186×132
7   **a** 228×192 **b** 256×171 **c** 238×184
8   **a** 324×156 **b** 308×164 **c** 287×176
9   **a** 336×198 **b** 362×184 **c** 378×176

4.5   Using multiplication in simple situations

Some simple long multiplications can be worked out mentally.

Look at Example 8 below and study the method carefully.

Example 8

Work out mentally: 500×60

$(5 \times 6) = 30$ and then three noughts must be added,
so $500 \times 60 = 30\,000$

Exercise 4J

Work out each of the following mentally.

1	90×40	**2**	70×30	**3**	50×30	**4**	80×40	**5**	70×60
6	60×40	**7**	90×50	**8**	70×20	**9**	60×30	**10**	90×60
11	80×20	**12**	90×30	**13**	200×40	**14**	300×20	**15**	400×20
16	600×20	**17**	200×20	**18**	300×30	**19**	400×30	**20**	600×40

Example 9

Aprille buys 4 choco bars at 17p per bar.
How much does she pay altogether?

$17p \times 4 = 28p + 40p = 68p$
Therefore the total cost is 68p.

Exercise 4K

1   A new-born kitten is 13 cm long.
    If the mother cat is 4 times longer, how long is the mother cat?

2   A dandelion in the garden is 16 cm tall.
    If a sunflower nearby is 5 times taller, how tall is the sunflower?

3   Toffee bars cost 23p each. If Julian buys 7 of them, how much does he pay?

4   Death Valley, in California, is 67 m below sea level. If the Dead Sea, in Palestine, is 6 times further below, how far below sea level is the Dead Sea?

5   An empty plastic bottle weights 117 grams, but when full of lemonade it is 8 times heavier.
    How heavy is the bottle when full?

6   The Wrekin, in Shropshire, is 335 m high, but Ben Nevis is 4 times higher.
    How high is Ben Nevis?

7   One Saturday 532 people turn up at a football ground for a reserve team match, but on the following Saturday 7 times as many people turn up when the first team play. How many people went to the first team match?

Example 10

A tall cabinet has shelves which each holds 45 books.
If the cabinet has 12 shelves how many books can it hold?

Each shelf holds 45 books.
So 12 shelves hold 45×12 books.
$$45 \times 12 = 540$$
So the cabinet can hold 540 books.

Exercise 4L

1   Meadow Lane School are having a day trip to the sea. The coaches used each have 38 seats and 13 of them are required.
    How many pupils are going on the trip if all the seats are occupied?

2   Mary has a dog who weighs 32 kg. She also has a horse who is 28 times heavier. How heavy is her horse?

3   A baker can stack 60 trays into his delivery van.
    If each tray holds 48 loaves, how many loaves can he deliver in his van?

4   A small village has only 156 inhabitants, but the market town nearby has 14 times as many. How many inhabitants does the market town have?

5   The River Thames is 336 km long, but the River Amazon is 19 times longer.
    How long is the River Amazon?

6   Hadrian's Wall is 120 km long, but the Great Wall of China is 23 times longer.
    How long is the Great Wall of China?

5 DIVISION

5.1 Division by counting

'Find how many times 4 goes into 12', and 'share 12 between 4 people' are
different ways of saying 'divide 12 by 4'.

Each of these can be represented by 12 ÷ 4, where '÷' is the symbol for
division (or $\frac{12}{4}$ or 12/4).

Example 1

a Find how many times 4 goes into 12. **b** Share 12 sweets between 4 people. **c** Find 15 ÷ 3.

a

Therefore 4 goes into 12 three times, so 12 ÷ 4 = 3.

b

When 12 sweets are shared between 4 people each one gets 3, so 12 ÷ 4 = 3.

c

Therefore 15 ÷ 3 = 5.

Exercise 5A

Work out each of the following by counting.

1 12 ÷ 3	**2** 15 ÷ 5	**3** 18 ÷ 6	**4** 12 ÷ 6	**5** 10 ÷ 5	**6** 20 ÷ 4
7 16 ÷ 4	**8** 20 ÷ 5	**9** 21 ÷ 3	**10** 9 ÷ 3	**11** 8 ÷ 4	**12** 6 ÷ 2

5.2 Dividing whole numbers by 10 and by 100

A number which ends with a nought can very easily be divided by 10.
Similarly a number which ends with two noughts can very easily be
divided by 100. Look at the following examples.

Example 2

Divide 70 by 10.

70 ÷ 10 = 7 (Each number is divided by 10, or each figure moves one place to the right.)

Example 3

Divide 500 by 100.

500 ÷ 100 = 5 (Each number is divided by 100, or each figure moves two places to the right.)

Exercise 5B

Divide each of the following by 10.

1 80 **2** 60 **3** 90 **4** 30 **5** 50 **6** 150 **7** 450 **8** 180

Divide each of the following by 100.

9 700 **10** 400 **11** 4200 **12** 8100 **13** 6000 **14** 5000

15 3800 away supporters arrived at a football ground by coach.
If 100 coaches were used and all were filled, how many travelled in each coach?

16 A bakery has 1500 loaves.
a If they exactly fill 100 trays, how many loaves can each tray hold?
b If 10 vans arrive and take all the loaves away, how many are loaded into each van if all vans take the same number?

5.3 Dividing by single-figure whole numbers

A multiplication table can be used for solving simple division problems.
An example is given below.

Example 4

Mrs Chavda has 24 chocolates. She shares them out equally between her 3 children.
How many does each child receive?

×	1	2	3	4	5	6	7	8	9	10
1	1	2	3	4	5	6	7	8	9	10
2	2	4	6	8	10	12	14	16	18	20
3	3	6	9	12	15	18	21	24	27	30
4	4	8	12	16	20	24	28	32	36	40
5	5	10	15	20	25	30	35	40	45	50
6	6	12	18	24	30	36	42	48	54	60
7	7	14	21	28	35	42	49	56	63	70
8	8	16	24	32	40	48	56	64	72	80
9	9	18	27	36	45	54	63	72	81	90
10	10	20	30	40	50	60	70	80	90	100

From the table 24 ÷ 3 = 8.

Therefore each child receives 8 chocolates.

Exercise 5C

Use the multiplication table to evaluate each of the following.

1 $45 \div 5$ **2** $35 \div 5$ **3** $72 \div 8$ **4** $56 \div 8$ **5** $48 \div 6$
6 $30 \div 6$ **7** $45 \div 9$ **8** $63 \div 9$ **9** $36 \div 9$ **10** $42 \div 7$

11 An electrician has a piece of wire which is 48 cm long. He has to cut it up into 8 equal pieces. How long will each piece be?

12 Janet pays the baker 30p for 5 buns.
How much does each bun cost?

13 Paul pays 32p for 8 erasers.
How much does each eraser cost?

14 Mushtaq pays 56p for 7 pencils.
How much does each pencil cost?

15 Shani has 18 kg of sugar. She finds that it fills 6 exactly similar bags.
How many kilograms does each bag hold?

16 Barbara has a piece of cotton which is 72 cm long.
If she has to cut it into 9 equal parts, how long will each part be?

17 A grocer has 54 eggs which he packs into cartons of 6.
How many cartons will he fill?

18 A greengrocer has 36 oranges which he places in packets of 4.
How many packets will he fill?

Example 5

Work out: **a** $72 \div 6$ **b** $135 \div 3$.

a $72 \div 6$

$6 \times 10 = 60$
$6 \times 2 = 12$
So $6 \times 12 = 72$

Tens	Units
6⌐7	¹2
1	2

Note 6 goes into 70 ten times. This leaves one ten to carry to the units column. 6 goes into 12 twice.

Therefore $72 \div 6 = 12$.

b $135 \div 3$

Hundreds	Tens	Units
3⌐1	¹3	¹5
	4	5

Therefore $135 \div 3 = 45$.

Exercise 5D

Find the answer which is different for each of the following.

1   **a** $48 \div 4$ **b** $26 \div 2$ **c** $36 \div 3$ **2**   **a** $69 \div 3$ **b** $46 \div 2$ **c** $96 \div 4$
3   **a** $72 \div 4$ **b** $85 \div 5$ **c** $54 \div 3$ **4**   **a** $98 \div 7$ **b** $90 \div 6$ **c** $56 \div 4$
5   **a** $90 \div 5$ **b** $38 \div 2$ **c** $57 \div 3$ **6**   **a** $138 \div 3$ **b** $192 \div 4$ **c** $240 \div 5$
7   **a** $168 \div 7$ **b** $156 \div 6$ **c** $216 \div 9$ **8**   **a** $185 \div 5$ **b** $296 \div 8$ **c** $117 \div 3$

5.4 Long division

Example 6
Find the answer which is different.

a $273 \div 13$ **b** $391 \div 17$ **c** $322 \div 14$

a
$$
\begin{array}{r}
21 \\
13\overline{)273} \\
-260 \quad \leftarrow 13 \times 20 \\
\hline
13 \\
-13 \quad \leftarrow 13 \times 1 \\
\hline
00
\end{array}
$$

b
$$
\begin{array}{r}
23 \\
17\overline{)391} \\
-340 \quad \leftarrow 17 \times 20 \\
\hline
51 \\
-51 \quad \leftarrow 17 \times 3 \\
\hline
00
\end{array}
$$

c
$$
\begin{array}{r}
23 \\
14\overline{)322} \\
-280 \quad \leftarrow 14 \times 20 \\
\hline
42 \\
-42 \quad \leftarrow 14 \times 3 \\
\hline
00
\end{array}
$$

The answer which is different is **a**.

Exercise 5E

Find the answer which is different for each of the following.

1 **a** $468 \div 13$ **b** $612 \div 17$ **c** $476 \div 14$ **2** **a** $946 \div 22$ **b** $966 \div 23$ **c** $882 \div 21$
3 **a** $714 \div 34$ **b** $792 \div 36$ **c** $672 \div 32$ **4** **a** $980 \div 28$ **b** $918 \div 27$ **c** $884 \div 26$
5 **a** $696 \div 29$ **b** $648 \div 27$ **c** $728 \div 28$ **6** **a** $850 \div 17$ **b** $960 \div 16$ **c** $950 \div 19$
7 **a** $750 \div 25$ **b** $600 \div 15$ **c** $360 \div 12$ **8** **a** $900 \div 18$ **b** $560 \div 14$ **c** $800 \div 16$

5.5 Using division in simple situations

Example 7
Work out mentally: $350 \div 70$.

$350 \div 70 = 35 \div 7 = 5$
(dividing the top and bottom each by 10)

Exercise 5F

Work these out mentally.

1 $270 \div 30$ **2** $480 \div 60$ **3** $150 \div 30$ **4** $160 \div 20$ **5** $540 \div 60$
6 $140 \div 20$ **7** $630 \div 70$ **8** $720 \div 90$ **9** $560 \div 80$ **10** $250 \div 50$
11 $360 \div 60$ **12** $160 \div 40$ **13** $640 \div 80$ **14** $200 \div 40$ **15** $300 \div 60$

Example 8

Mrs Marks spends 48p on 4 bars of chocolate. How much does each bar cost?

$48p \div 4 = 12p$ (Check: $4 \times 12p = 48p$)

Therefore each bar costs 12p.

Exercise 5G

1   There are 76 pupils in a small nursery school and they are equally divided between the school's 4 houses.
How many pupils are there in each house?

2   There are 738 pupils at Grove Lane School, and they are equally divided between the 6 years.
How many pupils are there in each year?

3   A multistorey car park has 7 levels. It has spaces for 805 cars and the spaces are equally divided between the 7 levels.
How many spaces are there on each level?

4   5 identical crates are loaded on to a van. Their total weight is the van's maximum load of 750 kg.
What is the weight of each crate?

Example 9

A milkman has 99 bottles and he has to put them into crates which hold 8 bottles each.
How many crates will he fill, and how many bottles will be left over?

99 must be divided by 8 $8 \overline{\smash{\big)}9\,{}^19}$
                                    12   remainder 3
He will fill 12 crates and have 3 bottles left over.

Example 10

A carpenter requires 43 screws for making a large cabinet.
If he can only buy the screws in packets of 4, how many packets must he buy and how many screws will he not use?

43 must be divided by 4 $4 \underline{|43}$
                                    10   remainder 3
10 packets will not be enough, so he must buy 11 packets and have 1 screw left over.

Exercise 5H

1 A shop manager has 80 cans of lemonade and he places them into packs of 6 in order to sell them.
How many packs will he fill and how many cans will be left over?

2 A farmer has 74 eggs and he places them into cartons of 6 in order to sell them.
How many cartons will he fill and how many eggs will be left over?

3 A hardware shop manager has 78 castors and he places them into packets of 4 in order to sell them.
How many packets will he fill and how many castors will be left over?

4 The manager of an electrical goods shop has 59 light bulbs and he places them into packets of 4 in order to sell them.
a How many packets will he fill?
b How many bulbs will be left over?

5 Buttons cost 7p each.
a How many can I buy with a 50p piece?
b What change will I receive?

6 Pencils cost 9p each.
a How many can I buy with a 50p piece?
b What change will I receive?

7 A builder requires 93 floor boards for a new house, but he can only buy them in bundles of 4.
a How many bundles will he require?
b How many boards will he not use?

8 A nurse requires 70 tablets but she can only find them in packets of 6.
a How many packets will she require?
b How many tablets will she not use?

9 An art teacher requires 22 special pencils for the children in her class, but she can only buy them in packets of 3.
a How many packets will she require?
b How many pencils will she not use?

10 Candace requires 35 cakes for a party, but she can only buy them in packets of 8.
a How many packets must she buy?
b How many cakes will not be required for the party?

Example 11

At Highfield School there are 450 pupils. If there are 18 pupils in each class how many classes are there altogether?

We need to work out $450 \div 18$:

$$
\begin{array}{r}
25 \\
18\overline{)450} \\
-360 \quad (18 \times 20) \\
\hline
90 \\
-90 \quad (18 \times 5) \\
\hline
0
\end{array}
$$

Therefore $450 \div 18 = 25$, so there are 25 classes.

Exercise 5J

1   A farmer has 600 bags of potatoes.
    If he sells the same number of bags to each
    of 25 greengrocers, how many bags does
    each one receive?

2   Mr Khan's car has a puncture and he has to
    raise the car through 210 millimetres
    before he can remove the wheel.
    If every complete turn of the jack handle
    lifts the car through 14 millimetres, how
    many times must he turn it?

3   At a garage the storage chamber under a
    petrol pump has 980 litres left inside it.
    How many petrol tanks, each of capacity
    35 litres, can it fill?

4   In a block of flats there are 180 dwellings
    which are equally divided between the 15
    floors.
    How many dwellings are there on each
    floor?

5   300 trains depart from a large station every
    day and there are the same number of
    departures from each of the 12 platforms.
    How many trains leave each platform
    daily?

6   One Saturday there were 198 footballers
    playing in the Premier division matches.
    Given that there are 11 players in each
    team, how many teams were playing?

7   864 people are sitting in a stand at a
    football ground.
    If there are 16 seats in each row, how
    many people are sitting in each row if
    every seat is occupied?

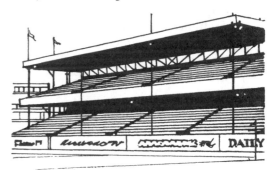

8   A hospital has 336 beds which are equally
    divided between its 14 wards.
    How many beds are there in each ward?

6   TIME

6.1   Understanding units of time

As people became aware of the cycles of the sun and the moon, and the changing nature of the seasons, it was necessary to describe and measure these periods of time, and then to subdivide them.

A **day** was chosen as the periodic time between the sun making successive appearances at its highest point.

A **week** was chosen as a period of 7 days.

A **month** was chosen as the periodic time between the moon making successive appearances at its fullest. (This in fact was called a lunar month and is 28 days.)

A **year**, initially thought to be twelve lunar months (or 336 days) but subsequently fixed at 365 days (366 days in a leap year), was chosen as a complete cycle of the seasons. There are, in fact, 13 lunar months in a complete year because 28 × 13 = 364 days. A leap year, every fourth year, is necessary as a more refined adjustment.

The twelve months were named January (31 days), February (28 or 29 days), March (31 days), April (30 days), May (31 days), June (30 days), July (31 days), August (31 days), September (30 days), October (31 days), November (30 days) and December (31 days). The number of days were chosen as shown in order to make up one complete year of 365 days (or 366 days in a leap year).

Each day is divided into 24 hours.

Each hour is subdivided into 60 minutes.

Each minute is subdivided again into 60 seconds.

It therefore follows that 1 hour (or 60 minutes) = 60 × 60 seconds = 3600 seconds.

Example 1
Change 4 hours to:
a minutes   **b** seconds.

a 4 hours = (4 × 60) minutes
   = 240 minutes
b 4 hours = (4 × 60) minutes × 60 seconds
   = 14 400 seconds

Example 2
Change 720 minutes to:
a hours   **b** seconds

a (720 ÷ 60) hours = 12 hours
b (720 × 60) seconds = 43 200 seconds

Example 3

Change 54 000 seconds to: **a** minutes   **b** hours.

a 54 000 seconds = (54 000 ÷ 60) minutes = 900 minutes
b 54 000 seconds = (54 000 ÷ 60) minutes ÷ 60 hours = 15 hours

Exercise 6A

Copy and complete the table below.

	Hours	Minutes	Seconds
1	8	480	28800
2	5	30	1800
3	20	1200	7200
4	50	3000	300000
5	4	240	14400
6	7	420	2560
7	9	540	32 400
8	25	1500	90 000

6.2   Reading and using a calendar

A calendar is a list of the days, weeks and months in a year. It is usually organised on a weekly or a monthly basis.

1998						
January	Monday		5	12	19	26
	Tuesday		6	13	20	27
	Wednesday		7	14	21	28
	Thursday	1	8	15	22	29
	Friday	2	9	16	23	30
	Saturday	3	10	17	24	31
	Sunday	4	11	18	25	

Individual dates may be written in different ways, e.g. January the 7th, the 7th of January, or 7 January. We shall use the style '7 January'.

Exercise 6B

Using the calendar on page 44 for January 1998 write down the day of the week on which each of the following dates occur.

1 1 January   **2** 5 January   **3** 13 January   **4** 29 January

On which date in the month is each of the following?

5 the first Monday   **6** the first Saturday   **7** the second Sunday
8 the third Thursday   **9** the fourth Wednesday   **10** the fifth Thursday

As 31 January 1998 fell on a Saturday, it follows that 1 February 1998 would fall on a Sunday. This enables us to make up the calendar for February 1998, which has 28 days.

1998						
February	Monday		2	9	16	23
	Tuesday		3	10	17	24
	Wednesday		4	11	18	25
	Thursday		5	12	19	26
	Friday		6	13	20	27
	Saturday		7	14	21	28
	Sunday	1	8	15	22	

(**Note:**   in each row the numbers go up by 7, e.g. 5 → 12 → 19 → 26. This is because there are 7 days from one week to the next.)

Exercise 6C

For questions 1 and 2 the above calendar for February 1998 is required.

1 On what day of the week will 1 March fall?

2 Make out a calendar for March 1998.

3 What will be the date in March on:
a the first Wednesday
b the second Friday
c the fourth Sunday?

4 Mumbi goes on an outward bound course starting on a Sunday and is away for seven days during the fourth week in March. Between which dates is she away?

5 A special religious group always celebrates Easter such that the days from Good Friday to Easter Monday inclusive occur as late as possible in March. On what date in 1998 will they celebrate:
a Good Friday
b Easter Monday?

Example 4

Part of a calendar is shown in each of parts **a** and **b** below. (They are not for the same month.)
Complete the rest of the dates for Tuesdays and Wednesdays in these two months.

a

Tuesday					
Wednesday			12	19	

b

Tuesday			16		
Wednesday					31

a

Tuesday		4	11	18	25
Wednesday		5	12	19	26

b

Tuesday		2	9	16	23	30
Wednesday		3	10	17	24	31

Exercise 6D

Part of a calendar is shown in each of the questions below. If all are different
months but all have 31 days, complete the rest of the dates for each case.

1

Saturday		9			
Sunday	3				

2

Saturday	1				
Sunday		9			

3

Saturday		14			
Sunday	1				

4

Wednesday				29	
Thursday					
Friday	3				

5

Wednesday		6			
Thursday					
Friday			22		

6

Wednesday			24		
Thursday					
Friday		12			

Example 5

Suppose today is Friday 16 October. Find each of the following:

a the date last Friday   **b** the date next Friday

c the date in two weeks' time   **d** the day and date in 10 days' time.

a $16 - 7 = 9$ so last Friday was the 9 October.

b $16 + 7 = 23$ so next Friday will be the 23 October.

c $16 + 7 + 7 = 30$ so in two weeks' time it will be Friday 30 October.

d $16 + 10 = 26$ so the date will be the 26 October. As $10 = 7 + 3$,
the day will be 3 days after next Friday and will
therefore be a Monday. So in 10 days' time it will
be Monday 26 October.

Exercise 6E

1   Suppose today is Saturday 10 March. Find each of the following.
    a The date last Saturday
    b the date next Saturday
    c the date in two weeks' time
    d the day and date in 9 days' time.

2   Suppose today is Sunday 13 August. Find each of the following.
    a The date last Sunday
    b the date next Sunday
    c the date in two weeks' time
    d the day and date in 10 days' time.

3   If today is Tuesday 17 July, find:
    a the date last Tuesday
    b the date two weeks ago
    c the date next Tuesday
    d the date in two weeks' time
    e the day and date in 12 days' time.

4   If today is Monday 15 October, find:
    a the date last Monday
    b the date two weeks ago
    c the date next Monday
    d the date in two weeks' time
    e the day and date in 13 days' time.

Example 6

If today is Monday 4 July, find each of the following.

a the date this coming Wednesday

b the date on Wednesday next week

c the day and date in 22 days' time.

a $4 + 2 = 6$ so the date on this coming Wednesday is 6 July.
b $4 + 7 + 2 = 13$ so the date on Wednesday next week is 13 July.
c $4 + 22 = 26$ so the date will be the 26 July. As $22 = 3 \times 7 + 1$, the day will be one day after a Monday, i.e. a Tuesday, so the day and date will be Tuesday 26 July.

Exercise 6F

1   If today is Monday 7 July, find each of the following.
    a The date this coming Thursday
    b the date on Thursday next week
    c the day and date in 17 days' time
    d the day and date in 23 days' time.

2   If today is Tuesday 5 April, find each of the following.
    a The date this coming Friday
    b the date on Friday next week
    c the day and date in 18 days' time
    d the day and date in 24 days' time.

3   If today is Wednesday 2 February, find:
    a the date this coming Friday
    b the day and date in 15 days' time
    c the day and date in 27 days' time, given that this year is a leap year.

4   If today is Wednesday 4 March, find:
    a the dates on this coming Saturday and Sunday
    b the day and date in 20 days' time
    c the day and date in 26 days' time.

6.3   Reading times

(a.m. and p.m., 12-hour and 24-hour clocks, analogue and digital clocks)

We now use two different types of clocks and watches, one type has a face with moving hands, the other has a display which simply shows numbers.

The clock with hands is called an **analogue** clock, since any movement of time can be shown, whereas the clock which just shows numbers is called a **digital** clock. A digital clock can only show whole numbers of hours, minutes and seconds, or very occasionally tenths of a second.

12-hour and 24-hour digital clocks
The day of 24 hours is split up into morning (a.m.) and afternoon (p.m.).

Most analogue clocks and some digital watches can only show up to 12 hours, so we have to attach the labels a.m. for a morning time and p.m. for an afternoon time.

The table below compares the two different types of digital watch.

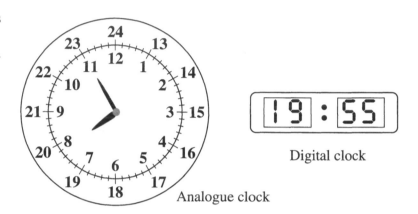

Digital clock

Analogue clock

12-hour clock	Read as	24-hour clock	Read as
1.30 am	One thirty a.m.	01.30	One thirty
7.45 a.m.	Seven forty-five a.m.	07.45	Seven forty-five
11.20 a.m.	Eleven twenty a.m.	11.20	Eleven twenty
12.00 noon	Twelve noon	12.00	Twelve noon
1.30 p.m.	One thirty p.m.	13.30	Thirteen thirty
7.45 p.m.	Seven forty-five p.m.	19.45	Nineteen forty-five
11.20 p.m.	Eleven twenty p.m.	23.20	Twenty-three twenty
12.00 midnight	Twelve midnight	24.00 or 00.00	Midnight

In each case the numbers before the dot refer to the hours and the numbers after the dot refer to the minutes. Some people refer to 01.30 and 07.45 on the 24-hour display as 'Oh' one thirty and 'Oh' seven forty-five and to 11.00 and 15.00 as eleven hundred hours and fifteen hundred hours.

Exercise 6G

For questions 1–6 a time on a digital watch display is shown. State each of the times in words.

1 11.15   **2** 10.40   **3** 09.20   **4** 08.15   **5** 17.30   **6** 22.35

For questions 7–14 a time on the twenty-four-hour clock is stated in words. Write each time in figures.

7   Ten fifteen   **8**   Eleven forty   **9**   Nine twenty-five   **10**   Seven forty-five
11 Thirteen twenty   **12** Eighteen forty-five **13** Nineteen forty   **14**   Twenty-two thirty

12-hour analogue clocks

Most analogue clocks have two hands, a short one to indicate the hours and a long one to indicate the minutes. The numbers on the face refer only to the hours, so you have to work out the minutes by imagining the dial divided into 60 divisions or five divisions between each of the hour numbers.

a
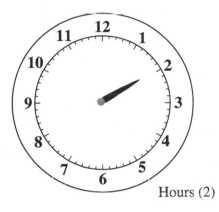
Hours (2)

b

Minutes (12)

Note   In **a** when the hour hand lies anywhere between the 2 and the 3 it is still indicating 2 hours. In **b** the hour numbers are multiplied by 5 to give the number of minutes ($2 \times 5 + 2 = 12$ minutes).

Example 7

What time does each clock show?

a

b

a The hour hand points between 1 and 2, i.e. 1 hour. The minute hand points at the 4, i.e. $4 \times 5 = 20$ minutes. So the time is one (or thirteen) twenty, or in figures 01.20 or 13.20 if after mid-day.

b The hour hand points between 5 and 6, i.e. 5 hours. The minute hand points at the second line past the nine, i.e. $9 \times 5 + 2 = 47$ minutes. So the time is five (or seventeen) forty-seven, or in figures 05.47 or 17.47.

Exercise 6H

For each of the following write down:
a the time shown on the 12-hour clock (which may be a.m. or p.m.)
b both possibilities on the 24-hour clock.

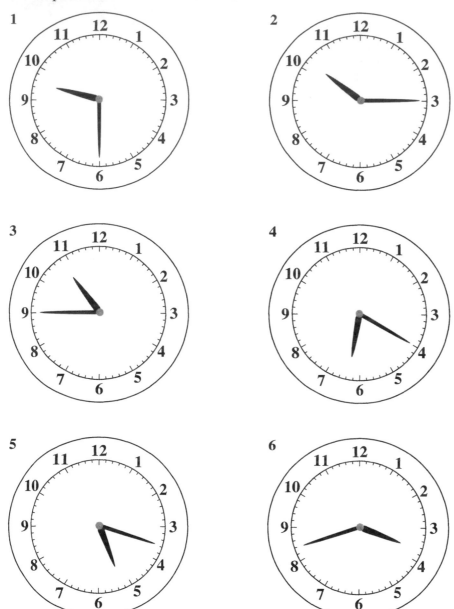

For questions 7–12 change each time to the 12-hour clock and draw each time on a clock face.

7 08.10   **8** 09.15   **9** 07.25   **10** 13.15   **11** 16.20   **12** 20.30

21416/510.76 ED

For questions 13–20 draw each time on a clock face.

13 eight thirty   **14** eleven fifteen   **15** two twenty   **16** six forty-five

17 thirteen forty-five   **18** sixteen forty   **19** twenty-one twenty   **20** twenty-two five

Calculating differences in times

Example 8

a I arrived at the football ground at 7.15 p.m. and I left the ground at 9.23 p.m.
How long was I in the ground?

b I left home at 6.47 p.m. and I returned at 10.15 p.m. For how long was I away from home?

a 7.15 p.m. to 9.15 p.m. is 2 hours, 9.15 to 9.23 p.m. is 8 minutes, so 7.15 p.m. to 9.23 p.m. is 2 hours and 8 minutes.

b 6.47 p.m. to 7.00 p.m. is 13 minutes (60 minutes in 1 hour), 7.00 p.m. to 10.00 p.m. is 3 hours, and 10.00 p.m. to 10.15 p.m. is 15 minutes, so the total time is 13 minutes + 3 hours + 15 minutes = 3 hours 28 minutes.

In **a** above it was easier to find the complete hours first and then the remaining minutes, whereas in **b** above it was better to work up to the hour and from the hour.

Example 9

a I arrived at the squash club at 19.03 and left at 22.22. How long was I there?

b I arrived home from work at 18.45 and left home the next morning at 07.20. For how long was I at home?

a 19.03 to 22.03 is 3 hours, and 22.03 to 22.22 is 9 minutes, so the total time is 3 hours and 9 minutes.

b 18.45 to 19.00 is 15 minutes, 19.00 to 24.00 is 5 hours, 00.00 to 07.00 is 7 hours, and 07.00 to 07.20 is 20 minutes (15 minutes + 5 hours + 7 hours + 20 minutes), so the total time is 12 hours and 35 minutes.

Again in Example 9**a** it is easier to find the complete hours first.

However, in Example 9**b** above it may be easier to find the time up to midnight and the time after midnight separately.

Exercise 6J

How long is it from:

1	10.20 a.m. to 11.35 p.m?	**2**	11.05 a.m. to 12.30 p.m?	**3**	2.25 p.m. to 7.50 p.m?
4	3.50 p.m. to 4.30 p.m?	**5**	12.55 p.m. to 1.40 p.m?	**6**	8.45 a.m. to 9.10 a.m.?

7   A film show at a cinema starts at 14.30 and ends at 16.45. How long does it last?

8   A ship leaves Liverpool at 13.15 and arrives at Douglas (Isle of Man) at 17.30.
How long does the voyage last?

9   One morning I arrived at a bus stop at 08.55, but no bus came until 09.20.
How long did I have to wait?

10   I left London in my car at 14.40 and arrived in Brighton at 16.15.
How long did my journey last?

6.4   Reading and using timetables

Apart from school timetables which show which class a teacher is taking
in a particular room, timetables are used for appointments and to show the
times of buses and trains.

Example 10

Look at the doctors' timetable for next Monday morning.

		Dr Jones	Dr Aval	Dr Singh	Dr Williams
Monday	9.00	Mr Bell	Miss English	(Not available)	Mr Patrick
	9.15	Mrs Bell	Mr Horne	Mr Ward	
	9.30		Mrs Horne	Miss Weston	Miss Lee
	9.45	Miss Jones	Mrs James	Mrs Kirby	Mr Brown
	10.00	Mr Green	Mr Sasha	Mr Smith	Mrs Hart
	10.15	Miss Feather	(Not available)		Mr Tenny
	10.30	Mr Amail	(Not available)	Mrs Davey	Miss Havil

a At what time and with whom is Mr Smith's appointment?

b Who is seeing Dr Williams at 10.15 a.m.?

c What is the earliest free appointment and with which doctor?

d What is the latest free appointment and with which doctor?

a	10.00 a.m. with Dr Singh	**b**	Mr Tenny
c	9.15 a.m. with Dr Williams	**d**	10.15 a.m. with Dr Singh

Exercise 6K

1   Several children apply to go to a new school. They are interviewed on
Monday by the head, deputy head or senior teacher.

		Head	Deputy Head	Senior Teacher
Monday	9.00	Jisanne	George	Jordan
	9.15	Marlon	Marcus	
	9.30		Ayo	Josiah
	9.45	Bobbie	Tony	Bernard
	10.00	Natalie	Naomi	Wendy
	10.15	Kate	Michelle	Anne
	10.30	Nicola		Laura

a   At what time and with whom are the following interviewed?
  i Marlon   **ii** Nicola   **iii** Michelle   **iv** Ayo   **v** Josiah   **vi** Anne
b   Who has an appointment with:
  i   the head at 9.45 a.m.   **ii**   the head at 10.15 a.m.
  iii the deputy head at 9.15 a.m.   **iv**   the deputy head at 10.00 a.m.
  v   the senior teacher at 9.00 a.m. **vi**   the senior teacher at 10.00 a.m.?
c   Bradley, Adam and Amy are late applicants. If they are to be
interviewed by the head, the deputy head and the senior teacher
respectively, at what times will their appointments have to be?

2   Several ladies are going to the hairdresser's on Friday morning. Their appointment details are
given below.

		Stylists			
		Charmaine (Cut and blow dry)	Rita (Shampoo and set)	Zoey (Perm)	Afiya (Dye)
Friday	9.00		Mrs Steiner	Miss Satur	Mrs Larn
	9.30	Miss Harris	Miss Bergman		
	10.00	Mrs Fox		Mrs Slade	Ms Gupta
	10.30	Ms Sherman	Mrs Vaughan	Ms Philips	
	11.00		Mrs Ratwana	Mrs O'Brien	Mrs Hornsby-Smith
	11.30	Mrs Ahmed	Ms Sing		Ms Brown
	12.00	Mrs Patel		Mrs Laiger	Joanna

a   At what time, with whom and for what purpose do each of the
following have an appointment?
  i   Mrs Ahmed   **ii** Miss Harris   **iii** Miss Bergman **iv** Mrs Ratwana
  v   Mrs Laiger   **vi** Ms Philips   **vii** Ms Brown?

(continued)

   b Who has an appointment for:
      i   a cut and blow dry at 10.30 a.m.   **ii**   a cut and blow dry at 12.00 a.m.
      iii a shampoo and set at 10.30 a.m.   **iv** a shampoo and set at 11.30 a.m.
      v a perm at 9.00 a.m.   **vi** a perm at 11.00 a.m.
      vii a dye at 11.00 a.m.   **viii** a dye at 12.00 a.m.?
   c Mrs White and Mrs McAndrew have decided that they want a perm
      and a dye respectively. Could they go to the hairdresser's at the
      same time on Friday morning and if so, when?

Example 11

New Milton Bus Timetable					
	Bus Routes				
Monday to Fridays	**190**	**191**	**192**	**191**	**191**
New Milton	09 27	10 42	11 42	14 12	16 42
Marryat Road		10 46	11 54	14 16	16 46
Hazelwood Avenue		10 48	11 56	14 18	16 48
Chatsworth Park	09 47	10 51	11 59	14 21	16 51
Hazelwood Avenue	09 51	10 54		14 24	16 54
Marryat Road	09 53	10 56		14 26	16 56
New Milton	10 06	11 00	12 19	14 30	17 00

The above timetable shows the times of buses from New Milton to
Chatsworth Park which then return to New Milton.
a What time does service 192 leave New Milton?
b What time does service 192 reach Chatsworth Park?
c How long does it take on service 192 to get from New Milton to Chatsworth Park?
d How long does it take on service 192 to return from Chatsworth Park to New Milton?
e What is the shortest time any bus takes from New Milton to Chatsworth Park?

a 11 42   **b** 11 59   **c** 17 minutes (11 42 to 11 59)
d 20 minutes (11 59 to 12 19)   **e** 9 minutes (10 42 to 10 51)

Exercise 6L

All questions refer to the bus timetable in the example above.

1   What time does the 190 leave New Milton?
2   What time does the 190 reach Chatsworth Park?
3   What time does the 192 return to New Milton?
4   How long does it take on the 190 to get from New Milton to Chatsworth Park?
5   After the 192 leaves New Milton, how long is it before it returns?

6 From New Milton to Chatsworth Park the 192 takes a longer route than the 191. Between which two points does it take a longer route?

7 On the return journey from Chatsworth Park to New Milton the 190 takes different times to the 191 between two pairs of points. Which are the two pairs of points?

8 Do you think that the 190 takes the same route from New Milton to Chatsworth Park as the 192 does from Chatsworth Park back to New Milton? Explain your answer.

Exercise 6M

Settle and Carlisle Railway Timetable					
Settle	07 15	09 45	11 45	14 15	17 30
Horton	07 25	09 55	11 55	14 25	17 40
Ribblehead	07 35	10 05	12 05	14 35	17 50
Dent	07 45	10 15	12 15	14 45	18 00
Garsdale	07 50	10 20	12 20	14 50	18 05
Kirkby Stephen	08 10	10 40	12 40	15 10	18 25
Appleby	08 25	10 55	12 55	15 25	18 40
Langwathby	08 40	11 10	13 10	15 40	18 55
Lazonby	08 45	11 15	13 15	15 45	19 00
Armathwaite	08 55	11 25	13 25	15 55	19 10
Carlisle	09 10	11 40	13 40	16 10	19 25
Carlisle	06 30	10 00	12 30	16 15	17 45
Armathwaite	06 45				
Lazonby	06 55				
Langwathby	07 00				
Appleby	07 15				
Kirkby Stephen	07 30				
Garsdale	07 50				
Dent	07 55				
Ribblehead	08 05				
Horton	08 15				
Settle	08 25				

(continued)

1   Suppose all trains take the same time between all stations.
    Copy and complete the Carlisle table.

2   How long does it take any train to travel from Settle to Carlisle?

3   Brenda goes from Settle to Carlisle for a day's shopping.
    What is the longest time she can have in Carlisle?

4   Marcus goes from Settle to Garsdale for a day's fell walking.
    What is the longest time he can have between arriving and departing?

5   Ayo goes from Settle to Kirkby Stephen to visit his friend for the day. If he leaves Settle on the first afternoon train, what is the longest time he can have?

6   Kanika goes from Settle to Appleby to visit a market, but she has to be back in Settle by early in the evening. Find
    a the time of the latest train she must catch from Appleby
    b the longest time she can have.

7   To what station does a train from Settle take exactly
    a 30 minutes
    b 1 hour 30 minutes to reach?

8   Ronnie lives near Dent station and he travels daily to Settle to work. How long does his train journey last?

9   Josiah lives in Horton and he travels daily to Appleby to work. How long does his train journey last?

10 Two trains pass each other midway between Settle and Horton. Which two trains are these?

7 USING YOUR CALCULATOR (1)
(+, −, × AND ÷ WITH WHOLE NUMBERS)

7.1 A first look at your calculator

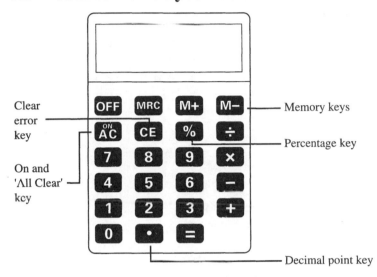

Clear error key

On and 'All Clear' key

Memory keys

Percentage key

Your calculator may have additional keys:

+/−

√

etc.

Decimal point key

Most simple calculators will have the majority of the keys shown above, although some may not have the memory keys (see page 167) or the % key. On some calculators the ON/OFF key is a single key and there are separate keys for clearing everything (**AC**) and clearing the last entry (**CE**), which can also be thought of as the 'clear error' key.

Example 1

Use your calculator to find 23 + 19.

Press your calculator keys as shown below:

AC **2** **3** **+** **1** **9** **=**   42

The answer (42), followed by a decimal point should appear at the right-hand end of the screen. It is necessary to press the **AC** key to start with in order to clear the calculator from any previous use. It is also essential to remember to press the **=** key.

Example 2

Use your calculator to find:

a 23 − 19   **b** 24 × 5   **c** 24 ÷ 8

a **AC** **2** **3** **−** **1** **9** **=** 4   **b** **AC** **2** **4** **×** **5** **=** 120

c **AC** **2** **4** **÷** **8** **=** 3

Clearing errors

If you make a mistake entering a number before you press the **+**, **−**, **×**, **÷** or **=** key, you can press the **CE** (clear error) key and then re-enter the number.

For example: **AC** **2** **4** **CE** **2** **3** **−** **9** **=** **4**   will calculate 23 − 19 rather than 24 − 19.

Exercise 7A

Use your calculator to find the answer which is different.

1	**a** 55 + 29	**b** 46 + 37	**c** 67 + 16		**2**	**a** 78 + 37	**b** 59 + 56	**c** 67 + 49
3	**a** 97 − 39	**b** 84 − 25	**c** 72 − 13		**4**	**a** 135 − 48	**b** 113 − 27	**c** 120 − 34
5	**a** 18 × 9	**b** 24 × 7	**c** 56 × 3		**6**	**a** 39 × 24	**b** 36 × 26	**c** 43 × 22
7	**a** 80 ÷ 5	**b** 84 ÷ 6	**c** 98 ÷ 7		**8**	**a** 299 ÷ 13	**b** 288 ÷ 12	**c** 506 ÷ 22

7.2   Order of operations

Not all calculators operate in the same way, so it is important to find out what type of calculator you have before trying anything other than the simplest of calculations.

Example 3 shows you how to find out which type of calculator you have.

Example 3

Use your calculator to find 2 + 3 × 4 by pressing the keys in this order

AC **2** **+** **3** **×** **4** **=**

You will get one of two possible answers: either 20 or 14. Which one you get will depend on the calculator you are using. If you have a simple 'four-rule' calculator (+, −, ×, ÷) you are likely to get 20, whereas if you have a 'scientific' calculator you will get 14.

The 'four-rule' calculators work in the order in which you enter the numbers and operations. These have what is known as **arithmetic** logic. For example, 2 + 3 × 4 becomes: 2 + 3 = 5, and 5 × 4 = 20.

'Scientific' calculators have the conventional **algebraic** logic built into them. This means that they work out any multiplications and divisions before any additions and subtractions.

With algebraic logic, 2 + 3 × 4 becomes: 3 × 4 = 12, and then 2 + 12 = 14.

The following example illustrates why you need to know which type of calculator you have.

Example 4

Use your calculator to find the cost of buyng one shirt (£12) and two pairs of socks (£3 each).

We need to find £12 + 2 × £3 so we would like to enter 12 + 2 × 3.

The 'scientific' calculator would give the correct answer of £18 (12 + 6), whereas the 'four-rule' calculator, with this sequence of key presses, would give an incorrect result of £42 (14 × 3).

You will see on page 168 how the use of the calculator's memory can get round this problem.

Exercise 7B

If you have a 'scientific' calculator you may enter the numbers as shown.

If you have a 'four-rule' calculator you will need to do the multiplication or division first.

1   Find the cost of buying one pair of trousers (£20) and three shirts (£7 each). $(20 + 3 \times 7)$
2   Find the cost of buying one jumper (£15) and four tee-shirts (£5 each). $(15 + 4 \times 5)$
3   Find the change from £20 after buying four pairs of socks (£3 each). $(20 - 4 \times 3)$
4   Find the change from £50 after buying two dresses (£23 each). $(50 - 2 \times 23)$
5   Find the cost of buying one pair of water skis (£150) and a half share in a speed boat which cost £1200. $(150 + \dfrac{1200}{2})$

6   Find my change from £50 if I pay a quarter share of a meal which cost £64. $(50 - \dfrac{64}{4})$

7.3   Using estimations to check calculations

It is very useful to make a rough estimate in order to check whether an addition or subtraction has been worked out correctly. Look at the following examples.

Example 5

Find the sum of 49 and 32 and check your answer with a rough estimate.

$49 + 32$ Adding 50 and   50   (49 to the nearest ten)
$= 81$ 30 is a rough   +30   (32 to the nearest ten)
                      estimate.   ────
                                            80

It can be seen that the estimate agrees roughly with the correct answer.

Example 6

Find the difference between 315 and 197 and check your answer with a rough estimate.

315 – 197   Subtracting 200   300   (315 to the nearest hundred)
= 118   from 300 is a   –200   (197 to the nearest hundred)
                rough estimate   100

It can be seen that the estimate agrees roughly with the correct answer.

To make rough estimates, two-figure numbers are corrected to the nearest ten, whereas three-figure numbers are corrected to the nearest hundred.

Exercise 7C

Use your calculator to find the sum and check your answer with a rough estimate.

1	86 and 24	**2**	48 and 27	**3**	76 and 39	**4**	28 and 9
5	281 and 122	**6**	417 and 381	**7**	521 and 279	**8**	593 and 380

Use your calculator to find the difference and check your answer with a rough estimate.

9	96 and 57	**10**	67 and 18	**11**	92 and 33	**12**	71 and 43
13	486 and 217	**14**	590 and 313	**15**	878 and 489	**16**	385 and 192

Example 7

Find the product of 41 and 29 and check your answer with a rough estimate.

$41 \times 29 = 1189$

Multiplying 40 by 30 is a rough estimate:

$40 \times 30 = 1200$

It can be seen that the rough estimate approximately agrees with the correct answer.

Exercise 7D

Use your calculator to find the product and check your answer with a rough estimate.

1	82 and 69	**2**	73 and 49	**3**	52 and 39	**4**	63 and 48	**5**	81 and 59
6	92 and 29	**7**	51 and 39	**8**	72 and 38	**9**	72 and 59	**10**	53 and 38

7.4   Approximating by rounding to the nearest whole number, to the nearest ten and to the nearest hundred

Any multiplication of whole numbers will always result in a whole number answer.

When a whole number is divided by another whole number the answer is not always a whole number.

Example 8

Use your calculator to find 38 ÷ 5.

Give your answer correct to the nearest whole number.

Press your calculator keys as shown below:

AC **3** **8** **÷** **5** **=**   `7.6`

The answer to the nearest whole number is 8 because the figure after the decimal point is more than 5.

Note   We would also round up to the next whole number if the figure after the decimal point was equal to 5 (i.e. 7.5 rounded up becomes 8) but when this figure is less than 5 we would round down (i.e. 7.4 becomes 7).

Exercise 7E

Use your calculator to work out these divisions. Give each answer correct to the nearest whole number.

1	29 ÷ 10	2	59 ÷ 10	3	178 ÷ 20	4	348 ÷ 40	5	21 ÷ 5
6	46 ÷ 5	7	61 ÷ 5	8	134 ÷ 20	9	261 ÷ 30	10	189 ÷ 15
11	73 ÷ 5	12	106 ÷ 20	13	279 ÷ 30	14	60 ÷ 25	15	237 ÷ 15
16	108 ÷ 20	17	30 ÷ 4	18	36 ÷ 8	19	88 ÷ 5	20	350 ÷ 20

Example 9

Use your calculator to find: 1254 ÷ 40.

Give your answer correct to the nearest whole number.

Press your calculator keys as shown below:

AC **1** **2** **5** **4** **÷** **4** **0** **=**   `31.35`

The answer to the nearest whole number is 31 because the first figure after the decimal point is less than 5.

Exercise 7F

Use the calculator to work out these divisions. Give each answer correct to the nearest whole number.

1	$473 \div 20$	**2**	$553 \div 20$	**3**	$1186 \div 40$	**4**	$874 \div 40$	**5**	$297 \div 20$
6	$377 \div 20$	**7**	$859 \div 20$	**8**	$110 \div 8$	**9**	$843 \div 20$	**10**	$2086 \div 40$
11	$1527 \div 20$	**12**	$1447 \div 20$	**13**	$3927 \div 60$	**14**	$1587 \div 60$	**15**	$117 \div 8$
16	$1347 \div 24$	**17**	$854 \div 16$	**18**	$1497 \div 24$	**19**	$931 \div 20$	**20**	$2182 \div 40$

Example 10

Find each of the following and give your answer to the nearest ten.

a 27×6 **b** 58×7 **c** 52×23 **d** 63×5

a $27 \times 6 = 162$, which is 160 to the nearest ten (2 is smaller than 5).
b $58 \times 7 = 406$, which is 410 to the nearest ten (6 is greater than 5).
c $54 \times 27 = 1458$, which is 1460 to the nearest ten (8 is greater than 5).
d $63 \times 5 = 315$, which is 320 to the nearest ten (5s are rounded up).

Exercise 7G

Use your calculator to work out these multiplications. Give each answer correct to the nearest ten.

1	34×7	**2**	36×18	**3**	63×9	**4**	27×8	**5**	43×19
6	134×4	**7**	57×13	**8**	58×4	**9**	107×9	**10**	136×7
11	87×28	**12**	99×52	**13**	69×32	**14**	97×16	**15**	49×38

Example 11

Find each of the following and give your answer to the nearest hundred.

a 24×76 **b** 48×37 **c** 35×50

a $24 \times 76 = 1824$, which is 1800 to the nearest hundred (24 is smaller than 50).
b $48 \times 37 = 1776$, which is 1800 to the nearest hundred (76 is greater than 50).
c $35 \times 50 = 1750$, which is 1800 to the nearest hundred (50 is rounded up).

Exercise 7H

Use your calculator to work out these multiplications. Give each answer correct to the nearest hundred.

1	93×24	**2**	86×19	**3**	69×67	**4**	99×56	**5**	96×51
6	144×22	**7**	88×76	**8**	89×21	**9**	54×32	**10**	98×42
11	78×27	**12**	251×24	**13**	126×32	**14**	256×16	**15**	63×49

7.5   Approximating by using significant figures

Significant figures

The number 1734 contains four figures.
The most significant is 1 because this is the number of thousands.
The least significant is 4 because this is the number of units.

We can write 1734 correct to one significant figure as 2000 since it is closer to 2000 than 1000.

We can write 1734 correct to three significant figures as 1730 since it is closer to 1730 than 1740.

Example 12

Write correct to three significant figures:

a 5438   b 8213   c 7345   d 6197
   544   *820*   *735*   *620*

a 5438 is 5440 correct to three significant figures.
   (The third figure is increased by one because the fourth figure is 5 or more.)
b 8213 is 8210 correct to three significant figures.
   (The fourth figure is less than 5 so the units are ignored.)
c 7345 is 7350 correct to three significant figures.
   (The third figure is also increased by one if the fourth figure is exactly 5.)
d 6197 is 6200 correct to three significant figures.
   (The fourth figure is greater than 5 and in this case 19 has to be increased to 20.)

Exercise 7J

Write correct to three significant figures.

1 4159 *4160*   2 5658 *5660*   3 2756 *2760*   4 6567 *6570*   5 3712 *3710*   6 4623 *4620*
7 6541 *6540*   8 9248 *9250*   9 8569 *8570*   10 2936 *2940*   11 8163 *8160*   12 4962 *4960*
13 3784 *3780*   14 6185 *6190*   15 5645 *5650*   16 5709 *5710*   17 5697 *5700*   18 6496 *6500*

Example 13

Write to two significant figures:
a 243   b 3961

a 243 is 240 correct to two significant figures.
   (The third figure is less than 5 so the units are ignored.)
b 3961 is 4000 correct to two significant figures.
   (The third figure is greater than 5 so in this case the 39 has to be increased to 40.)

Exercise 7K

Write correct to two significant figures:

1	581	**2**	284	**3**	683	**4**	378	**5**	579	**6**	645
7	965	**8**	308	**9**	203	**10**	498	**11**	697	**12**	295

Exercise 7L

Write correct to two significant figures:

1	8394	**2**	7372	**3**	3426	**4**	7648	**5**	8653	**6**	6076
7	3094	**8**	3987	**9**	2964	**10**	6952	**11**	7914	**12**	3701

7.6   Using your calculator in simple whole number situations

> **Example 14**
>
> Four bars of chocolate cost 17p, 23p, 24p and 28p.
> Find the total cost and the change from £1.
>
>
> Total cost = (17 + 23 + 24 + 28) = 92p
> Change from £1 = (100 – 92) = 8p

Exercise 7M

1 Four cakes cost 18p, 21p, 26p and 28p.
Find the total cost and the change from £1.

2 Candace uses 50 grams of jam for some
sandwiches, 75 grams for a cake and
115 grams for a sponge pudding.
If she uses a jar which contains 300 grams,
how much is left in the jar?

For questions 3 and 4 give your answer correct
to the nearest whole number.

3 A piece of string is 86 cm long. It is cut up
into 5 equal lengths.
How long is each length?

4 A builders' merchant has 512 kg of cement
and he uses it to fill 20 identical bags.
How much does he put into each bag?

For questions 5 and 6 give your answer correct
to the nearest ten.

5 A train consists of 11 coaches which are
each 23 metres long.
Find the total length of the train.

6 A staircase consists of 26 stairs of height
21 cm.
What is the vertical height of the staircase?

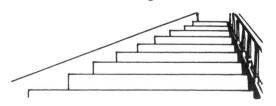

Sometimes, for a practical reason, the answer to a division calculation has to be rounded up to the next higher whole number, whatever the decimal figures may be. Example 15 shows this.

Example 15

A lift cannot carry more than 15 people at once.

If 51 people want to use the lift, find:

a the number of ascents that the lift will have to make

b the number of people in the lift during the last ascent if it is to be full for all the others.

a $51 \div 15 = 3.4$

The cage must take 4 ascents because 3 would not be enough.

b $15 \times 3 = 45$

The number of people in the cage for the last ascent is: $51 - 45 = 6$.

Exercise 7N

1 A haulage contractor has some car transporters but they cannot carry more than 10 cars at once.
If 53 cars have to be moved, find:
a the number of transporters required
b the number of cars on the last transporter if that is the only one which is not to be full.

2 Kanika has some egg cartons which can each hold 6 eggs. If she wants to pack 21 eggs into cartons, find:
a the number of cartons she requires
b the number of eggs she will place in the last carton if that is the only one she is not going to fill.

3 A train of coal trucks is to be used to move some coal from a colliery to a power station, but each truck can only carry 30 tonnes.
If 405 tonnes of coal have to be moved, find:
a the number of trucks required
b the number of tonnes in the truck at the back of the train if that is the only one that is not full.

4 Some lorries are to be used for moving earth but each lorry can only carry 8 tonnes. If 42 tonnes have to be moved, find:
a the number of lorries required
b the number of tonnes in the last lorry if all of the others are to be full.

5 A museum shows a video film for its visitors but the theatre room has only 30 seats. If on one particular day 168 people want to see the video, find:
a the number of showings they will have to hold
b the number of people in the theatre for the last showing if it is to be full for all the others.

Example 16

A carpenter requires 93 lengths of floorboard for a new house.

If the boards are only sold in bundles of 6 find:

a the number of bundles he must buy

b the number of length that he will not use.

a $93 \div 6 = 15.5$

Therefore he must buy 16 bundles because 15 would not be enough.

b $16 \times 6 = 96$

The number of boards not used is: $96 - 93 = 3$.

Exercise 7P

1 Tnisha requires 17 buttons for repairing some dresses.
If the buttons she requires are only sold in packets of 5, find:
  a the number of packets she must buy
  b the number of buttons she will not use.

2 A secretary requires 51 envelopes.
If they are only sold in packets of 6, find:
  a the number of packets she must buy
  b the number of envelopes she will not use.

3 A man requires 42 light bulbs for his new house.
If the bulbs he wants are only sold in packets of 8, find:
  a the number of packets he must buy
  b the number of bulbs he will not use.

4 A team of cooks requires 56 eggs for making some cakes.
If the eggs are sold in cartons of 10, find:
  a the number of cartons they require
  b the number of eggs they will not use.

5 The secretary in question 2 requires 39 stamps because she has none left in her office.
If a nearby shop only sells stamps in books of 12, find:
  a the number of books she must buy
  b the number of stamps she will not use.

8 DECIMALS

8.1 Understanding decimals and the decimal notation

Representing decimals on a number line

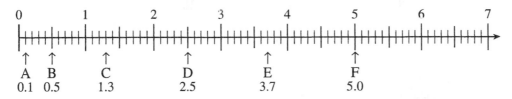

On the number line above each of the whole numbers has been divided into ten equal divisions. We can use decimals to describe the points listed below.

The point A is **one** tenth of the distance between 0 and 1, i.e. 0.1.
The point B is **five** tenths of the distance between 0 and 1, i.e. 0.5.
The point C is **three** tenths of the distance between 1 and 2, i.e. 1.3.
The point D is **five** tenths of the distance between 2 and 3, i.e. 2.5.
The point E is **seven** tenths of the distance between 3 and 4, i.e. 3.7.
The point F is exactly at 5. This can also be written as 5.0.

Example 1

a Show the point 1.4 on the number line.
b Write down the decimals which describe the points P and Q.

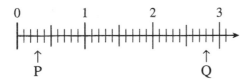

Where is 1.4?

a The position of 1.4 is as shown.
(Its position is four tenths of the distance between 1 and 2.)

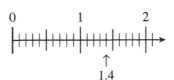

b P is the point 0.3, Q is the point 2.8.

Exercise 8A

For questions 1–10 copy the number line illustrated and then mark the decimal number for each question on it.

1	1.2	**2**	1.5	**3**	1.8	**4**	2.2	**5**	2.4
6	2.6	**7**	2.9	**8**	0.2	**9**	0.6	**10**	3.0

For questions 11–20 give the decimal number that the letter on the number line represents.

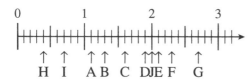

11	A	**12**	B	**13**	C	**14**	D	**15**	E
16	F	**17**	G	**18**	H	**19**	I	**20**	J

If we wanted to show a point between 1.3 and 1.4 on a number line, we could divide the gap into ten divisions and each division would then be one one hundredth of the distance between 1 and 2. 1.36 is illustrated on the number line below.

Example 2

a Show the point 2.34 on the number line.

b Write down the decimals which describe the points P and Q.

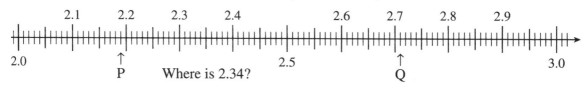

a The position of 2.34 is as shown.
(Its position is four tenths of the distance between 2.3 and 2.4.)

b P is the point 2.19, Q is the point 2.71.

Exercise 8B

For questions 1–10 copy the number line illustrated and then mark the decimal number for each question on it.

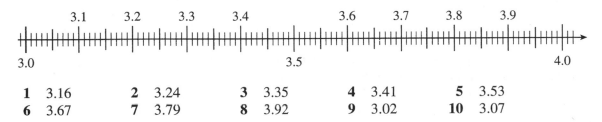

| **1** 3.16 | **2** 3.24 | **3** 3.35 | **4** 3.41 | **5** 3.53 |
| **6** 3.67 | **7** 3.79 | **8** 3.92 | **9** 3.02 | **10** 3.07 |

For questions 11–20 give the decimal number that the letter on the number line represents.

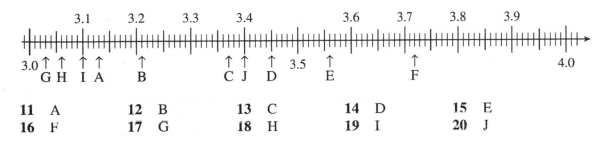

| **11** A | **12** B | **13** C | **14** D | **15** E |
| **16** F | **17** G | **18** H | **19** I | **20** J |

Decimals and place value

We used the column headings of units, tens, hundreds, etc. to denote the place value of each figure in a number such as 732:

Hundreds	Tens	Units
7	3	2

We can include columns to the right to show the place value of numbers which include decimal parts:

Hundreds	Tens	Units		Tenths	Hundredths
7	3	2	.	5	1

The first figure to the right of the decimal point (.) has a value of five tenths and the second such figure has a value of one hundredth. We can shorten the column headings to:

H	T	U	.	t	h

Example 3

Write down the place value of each figure in: **a** 7.35   **b** 73.54.

a 7 is seven units
3 is three tenths
5 is five hundredths

b 7 is seven tens
3 is three units
5 is five tenths
4 is four hundredths

Exercise 8C

Write down the place value of each figure in each of the following.

1	9.2	**2**	7.3	**3**	5.9	**4**	12.3	**5**	15.2	**6**	18.9
7	135.2	**8**	269.3	**9**	326.9	**10**	2.46	**11**	1.37	**12**	3.24
13	13.26	**14**	14.38	**15**	21.85	**16**	21.05	**17**	34.08	**18**	10.09

Measurements involving mixed units can often be written out more simply by using a decimal point. Look carefully at Example 4 below.

Example 4

Give the length of the screwdriver.

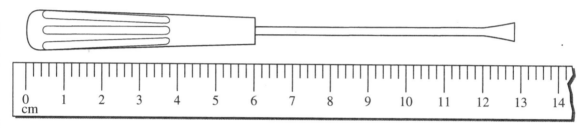

The small divisions on the ruler are 2 millimetres each, so the length of the screwdriver is 12 centimetres 8 millimetres.

This can be written as 12.8 centimetres (12.8 cm), or 128 millimetres (128 mm).

Exercise 8D

Give the length of each of the following in: **a** cm   **b** cm and mm.

1

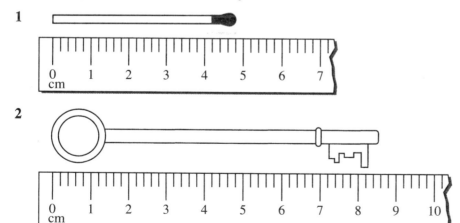

2

3

4

5

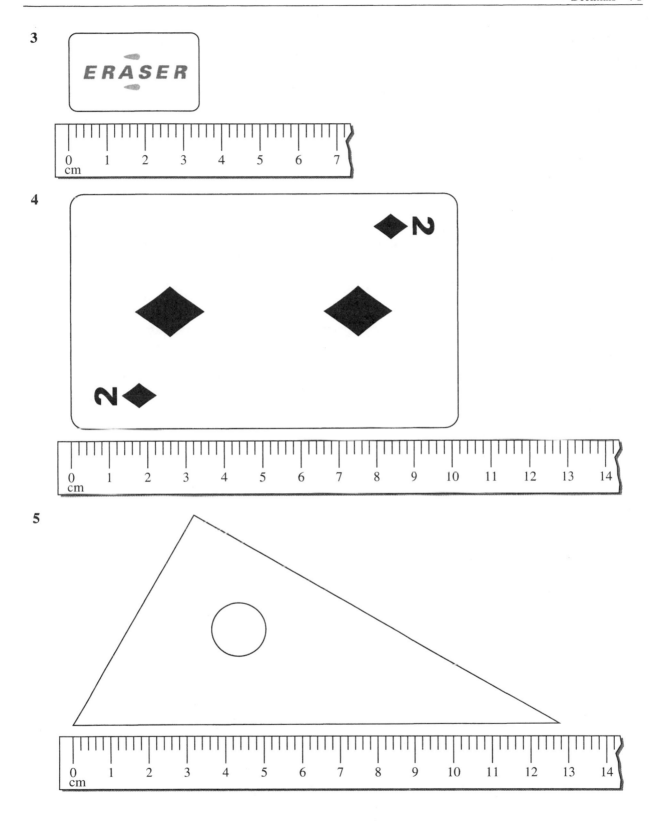

Example 5

A sewing needle is 5 cm 7 mm in length.

What is its length in: **a** cm   **b** mm?

a 5 cm 7 mm = 5.7 cm   **b** 5 cm 7 mm = 57 mm

Exercise 8E

Copy and complete the table below.

	Object	Length (cm and mm)	Length (cm)	Length (mm)
1	Screw	5 cm 3 mm		
2	Hairpin	4 cm 8 mm		
3	Bus ticket	9 cm 1 mm		
4	Coloured crayon	13 cm 6 mm		
5	Toothbrush		15.4 cm	
6	Tube of toothpaste		12.9 cm	
7	Hammer		20.6 cm	
8	Chisel			214 mm
9	Bicycle pump			319 mm
10	Pair of scissors			108 mm

Example 6

The measuring tape, which is marked in metres and centimetres, is being used to measure the length of a piece of wood. Give the length of the piece of wood.

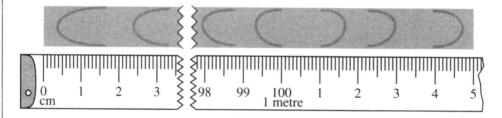

The length is:

   1 metre 5 centimetres or 1.05 metres or 105 centimetres.

Exercise 8F

1   The table below gives the height of three pupils in Normans House at
    Littletots Junior School. Copy and complete the table.

Pupil	Height (m and cm)	Height (m)	Height (cm)
Jim	1 m 23 cm		
Anne	1 m 40 cm		
Laura	1 m 3 cm		

2   The table below gives the height of three pupils in Vikings House at
    Littletots Junior School. Copy and complete the table.

Pupil	Height (m and cm)	Height (m)	Height (cm)
Kanika		1.17 m	
Marcus		1.02 m	
Josiah		1.2 m (or 1.20 m)	

3   The table below gives the height of three pupils in Saxons House at
    Littletots Junior School. Copy and complete the table.

Pupil	Height (m and cm)	Height (m)	Height (cm)
Marlon			118 cm
Deena			110 cm
Helen			104 cm

4   The table below shows several dimensions. Copy and complete the table.

Dimension to be measured	Measurement made (m and cm)	Measurement made (m)	Measurement made (cm)
Height of a wall mirror	1 m 25 cm		
Height of a clothes post	2 m 40 cm		
Height of a tall cabinet		1.95 m	
Length of a bed		2.05 m	
Length of a bicycle			185 cm
Length of a car			505 cm

8.2   Ordering decimals and appreciating place values

On page 4 we studied the relationship between place values in whole numbers. We will now extend this to consider the place values of decimal numbers.

Example 7
Write down the place value of each figure in: 32.756.

The figure 3 means **three** tens.
The figure 2 means **two** units.
The figure 7 in the first decimal place means **seven** tenths.
The figure 5 in the second decimal place means **five** hundredths.
The figure 6 in the third decimal place means **six** thousandths.

Note the following:
   0.75 can be regarded as either $\frac{7}{10} + \frac{5}{100}$ or $\frac{75}{100}$
   0.756 can be regarded as either $\frac{7}{10} + \frac{5}{100} + \frac{6}{1000}$ or $\frac{756}{1000}$

Exercise 8G

Write down the place value of each figure in:

1 43.68	**2** 57.32	**3** 56.432	**4** 78.694	**5** 2.734	**6** 8.263
7 6.57	**8** 4.93	**9** 35.8	**10** 53.4	**11** 8.2	**12** 2.9

Example 8
Write in descending order of size: 0.7   0.57   0.399   0.81

The four numbers can be written as follows: 0.700   0.570   0.399   0.810
Therefore the order of descending size is:
   0.810   0.700   0.570   0.399
or 0.81   0.7   0.57   0.399

Exercise 8H

Write in descending order of size.

1 0.47, 0.29, 0.56, 0.38	**2** 0.23, 0.12, 0.45, 0.34	**3** 0.49, 0.67, 0.58, 0.76
4 0.824, 0.644, 0.915, 0.735	**5** 0.730, 0.640, 0.912, 0.821	**6** 0.437, 0.300, 0.616, 0.520
7 0.319, 0.68, 0.4, 0.591	**8** 0.76, 0.85, 0.675, 0.9	**9** 0.5, 0.45, 0.73, 0.647

> **Example 9**
> Write in ascending order of size:
>   3.042   3.42   3.024   3.24
>
> The order of ascending size is:
>   3.024   3.042   3.24   3.42

Exercise 8J

Write in ascending order of size.

1   8.657, 8.765, 8.576, 8.756, 8.675
2   4.312, 4.213, 4.321, 4.231, 4.123, 4.132
3   3.504, 3.405, 3.054, 3.54, 3.045, 3.45
4   5.706, 5.067, 5.76, 5.076, 5.67, 5.607
5   1.32, 1.23, 1.302, 1.023, 1.203, 1.032
6   4.56, 4.65, 4.605, 4.065, 4.056, 4.506
7   8.099, 8.009, 8.9, 8.99, 8.09, 8.909
8   6.55, 6.055, 6.5, 6.05, 6.005, 6.505

8.3   Addition and subtraction of decimals

> **Example 10**
> Find   **a** 6.4 + 2.8   **b** 6.4 − 2.8
>
> **a**
> | Units | . | Tenths |
> |---|---|---|
> | 6 | . | 4 |
> | + 2 | . | 8 |
> | 9 | . | 2 |
> | 1 | | |
>
> Therefore 6.4 + 2.8 = 9.2
>
> **Note** 0.4 + 0.8 is four tenths plus eight tenths, or twelve tenths, which is one unit and two tenths, hence the need to carry one (or ten tenths) from the tenths column to the units column
>
> **b**
> | Units | . | Tenths |
> |---|---|---|
> | $\cancel{6}^5$ | . | ^{14} |
> | − 2 | . | 8 |
> | 3 | . | 6 |
>
> Therefore 6.4 − 2.8 = 3.6
>
> **Note** We need to carry ten tenths from the units column to the tenths column so that we can subtract eight tenths from fourteen tenths.

Exercise 8K

Work out the value of each of the following.

1   5.3 + 2.6
2   4.2 + 3.5
3   6.9 + 2.5
4   7.9 + 2.4
5   8.8 + 3.6
6   5.6 − 3.1
7   8.2 − 2.9
8   9.3 − 1.8
9   7.1 − 5.7
10   6.0 − 3.7

Example 11

Find   **a** $6.48 + 2.81$ **b** $6.48 - 2.81$

a
Units		Tenths	Hundredths
6	.	4	8
+ 2₁	.	8	1

$$\begin{array}{ccc} 9 & . & 2 & 9 \end{array}$$

Therefore $6.48 + 2.81 = 9.29$

Note   Again we need to carry one unit (or ten tenths) from the tenths column to the units column.

b
Units		Tenths	Hundredths
$\cancel{6}^5$	.	¹4	8
− 2	.	8	1

$$\begin{array}{ccc} 3 & . & 6 & 7 \end{array}$$

Therefore $6.48 - 2.81 = 3.67$

Note   Again we need to carry ten tenths from the units column to the tenths column.

Exercise 8L

Work out each of the following.

1	$3.52 + 4.17$	**2**	$5.31 + 1.27$	**3**	$5.83 + 3.46$	**4**	$4.95 + 2.62$	**5**	$7.84 + 4.65$
6	$6.79 - 3.54$	**7**	$8.25 - 3.83$	**8**	$9.69 - 2.97$	**9**	$8.03 - 5.25$	**10**	$9.00 - 7.54$

8.4   Multiplying decimals by whole numbers

In place value the value of each place is ten times the value of the place on its right:

Hundreds   (× 10)   Tens   (× 10)   Units   (× 10)   Tenths   (× 10)   Hundredths

Example 12

Find   **a** 0.3×10 **b** 2.3×10 **c** 0.3×100 **d** 2.3×100

	Units		Tenths			Tens	Units		Tenths
a	0	.	3	$\times 10 =$			3	.	0
b	2	.	3	$\times 10 =$		2	3	.	0

Note   Each figure moves one place to the left.

	Tens	Units		Tenths			Hundreds	Tens	Units		Tenths
c		0	.	3	$\times 100 =$			3	0	.	0
d		2	.	3	$\times 100 =$		2	3	0	.	0

Note   Each figure moves two places to the left.

Exercise 8M

Work out each of the following.

1	**a** 0.4×10	**b** 0.4×100	**2**	**a** 0.6×10	**b** 0.6×100	**3**	**a** 0.2×10	**b** 0.2×100
4	**a** 0.7×10	**b** 0.7×100	**5**	**a** 0.5×10	**b** 0.5×100	**6**	**a** 0.9×10	**b** 0.9×100
7	**a** 1.8×10	**b** 1.8×100	**8**	**a** 1.6×10	**b** 1.6×100	**9**	**a** 1.5×10	**b** 1.5×100
10	**a** 2.5×10	**b** 2.5×100	**11**	**a** 2.9×10	**b** 2.9×100	**12**	**a** 2.3×10	**b** 2.3×100

Example 13

Find   **a** 0.3×4 **b** 0.7×5

a 0.3×4 = three tenths $\times 4$ = twelve tenths = one unit plus two tenths = 1.2

b 0.7×5 = seven tenths $\times 5$ = thirty-five tenths = three units plus five tenths = 3.5

Exercise 8N

Evaluate each of the following.

1 0.8×6	**2** 0.8×4	**3** 0.7×3	**4** 0.7×8	**5** 0.7×2	**6** 0.9×5
7 0.9×7	**8** 0.1×9	**9** 0.8×5	**10** 0.4×5	**11** 0.5×4	**12** 0.5×6

Example 14

Find   **a** 7.4×3 **b** 7.4×5

a We could find 7.4×3 as $7.4 + 7.4 + 7.4 = 22.2$

Or by setting it out as multiplication:

Tens	Units	Tenths
	7 .	4
$\times$		3
2	2 .	2
2	1	

Note We need to carry one unit (ten tenths) from the tenths column to the units column and then two tens from the units column to the tens column.

Therefore $7.4 \times 3 = 22.2$.

b

Tens	Units	Tenths
	7 .	4
$\times$		5
3	7 .	0
3	2	

Note We need to carry two units (twenty tenths) from the tenths column to the units column and three tens from the units column to the tens column.

Therefore $7.4 \times 5 = 37.0$

Exercise 8P

Evaluate each of the following.

1 4.3×2	**2** 2.3×3	**3** 3.2×3	**4** 2.1×4	**5** 3.1×2	**6** 1.2×3
7 2.4×3	**8** 3.8×2	**9** 2.3×4	**10** 1.3×5	**11** 1.6×6	**12** 1.7×4
13 4.5×6	**14** 3.5×8	**15** 5.6×5	**16** 7.4×5	**17** 5.3×3	**18** 6.4×2

Example 15

Find   **a i** 0.31×10 **ii** 2.31×10
    b i 0.31×100 **ii** 2.31×100

a i $0.31 \times 10 = 3.1$ **Note**   Each figure moves one place to the left.
 ii $2.31 \times 10 = 23.1$ Each figure moves one place to the left.
b i $0.31 \times 100 = 31.0$ Each figure moves two places to the left.
 ii $2.31 \times 100 = 231.0$ Each figure moves two places to the left.

Exercise 8Q

Multiply each of the following by: **a** 10   **b** 100.

1 0.45	**2** 0.37	**3** 0.61	**4** 0.93
5 0.72	**6** 0.05	**7** 0.08	**8** 0.03
9 3.04	**10** 4.06	**11** 4.02	**12** 5.01
13 5.10	**14** 7.30	**15** 6.50	**16** 0.90

Example 16

Find   **a** 0.31×4 **b** 0.73×5

a 0.31×4

Units	Tenths	Hundredths
0 .	3	1
× 4		
1 .	2	4
1		

Note   We need to carry one (or ten tenths) from the tenths column to the units column.

Therefore $0.31 \times 4 = 1.24$

b 0.73×5

Units	Tenths	Hundredths
0 .	7	3
× 5		
3 .	6	5
3	1	

Note   We need to carry one tenth (ten hundredths) from the hundredths column to the tenths column and three units (thirty tenths) from the tenths column to the units column.

Therefore $0.73 \times 5 = 3.65$

Exercise 8R

Evaluate each of the following.

1	0.42×3	**2**	0.74×2	**3**	0.63×3	**4**	0.31×5	**5**	0.41×4
6	0.62×4	**7**	0.72×3	**8**	0.71×5	**9**	0.61×7	**10**	0.69×5
11	0.56×5	**12**	0.85×4	**13**	0.05×7	**14**	0.09×6	**15**	0.05×8

Example 17

Find **a** 7.43×3 **b** 7.43×5

a We could find 7.43×3 as $7.43 + 7.43 + 7.43 = 22.29$

Or by setting it out as a multiplication:

Tens	Units		Tenths	Hundredths
	7	.	4	3
$\times$	3			
2,	2	.	2	9
2	1			

Note We need to carry one unit (ten tenths) from the tenths column to the units column and two tens from the units column to the tens column.

Therefore $7.43 \times 3 = 22.29$

b

Tens	Units		Tenths	Hundredths
	7	.	4	3
$\times$	5			
3	7	.	1	5
3	2		1	

Note We need to carry ten hundredths (one tenth) from the hundredths column to the tenths column, twenty tenths (two units) from the tenths column to the units column and thirty units (three tens) from the units column to the tens column.

Therefore $7.43 \times 5 = 37.15$

Exercise 8S

Find the value of each of the following.

1	3.24×2	**2**	2.32×3	**3**	2.21×4	**4**	1.31×3	**5**	2.31×4
6	2.62×3	**7**	4.74×2	**8**	1.31×5	**9**	3.42×4	**10**	8.93×2
11	3.75×8	**12**	2.04×8	**13**	5.07×5	**14**	6.04×5	**15**	3.05×6

8.5   Dividing decimals by whole numbers

In place value the value of each place is one tenth of the value of the place on its left:

Hundreds   ($\div 10$)   Tens   ($\div 10$)   Units   ($\div 10$)   Tenths   ($\div 10$)   Hundredths

---

Example 18

Find   **a i** $23 \div 10$ **ii** $2.3 \div 10$
          b i $231 \div 100$ **ii** $23.1 \div 100$

a

	Tens	Units	Tenths		Units	Tenths	Hundredths	Notes
i	2	3 .		$\div 10 =$	2 .	3		Each figure moves one
ii		2 .	3	$\div 10 =$	0 .	2	3	place to the right.

b

	Hundreds	Tens	Units	Tenths		Units	Tenths	Hundredths	Thousandths
i	2	3	1		$\div 100 =$	2 .	3	1	
ii		2	3 .	1	$\div 100 =$	0 .	2	3	1

Each figure moves two places to the right.

Exercise 8T

Find the value of each of the following.

1	$36 \div 10$	**2**	$52 \div 10$	**3**	$1.5 \div 10$	**4**	$4.5 \div 10$	**5**	$0.7 \div 10$
6	$0.3 \div 10$	**7**	$256 \div 100$	**8**	$325 \div 100$	**9**	$504 \div 100$	**10**	$805 \div 100$
11	$670 \div 100$	**12**	$430 \div 100$	**13**	$37.2 \div 100$	**14**	$96.5 \div 100$	**15**	$6.52 \div 100$
16	$8.46 \div 100$	**17**	$7.5 \div 100$	**18**	$2.6 \div 100$				

Example 19

Find   **a** $13 \div 2$ **b** $13.4 \div 2$ **c** $27.4 \div 5$

a $13 \div 2$

$$\begin{array}{r} 6.5 \\ 2)\overline{13.0} \\ -12.0 \quad (6 \times 2) \\ \hline 1.0 \\ -1.0 \quad (0.5 \times 2) \\ \hline 0.0 \end{array}$$

b $13.4 \div 2$

$$\begin{array}{r} 6.7 \\ 2)\overline{13.4} \\ -12.0 \quad (6 \times 2) \\ \hline 1.4 \\ -1.4 \quad (0.7 \times 2) \\ \hline 0.0 \end{array}$$

c $27.4 \div 5$

$$\begin{array}{r} 5.48 \\ 5)\overline{27.40} \\ -25.00 \quad (5 \times 5) \\ \hline 2.40 \\ -2.00 \quad (0.4 \times 5) \\ \hline 0.40 \\ -0.40 \quad (0.08 \times 5) \\ \hline 0.00 \end{array}$$

Therefore $13 \div 2 = 6.5$ Therefore $13.4 \div 2 = 6.7$ Therefore $27.4 \div 5 = 5.48$

Exercise 8U

Work out each of the following.

1	13 ÷ 5	**2**	19 ÷ 2	**3**	34 ÷ 4	**4**	36 ÷ 5	**5**	27 ÷ 6
6	21 ÷ 4	**7**	62 ÷ 8	**8**	15 ÷ 4	**9**	50 ÷ 8	**10**	37.6 ÷ 4
11	28.8 ÷ 4	**12**	24.9 ÷ 3	**13**	18.8 ÷ 2	**14**	21.4 ÷ 4	**15**	23.6 ÷ 5
16	17.1 ÷ 2	**17**	28.5 ÷ 6	**18**	35.9 ÷ 5	**19**	24.6 ÷ 4	**20**	42.4 ÷ 5

8.6 Calculations using money and simple measurements

Very often quantities can be written our more simply by using a decimal point.

For example:
Two pounds and thirty-five pence is usually written as £2.35.
Three metres and twenty-four centimetres is 3.24 metres.

Example 20

If I go to a shop and buy a shirt which costs £8.45 and a tie which
costs £2.75, find:

a how much I spend

b the change I receive if I pay with a £20 note.

a The amount I spend = £8.45 + £2.75

> The figures and decimal points
> are correctly arranged in columns.

$$\begin{array}{r} £8.45 \\ +£2.75 \\ \hline £11.20 \end{array}$$

I therefore spend £11.20.

b My change from a £20 note = £20 − £11.20

> The figures and decimal points are
> again correctly arranged in columns.

$$\begin{array}{r} £20.00 \\ -£11.20 \\ \hline £8.80 \end{array}$$

My change is therefore £8.80.

Exercise 8V

1   Marcus goes into a shop and buys a pair of shorts which cost £4.95 and a pair of trainer shoes which cost £10.15. Find:
   a how much he spends
   b his change out of a £20 note.

2   Josiah goes to a market and buys a hammer which costs £3.25 and a screwdriver which costs £2.45. Find:
   a how much he spends
   b his change out of a £10 note.

3   Jean goes to a sale and buys a table lamp which costs £7.95 and a spare bulb which costs 45p (£0.45). Find:
   a how much she spends
   b her change out of a £10 note.

4   Barbara requires two lengths of tape: one of length 1 metre 75 centimetres and the other of length 1 metre 15 centimetres. If the tape is only sold in 2 metre and 3 metre lengths, find each of the following:
   a the total length she requires
   b the length of the piece she must buy
   c the length of tape she will have left over.

5   Ayo requires two lengths of copper piping, one of length 1 metre 35 centimetres and one of length 45 centimetres (0.45 metres). If the copper piping is only sold in 2 metre or 3 metre lengths, find each of the following:
   a the total length he requires
   b the length of the piece he must buy
   c the length of piping he will have left over.

Example 21

Becky buys 4 pens which cost £1.35 each. Find:
a the total cost
b the change from a £10 note.

a Total cost = £1.35 × 4

There are two figures after the decimal point, but the multiplication is done without the decimal point.

$$
\begin{array}{r}
135 \\
\times\ 4 \\
\hline
540
\end{array}
$$

The answer must include two figures after the decimal point in order to match the information.

So the total cost is £5.40.

b   Her change from a £10 note = £10 − £5.40

The figures and decimal points are correctly arranged in columns.

$$
\begin{array}{r}
£10.00 \\
-£5.40 \\
\hline
£4.60
\end{array}
$$

So her change is £4.60.

Exercise 8W

1 Tnisha buys 4 small dolls which cost £1.85 each. Find:
   a the total cost
   b her change from a £10 note.

2 Rita requires 5 pieces of elastic material which are each 46 cm (0.46 m) long.
   If the elastic material is only sold in 2 metre or 3 metre lengths, find each of the following:
   a the total length she requires
   b the length of the piece she must buy
   c the length of elastic material that she will have left over.

3 Julian buys 8 torch batteries which cost 60p (£0.60) each. Find:
   a the total cost
   b the change from a £5 note.

4 Laura requires 6 pieces of decorative string for tying up some parcels and each one must be 30 cm (0.3 m) long.
   If the string is only sold in 2 metre or 3 metre lengths, find each of the following:
   a the total length she requires
   b the length of the piece she must buy
   c the length of string that she will have left over.

Example 22

If 5 pens costs 44p, find the cost of:

a 1 pen   b 3 pens

Give each answer correct to the nearest penny.

a 44p ÷ 5 = 8.8p or 9p to the nearest penny.
b 8.8p × 3 = 26.4p or 26p to the nearest penny.

Exercise 8X

1 If 5 pencils cost 43p, find, to the nearest penny, the cost of:
   a 1 pencil   b 6 pencils   c 3 pencils   d 8 pencils   e 4 pencils.

2 If 5 liquorice sticks cost 32p, find, correct to the nearest penny, the cost of:
   a 1 stick   b 6 sticks   c 8 sticks   d 3 sticks   e 4 sticks.

3 There are 5 diaries on a table and they form a pile of height 11 cm.
   a Find the thickness of 1 diary.
   Find the height of a pile of these diaries if it consists of:
   b 6 diaries   c 7 diaries   d 2 diaries   e 4 diaries   f 9 diaries.
   (Give each answer to the nearest centimetre.)

4 There are 5 sausages in a string and the length of the string is 38 cm.
   a Find the length of one sausage.
   Find the length of a string of these sausages if the string consists of:
   b 6 sausages   c 8 sausages   d 3 sausages   e 9 sausages   f 4 sausages.
   (Give each answer correct to the nearest centimetre.)

5 There are 5 exercise books on a desk and they form a pile of height 4 cm.
   a Find the thickness of one book.
   Find the height of a pile of these books if it consists of:
   b 6 books   c 7 books   d 2 books   e 4 books   f 9 books.
   (Give each answer correct to the nearest centimetre.)

9   LENGTH

9.1   Understanding units of length in the metric and imperial systems

At present we still have two different systems of measurement in common use. Sometimes we use the imperial system and sometimes we use the metric system.

Originally the units of length in the imperial system were linked to parts of the body.

1 **inch (in).**   One inch was about the width of the top joint of a man's thumb.

1 **foot (ft)** = 12 inches.   One foot was about the length of a man's foot from toe to heel.

1 **yard (yd)** = 3 feet = 36 inches.   One yard was about the length of a man's full stride when walking.(It is also about the distance from the tip of a man's nose to the end of his finger when his arm is fully stretched.)

1 **mile** = 1760 yards.

In the metric system all units are linked to the metre by powers of ten.

1 **metre (m)** = 39.37 inches.   One metre is also about the length of a man's full stride.

1 **decimetre (dm)** = 0.1 metres.   'Deci' is the Latin word for a 1/10 part.

1 **centimetre (cm)** = 0.01 metres.   'Centi' is the Latin word for a 1/100 part.

1 **millimetre (mm)** = 0.001 metres.   'Milli' is the Latin word for a 1/1000 part.

1 **kilometre (km)** = 1000 metres.   'Kilo' is the Latin word for 1000.

The table below shows the most commonly used imperial units and their metric equivalents.

Quantity to be measured	Imperial unit	Accurate conversion to and from metric equivalent	Approximate conversion to and from metric equivalent
Length	1 inch (1″ or 1 in)	1 in = 2.54 cm 1 cm = 0.3937″	1″ = 2.5 (or 2½) cm 1 cm = 0.4″
	1 foot (1′ or 1 ft) (1 ft = 12 in)	1 ft = 0.3048 m 1 m = 3.281 ft	1′ = 0.3 m 1 m = 3.3′
	1 yard (1 yd) (1 yd = 36 in)	1 yd = 0.9144 m 1 m = 1.094 yd	1 yd = 0.9 m 1 m = 1.1 yd
	1 mile (1 mile = 1760 yd)	1 mile = 1.6093 km 1 km = 0.6214 miles	1 mile = 1.6 km 1 km = 0.625 miles (or $\frac{5}{8}$ mile)

Example 1

Write down the lengths of the lines AB, CD, EF, and XY which are drawn on the grid of 1 centimetre squares.

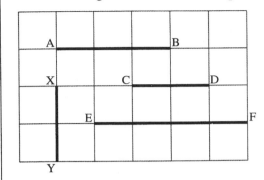

AB is 3 centimetres (cm)
CD is 2 centimetres (cm)
EF is 4 centimetres (cm)
XY is 2 centimetres (cm)

Exercise 9A

Write down the length of :

1 AB   2 CD
3 EF   4 GH
5 KL   6 MN
7 PQ   8 RS
9 TU   10 VW

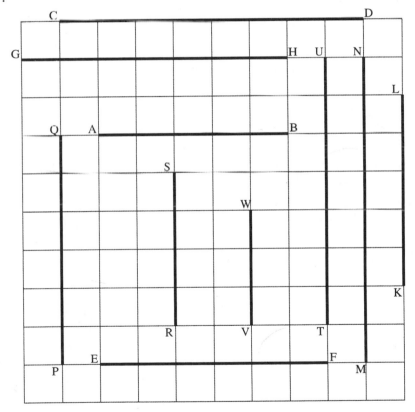

(continued)

Example 2

Use the given centimetre ruler to state how long each line is.

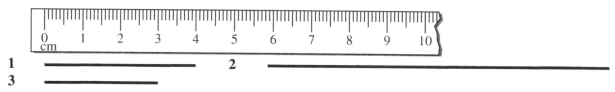

a   A ————————— B

b   C ——————————————— D

c   E ——————————— F

a   AB = 3 cm

b   CD = 7 cm

c   EF = 6 – 2 = 4 cm

Exercise 9B

For questions 1–3 use the given centimetre ruler to state how long each line is.

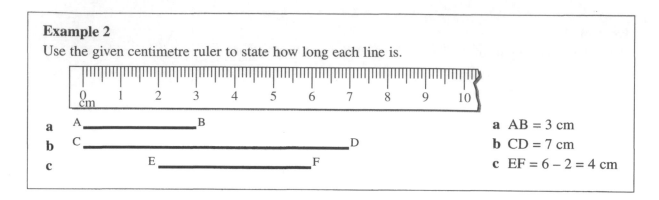

1   ============   2   ————————————————

3   ==========

9.2   Reading and measuring lengths

(including perimeters of simple shapes)

A ruler is normally about 30 centimetres long and marked in centimetres and millimetres. This means that lengths can be measured more accurately than they can with a ruler which is only marked in centimetres. On many rulers every fifth millimetre is shown with a longer mark.

Example 3

Write down the length of: **a** the handle   **b** the shaft   **c** the whole screwdriver

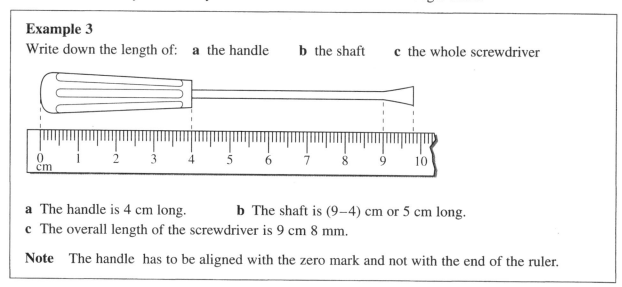

a The handle is 4 cm long.   **b** The shaft is (9–4) cm or 5 cm long.

c The overall length of the screwdriver is 9 cm 8 mm.

Note   The handle has to be aligned with the zero mark and not with the end of the ruler.

Exercise 9C

1   Write down the length of the needle.

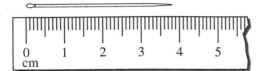

2   Write down the length of the pin.

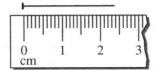

3   Write down the length of the hinge.

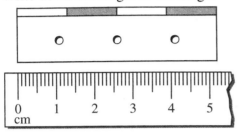

4   Write down the length of the tweezers.

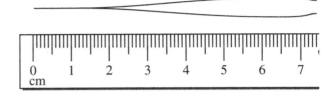

5   Write down:
   a the overall length of the dart
   b the length of the flight
   c the length of the stem
   d the length of the pointed end.

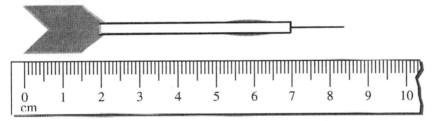

Example 4

We can write 1 cm 3 mm as 13 mm or as 1.3 cm.

State the length of the line below in:

a cm and mm   **b** mm   **c** cm.

a 2 cm 3 mm   **b** 23 mm   **c** 2.3 cm

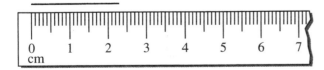

Exercise 9D

Measure the length of each of the lines and state each length in:
a cm and mm   **b** mm   **c** cm.

1 ▬▬▬▬▬▬▬▬▬▬▬▬

2 ▬▬▬▬▬▬▬▬▬▬▬▬▬

3 ▬▬▬▬▬▬▬▬▬▬▬▬▬▬▬

4 ▬▬▬

5 ▬▬▬▬▬▬▬▬▬▬

Finding perimeters of simple shapes

The perimeter of a shape is the total distance around the outside of the shape.

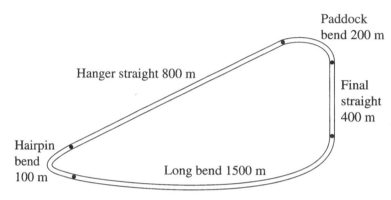

Paddock bend 200 m
Hanger straight 800 m
Final straight 400 m
Hairpin bend 100 m
Long bend 1500 m

Example 5

Find the perimeter of the race track illustrated above.

The perimeter is: (1500 + 100 + 800 + 200 + 400) m = 3000 m.

Exercise 9E

1 Find the perimeter of the playground at John's school.

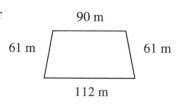

22 m
16 m
14 m
30 m

2 Find the perimeter of the car park.

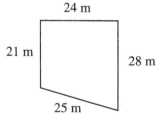

24 m
21 m
28 m
25 m

3 Find the perimeter of the bus station.

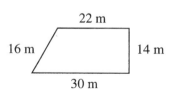

90 m
61 m
61 m
112 m

4 Find the perimeter of the village green.

60 m
41 m   Village Green   41 m
78 m

For regular shapes there is often a quick way of finding the perimeter.

Example 6

Find the perimeter of:

a a square of side length 5 cm

b an equilateral triangle of side
length 5 cm.

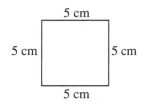 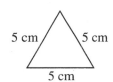

a Perimeter = 4×5 cm = 20 cm

b Perimeter = 3×5 cm = 15 cm

Exercise 9F

1 Find the perimeter of the square if the side length l is:

   a 6 cm   **b** 9 cm   **c** 15 cm

   d 24 mm   **e** 65 mm   **f** 90 mm

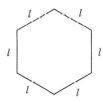

2 Find the perimeter of the equilateral triangle if the side length l is:

   a 8 cm   **b** 6 cm   **c** 20 cm

   d 45 mm   **e** 72 mm   **f** 96 mm

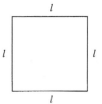

3 Find the perimeter of the regular hexagon if the side length l is:

   a 12 cm   **b** 18 cm   **c** 25 cm

   d 42 mm   **e** 75 mm   **f** 60 mm

Example 7

Find the perimeter of
the rectangle illustrated.

Length = 3 cm

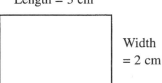

Width
= 2 cm

Perimeter = $((2 \times 3) + (2 \times 2))$ cm

          = $(6 + 4)$ cm

          = 10 cm

So the perimeter is 10 cm.

Exercise 9G

For questions 1–4 find which rectangles (**a**, **b** or **c**) has a different perimeter from the other two.

1 **a** Length = 25 cm   **b** Length = 28 cm   **c** Length = 21 cm
        Width = 15 cm   Width = 12 cm   Width = 17 cm

2 **a** Length = 55 cm   **b** Length = 49 cm   **c** Length = 62 cm
        Width = 25 cm   Width = 33 cm   Width = 18 cm

3 **a** Length = 75 cm   **b** Length = 53 cm   **c** Length = 68 cm
        Width = 21 cm   Width = 43 cm   Width = 24 cm

4 **a** Length = 113 mm   **b** Length = 150 mm   **c** Length = 124 mm
        Width = 65 mm   Width = 26 mm   Width = 52 mm

For questions 5–7 measure the side lengths of the rectangle and find its perimeter.
(**Note**   each square is a $\frac{1}{2}$ cm square.)

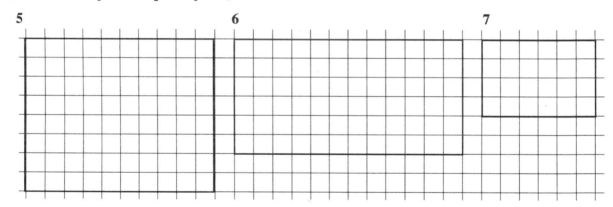

For questions 8 and 9 measure the side lengths of the shape and find its perimeter.

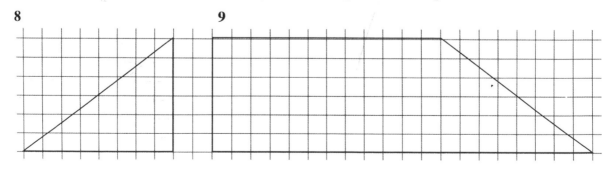

The circumference of a circle

Reminder 1

The circumference (or perimeter) of a circle of diameter D cm is $\pi \times D$ or πD cm, where $\pi = 3.14$ (correct to two decimal places).

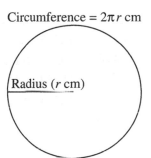

Circumference = πD cm

Diameter (D cm)

Note   the diameter is twice the length of the radius, so $D = 2r$.

Reminder 2

The circumference of a circle of radius r cm is $2 \times \pi \times r$ or $2\pi r$ cm.

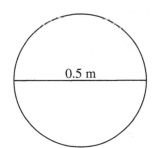

Circumference = $2\pi r$ cm

Radius (r cm)

Example 8

Find the circumference of a circle of diameter 0.5 m (take $\pi = 3.14$).

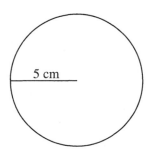

0.5 m

Circumference = $\pi \times 0.5$ m
$= (3.14 \times 0.5)$ m
$= 1.57$ m

Example 9

Find the circumference of a circle of radius 5 cm ($\pi = 3.14$).

5 cm

Circumference = $2\pi \times 5$ cm
$= (2 \times 3.14 \times 5)$ cm
$= 31.4$ cm

Exercise 9H

Find the circumference of the circle for each of the following cases.
Take π = 3.14.

1 Diameter = 5 cm	**2** Diameter = 4 cm	**3** Diameter = 15 cm
4 Diameter = 35 cm	**5** Diameter = 4.5 cm	**6** Diameter = 7.5 cm
7 Radius = 3 cm	**8** Radius = 10 cm	**9** Radius = 25 cm
10 Radius = 22.5 mm	**11** Radius = 12.5 mm	**12** Radius = 0.75 m

---

Example 10

A birthday cake has a diameter of 40 cm.
What length of ribbon is required to go round it, assuming it has a
1 cm overlap? Take π = 3.14.

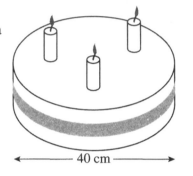

Circumference of cake = (3.14 × 40) cm
                       = 125.6 cm
So the length of ribbon = Circumference + overlap
                       = (125.6 + 1) cm
                       = 126.6 cm

40 cm

Exercise 9J

(Take π = 3.14)

1   A cotton reel has a drum of diameter 3.5 cm. Find:
   a the circumference of the drum
   b the length of cotton on a full reel if it is wound
      round 2000 times.

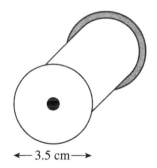

← 3.5 cm →

2   A tin of beans has a diameter of 7 cm.
   What length of label is required
   to go round it assuming an overlap of 1 cm?

7.5 cm

B·E·A·N·S   B·E·A·N·S   B·E·A·N·S

3   A cigar has a maximum diameter of 10.5 mm. It has a piece of foil wrapped around its maximum diameter with an overlap of 1 mm.
What is the length of the foil?

10.5 mm

4   A bowl has a diameter of 20 cm. Find:
   a the circumference of the bowl
   b the number of times it rotates while it rolls 15.7 m (1570 cm) across a bowling green before stopping.

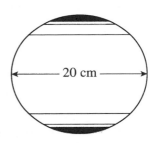

— 20 cm —

5   The circumference of a circle is 31.4 cm. Find:
   a the diameter   **b** the radius.

6   The circumference of a circle is 157 mm. Find:
   a the diameter   **b** the radius.

9.3   Converting between units of length in the metric and imperial systems

Three important units of length are the metre, centimetre and millimetre.
These three units are connected as follows:

   10 millimetres (mm) = 1 centimetre (cm)
   100 centimetres (cm) = 1 metre (m)

It therefore follows that 1 metre is equal to 100 centimetres or 1000 millimetres.

Example 11
Change 3 metres to: **a** centimetres   **b** millimetres.

a 3 metres = 3 × 100 centimetres = 300 centimetres
b 3 metres = 3 × 1000 millimetres = 3000 millimetres

Example 12
Change 1900 centimetres to: **a** metres   **b** millimetres.

a 1900 centimetres = 1900 ÷ 100 metres = 19 metres
b 1900 centimetres = 1900 × 10 millimetres = 19 000 millimetres

---

Example 13

Change 40 000 millimetres to: **a** metres   **b** centimetres.

a 40 000 millimetres = 40 000 ÷ 1000 metres = 40 metres
b 40 000 millimetres = 40 000 ÷ 10 centimetres = 4000 centimetres

Exercise 9K

Copy and complete the table below.

	Metres	Centimetres	Millimetres
1	7	7 × 100 =	7 × 1000 =
2	15		
3		2100	
4		1400	
5			5000
6			30 000

Example 14

A sewing needle is 5 cm 7 mm in length.
What is its length in: **a** cm   **b** mm?

a 5 cm 7 mm = 5.7 cm   **b** 5 cm 7 mm = 57 mm

Exercise 9L

Copy and complete this table:

	Object	Length (cm and mm)	Length (cm)	Length (mm)
1	Screwdriver	16 cm 2 mm		
2	Toy lorry		25.2 cm	
3	Knitting needle			284 mm

Look carefully at the illustration below. A measuring tape, which is marked in metres and centimetres, is being used to measure the length of a piece of wood.

The length is 1 metre 5 centimetres or 1.05 metres or 105 centimetres.

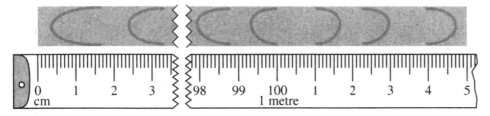

Exercise 9M

The table below gives the height of ten children. Copy and complete the table.

	Pupil	Height (m and cm)	Height (m)	Height (cm)
1	Joshua	1 m 36 cm		
2	Mandeep	1 m 6 cm		
3	Jotinder		1.38 m	
4	Lucy		1.3 m (or 1.30 m)	
5	Amy			134 cm
6	Jane			86 cm

Here is a reminder of the metric length table:

10 millimetres (mm)   = 1 centimetre (cm)
100 centimetres (or 1000 millimetres) = 1 metre (m)

Example 15

Convert 71 metres to: **a** centimetres   **b** millimetres.

a 71 m = 71 × 100 cm = 7100 cm
b 71 m = 71 × 1000 mm = 71 000 mm

Example 16

Convert 2.3 metres to: **a** centimetres   **b** millimetres.

a 2.3 m = 2.3 × 100 cm = 230 cm
b 2.3 m = 2.3 × 1000 mm = 2300 mm

Exercise 9N

Convert each of the following to: **a** centimetres   **b** millimetres.

1	35 m	**2**	23 m	**3**	47 m	**4**	52 m	**5**	4.9 m	**6**	3.6 m
7	2.5 m	**8**	7.3 m	**9**	0.3 m	**10**	0.7 m	**11**	0.25 m	**12**	0.08 m

---

Example 17

Convert 4973 mm to: **a** centimetres   **b** metres.

a 4973 mm = 4973 ÷ 10 cm = 497.3 cm
b 4973 mm = 4973 ÷ 1000 m = 4.973 m

Example 18

Convert 79 millimetres to: **a** centimetres   **b** metres.

a 79 mm = 79 ÷ 10 cm = 7.9 cm
b 79 mm = 79 ÷ 1000 m = 0.079 m

Exercise 9P

Convert each of the following to: **a** centimetres   **b** metres.

1	2439 mm	**2**	5264 mm	**3**	2750 mm	**4**	2500 mm
5	725 mm	**6**	379 mm	**7**	96 mm	**8**	78 mm

Converting imperial units

Here is a reminder of the main imperial units of length and the
relationships between them:

1 foot = 12 inches   1 yard = 3 feet = 36 inches   1 mile = 1760 yards

---

Example 19

Convert the following lengths to: **i** feet   **ii** inches.
a 5 yards   **b** 1 mile

a i   5 yards = (5 × 3) feet = 15 feet
   ii 15 feet = (15 × 12) inches = 180 inches
b i   1 mile = 1760 yards = (1760 × 3) feet = 5280 feet
   ii 5280 feet = (5280 × 12) inches = 63 360 inches

Exercise 9Q

For questions 1–6 convert to: **a** feet **b** inches.

1 8 yards **2** 6 yards **3** 3 yards **4** 12 yards **5** 15 yards
6 The swimming pool in Grove Park is 45 yards long and 20 yards wide.

For questions 7–10 convert to: **a** yards **b** feet.

7 2 miles **8** 5 miles **9** 6 miles **10** The Forth Bridge is 1.5 miles long.

Example 20
Convert the following lengths to: **i** feet **ii** yards.
a 72 inches **b** 360 inches

a i 72 inches = (72 ÷ 12) feet = 6 feet
  ii 6 feet = (6 ÷ 3) yards = 2 yards
b i 360 inches = (360 ÷ 12) feet = 30 feet
  ii 30 feet = (30 ÷ 3) yards = 10 yards

Exercise 9R

For each of the following convert the length to: **a** feet **b** yards.

1 108 inches **2** 720 inches **3** 144 inches **4** 504 inches **5** 324 inches
6 The playground at Josiah's school is 1260 inches long and 1152 inches wide.

Converting metric lengths to imperial lengths and vice versa

Example 21
a A shelf is 40 inches long. What is its length in centimetres, given that 1 inch equals 2.5 centimetres?
b A lead for a large dog is 55 centimetres long. What is its length in inches, given that 1 centimetre = 0.4 inches?

a 40 inches = 40 × 2.5 centimetres = 100 centimetres
b 55 centimetres = 55 × 0.4 inches = 22 inches

Exercise 9S

For questions 1–4 convert the dimension in inches to centimetres, given that 1 inch equals 2.5 centimetres.

1 A door is 36 inches wide.
2 A cricket stump is 26 inches long.
3 A tie is 34 inches long.
4 Tom's younger brother James is 46 inches tall.

(continued)

For questions 5–8 convert the dimension in centimetres to inches, given that 1 centimetre = 0.4 inches.

5   A cricket bat is 75 centimetres long.

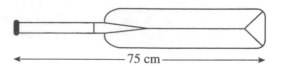

75 cm

6   A walking stick is 70 centimetres long.
7   A broom handle is 120 centimetres long.
8   Julie's younger sister Diane is 105 centimetres tall.

Example 22

a The cliff at Achill Island in Ireland, which is the tallest in the British Isles, is 2190 feet high.
Given that 1 foot = 0.3 metres, find its height in metres.

b The tallest of the Egyptian pyramids is 150 metres high.
Given that 1 metre = 3.3 feet, find its height in feet.

a 2190 feet = 2190 × 0.3 metres = 657 metres
b 150 metres = 150 × 3.3 feet = 495 feet

Exercise 9T

For questions 1–4 convert the dimension in feet to metres, given that 1 foot = 0.3 metres.

1   A garage is 10 feet high.

2   A bus is 50 feet long.

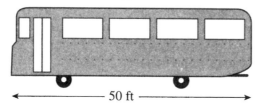

50 ft

3   The highest main road in England, which is between Alston and Wearhead, reaches a height of 2050 feet above sea level.

4   The highest mountain in Western Europe, which is Mont Blanc, has a height of 15 760 feet above sea level.

For questions 5–8 convert the dimension in metres to feet, given that 1 metre = 3.3 feet.

5   A ship is 70 metres long.

6   The highest railway bridge in the world is at Les Fades in Central France. It is 130 metres high.

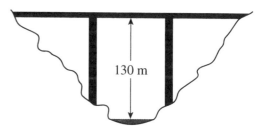

130 m

7   The highest mountain in the world, which is Mount Everest, has a height of 8850 metres above sea level.

8   The deepest land depression in the world is that of the Dead Sea. The surface of the Dead Sea is 390 metres below sea level.

Example 23

a The playground at Sally's school is 70 yards long. Given that 1 yard = 0.9 metres, find its length in metres.

b The football pitch at Paul's school is 80 metres long. Given that 1 metre = 1.1 yards, find its length in yards.

a 70 yards = 70 × 0.9 metres = 63 metres   b 80 metres = 80 × 1.1 yards = 88 yards

Exercise 9U

For questions 1–4 convert the dimension in yards to metres, given that 1 yard = 0.9 metres.

1 The lamp posts in Larch Avenue are 30 yards apart.
2 A viaduct is 750 yards long.
3 The distance between the underground stations at Hyde Park Corner and Green Park is 940 yards.
4 John lives 1250 yards from his school.

For questions 5–8 convert the dimension in metres to yards, given that 1 metre = 1.1 yards.

5 Beech Avenue is 60 metres long.
6 When you take your driving test you are asked to read a car number plate from a distance of 20 metres.
7 A railway tunnel is 760 metres long.
8 Mary lives 830 metres from her school.

Example 24

a The distance from London to Leeds is 190 miles. Given that 1 mile = 1.6 kilometres, convert this distance to kilometres.

b The distance from Paris to Lyon is 472 kilometres. Given that 1 kilometre = 0.625 (or $\frac{5}{8}$) miles, convert this distance to miles.

a 190 miles = 190 × 1.6 kilometres = 304 kilometres
b 472 kilometres = 472 × 0.625 miles = 295 miles

Exercise 9V

For questions 1–4 convert the distance in miles to kilometres, given that 1 mile = 1.6 kilometres.

1 London to Glasgow, 400 miles   2 London to Manchester, 185 miles
3 London to Bristol, 120 miles   4 London to Southend, 35 miles

For questions 5–8 convert the distance in kilometres to miles, given that 1 kilometre = 0.625 (or $\frac{5}{8}$) miles.

5 Paris to Nice, 920 kilometres   6 Paris to Calais, 280 kilometres
7 Paris to Milan, 856 kilometres   8 Paris to Rome, 1480 kilometres

10 USING YOUR CALCULATOR (2)
(+, −, × AND ÷ WITH DECIMALS)

10.1 Addition and subtraction using decimals

Using a calculator makes most arithmetic processes easier.

Several examples are shown below.

Press the **AC** key to clear your calculator before each new calculation.
The decimal point key is the **·** key and the **=** key must be pressed at the end of every calculation.

Example 1

Use your calculator to find the 'odd answer out'.

a 85 + 56 + 5   **b** 98.3 + 11.1 + 35.6   **c** 103 + 36.1 + 6.9

Using a calculator gives the answers: **a** 146   **b** 145   **c** 146
Therefore the 'odd answer out' is **b**.

Exercise 10A

Use your calculator to find the 'odd answer out' for each of the following.

1 **a** 53.64 + 9.24 + 8.52   **b** 61.16 + 4.52 + 5.82   **c** 58.15 + 6.83 + 6.42
2 **a** 9.2 + 5.4 + 3.4   **b** 8.3 + 3.5 + 6.2   **c** 7.1 + 4.6 + 7.3
3 **a** 325 + 187 + 216   **b** 269 + 195 + 274   **c** 413 + 209 + 106

Example 2

Use your calculator to find the 'odd answer out'.

a 31.5 − 25.9   **b** 15.2 − 9.6   **c** 24 − 18.3

Using a calculator gives the answers: **a** 5.6   **b** 5.6   **c** 5.7
The 'odd answer out' is **c**.

Exercise 10B

Use your calculator to find the 'odd answer out' for each of the following.

1 a 61.45 − 34.7   **b** 53.65 − 26.8   c 39.95 − 13.1
2 a 735 − 469   **b** 984 − 728   c 813 − 557
3 a 9 − 4.39   **b** 8.2 − 3.69   c 7.25 − 2.64
4 a 14.27 − 9.145   **b** 13.065 − 7.84   c 5.6 − 0.475

Example 3

A carpenter has a 17 metre length of skirting board.

He cuts off six pieces whose lengths are:

1 m 70 cm, 2 m 60 cm, 1 m 30 cm, 3 m 80 cm, 2 m 90 cm and 4 m 30 cm.

Find:

a the total length he cuts off

b the length of skirting board he has left.

a $1.70 + 2.60 + 1.30 + 3.80 + 2.90 + 4.30 = 16.60$

The length cut off is 16 m 60 cm.

b $17 - 16.60 = 0.40$

The length left is 40 cm.

Exercise 10C

For questions 1 and 2 find:

    a the total amount paid
    b the change from a £10 note.

1 Joan goes to the greengrocer's where she spends £1.35 on apples, £1.17 on pears, £1.05 on oranges, £1.10 on tomatoes and £1.48 on potatoes.

2 George goes to the electrical spares shop where he spends £1.80 on electric plugs, £1.75 on electric wire, £2.36 on light bulbs, £1.04 on cable clips and 30p (£0.30) on fuses.

3 Simone goes to an art shop where she spends £3.50 on paint, £2.55 on brushes, £1.18 on turps, £1.42 on pencils and 80p on erasers. Find:
    a the total amount she spends
    b the change from a £20 note.

4 Tony has a reel which contains 10 metres of wire. He cuts off six pieces whose lengths are: 1 m 50 cm, 1 m 20 cm, 1 m 15 cm, 1 m 30 cm, 1 m 55 cm and 1 m 65 cm. Find:
    a the total length he cuts off
    b the length of wire left on the reel.

10.2 Multiplication and division using decimals

Example 4

Use your calculator to find the 'odd answer out'.

a 45×16 **b** 50×14.4 **c** 60×12.5

Using a calculator gives the answers: **a** 720   **b** 720   **c** 750

The 'odd answer out' is **c**.

Exercise 10D

Use your calculator to find the 'odd answer out' for each of the following.

1 **a** 31.2×2.6 **b** 36.3×2.4 **c** 48.4×1.8
2 **a** 272×3.5 **b** 530×1.8 **c** 212×4.5
3 **a** 48×0.54 **b** 81×0.32 **c** 191×0.12

Example 5

Use your calculator to find the 'odd answer out'.
a $153 \div 3.6$ **b** $170.1 \div 4.2$ **c** $27.2 \div 0.64$

Using a calculator gives the answers: **a** 42.5   **b** 40.5   **c** 42.5
The 'odd answer out' is **b**.

Exercise 10E

Use your calculator to find the 'odd answer out' for each of the following.

1 **a** $8.85 \div 2.95$ **b** $5.55 \div 1.85$ **c** $9.8 \div 2.45$
2 **a** $51.6 \div 15$ **b** $96.6 \div 28$ **c** $55.2 \div 16$
3 **a** $18 \div 0.03$ **b** $30.4 \div 0.05$ **c** $9.12 \div 0.015$

Example 6

Find:
a the cost of 3 shirts at £7.99 each together with 2 ties at £3.99 each
b the change from a £50 note.

a 3 shirts cost £7.99 × 3 = £23.97. 2 ties cost £3.99 × 2 = £7.98.
Therefore the total cost is: £23.97 + £7.98 = £31.95.
b The change from a £50 note is: £50 − £31.95 = £18.05.

Exercise 10F

For questions 1–4 find:

    a the total cost
    b the change from a £50 note.

1 3 children's tickets for an excursion at £4.25 each and 2 adult's tickets for the same excursion at £8.50 each

2 3 cardigans at £4.95 each and 2 blouses at £3.75 each

3 4 dressing gowns at £8.95 each and 3 towels at £1.55 each

4 4 jumpers at £5.15 each and 3 handbags at £2.45 each

Example 7

On one market stall 3 kilograms of apples cost £4.86. On a second stall 2 kilograms of the same apples cost £3.26. Which is the better buy?

1 kilogram at the first stall costs: £4.86 ÷ 3 = £1.62
1 kilogram at the second stall costs: £3.26 ÷ 2 = £1.63

The apples on the first stall are the better buy (because they are cheaper).

Exercise 10G

For all questions find which is the better buy.

1   3 kg of cherries costing £7.92 or 2 kg of the same cherries costing £5.26
2   4 kg of plums costing £4.92 or 3 kg of the same plums costing £3.66
3   4 kg of bananas costing £4.52 or 3 kg of the same bananas costing £3.42
4   6 lemons costing £1.44 or 5 similar ones costing £1.15
5   9 limes costing £2.52 or 8 similar ones costing £2.32

Example 8

Which is the best buy?
i   3 litres of squash for £2.01   ii   2 litres of squash for £1.30   iii   1.5 litres of squash for 99p

i If 3 litres cost £2.01, then the price per litre is: £2.01 ÷ 3 = £0.67 = 67p
ii If 2 litres cost £1.30, then the price per litre is: £1.30 ÷ 2 = £0.65 = 65p
iii If 1.5 litres cost 99p, then the price per litre is: 99p ÷ 1.5 = 66p

Therefore **ii** is the best buy.

Exercise 10H

For questions 1–3 find which is the better buy.

1   a 3 kg packet of sultanas costing £3.75 or a 2.5 kg packet of the same sultanas costing £3.15

2   a 2 kg packet of flour costing £1.52 or a 1.5 kg packet of the same flour costing £1.11

3   a 2 kg packet of sugar lumps costing £1.94 or a 1.5 kg packet of the same sugar lumps costing £1.47

For questions 4 and 5 find which is the best buy.

4   i   a 2.5 litre carton of milk costing £2.05
    ii a 2 litre carton of milk costing £1.60
    iii a 1.5 litre carton of milk costing £1.17

5   i   a 1.5 litre bottle of cooking oil costing £1.62
    ii a 1.25 litre bottle of cooking oil costing £1.40
    iii a 1.2 litre bottle of cooking oil costing £1.26

10.3 Approximating by using decimal places

The number 29.346 contains three decimal places. If we want to approximate this number we can write it correct to two or to one decimal place(s).

Correct to two decimal places it is 29.35 (because the third decimal figure is a 6).
Correct to one decimal place it is 29.3 (because the second decimal figure is a 4).

Example 9

Write correct to two decimal places:

a 4.286   b 2.132   c 5.195

a 4.286 is 4.29 correct to two decimal places.
(The second decimal figure is increased by 1 because the third decimal figure is greater than 5.)

b 2.132 is 2.13 correct to two decimal places.
(The third decimal figure is less than 5, so it is ignored.)

c 5.195 is 5.20 correct to two decimal places.
(The third decimal figure is equal to 5 and in this case 19 has to be increased to 20.)

Exercise 10J

Write each of the following correct to two decimal places.

1	2.348	**2**	3.647	**3**	4.746	**4**	9.139	**5**	5.481
6	4.283	**7**	2.784	**8**	5.245	**9**	6.308	**10**	3.509
11	9.502	**12**	6.804	**13**	3.298	**14**	2.395		

Example 10

Write correct to one decimal place:

a 5.26   b 6.024

a 5.26 is 5.3 correct to one decimal place.
(The first decimal figure is increased by 1 because the second decimal figure is greater than 5.)

b 6.024 is 6.0 correct to one decimal place.
(The second decimal figure is less than 5 so it is ignored.)

Exercise 10K

Write each of the following correct to one decimal place.

1	2.63	**2**	5.91	**3**	3.84	**4**	8.23	**5**	5.29
6	3.46	**7**	7.57	**8**	4.65	**9**	6.15	**10**	9.08
11	5.07	**12**	3.03	**13**	8.01	**14**	4.97	**15**	2.96

Exercise 10L

Write each of the following correct to one decimal place.

1	3.692	**2**	6.581	**3**	7.465	**4**	5.873	**5**	8.396
6	6.524	**7**	5.716	**8**	4.826	**9**	9.317	**10**	3.985
11	2.964	**12**	6.706	**13**	7.504	**14**	4.093	**15**	4.251

Exercise 10M

Copy and complete the table below.

	Number	Number correct to four decimal places	Number correct to three decimal places	Number correct to two decimal places	Number correct to one decimal place
1	8.518 46				
2	4.737 25				
3	2.982 37				
4	8.527 38				
5	2.736 17				
6	4.615 39				
7	26.512 69				
8	37.324 58				

Example 11

Write correct to two decimal places:

a 0.846   **b** 0.073

a 0.846 is 0.85 correct to two decimal places.
(The second decimal figure is increased by 1 because the third decimal figure is greater than 5.)

b 0.073 is 0.07 correct to two decimal places.
(The third decimal figure is less than 5 so it is ignored. Note that the nought after the decimal point does count as a decimal place even though it does not count as a significant figure.)

Exercise 10N

Write each of the following correct to two decimal places.

1	0.354	**2**	0.761	**3**	0.823	**4**	0.904	**5**	0.801
6	0.629	**7**	0.738	**8**	0.576	**9**	0.415	**10**	0.307
11	0.408	**12**	0.017	**13**	0.029	**14**	0.024		

It is possible to correct any quantity to a given number of decimal places by using a calculator in its 'fix' mode, but the manual for your model of calculator must be consulted to see how to do this.

10.4   Checking your answers by using inverse operations

It is always useful to do a rough estimate to get an idea of the likely size of an answer before using your calculator, because it is very easy to press the wrong key by mistake.

In addition and multiplication it can also be a check if you do the sum a different way.

Example 12

Find   **a** $4.3 + 5.2 + 7.1$ **b** 2.6×4.3

a $4.3 + 5.2 + 7.1 = 16.6$

We could also find this in reverse order:

$7.1 + 5.2 + 4.3 = 16.6$

As both answers agree this must be the correct answer.

b $2.6 \times 4.3 = 11.18$

We could also do this as:

$4.3 \times 2.6 = 11.18$

Again, as both answers agree, 11.18 is the correct answer.

Exercise 10P

Find each of the following and check each answer by doing the working in reverse order.

1	$2.9 + 3.6 + 4.2$	**2**	$15.2 + 11.5 + 9.3$	**3**	$5.6 + 1.23 + 3.27$
4	$6.24 + 1.37 + 4.59$	**5**	$4.58 + 2.77 + 1.35$	**6**	$7.29 + 4.37 + 0.84$
7	8.5×2.4	**8**	9.2×3.5	**9**	6.8×0.75
10	9.6×0.05	**11**	2.5×0.08	**12**	0.6×0.025

The method for addition and multiplication does not work for subtraction or division because $8 \div 4$, for example, does not give the same result as $4 \div 8$.

We can, however, check subtraction and division as shown below.

Example 13

Find   **a** $14.6 - 3.9$ **b** $17.94 \div 3.9$

a $14.6 - 3.9 = 10.7$

Since addition is the opposite (or inverse) of subtraction we can add 3.9 to the answer of 10.7 and see if we get 14.6 back:

$10.7 + 3.9 = 14.6$ as expected, so $14.6 - 3.9$ does equal 10.7

b $17.94 \div 3.9 = 4.6$

Since multiplication is the opposite (or inverse) of division we can multiply the answer of 4.6 by 3.9 and see if we get 17.94 back:

$4.6 \times 3.9 = 17.94$ as expected, so $17.94 \div 3.9$ does equal 4.6

Exercise 10Q

Find each of the following and check each answer with an inverse operation.

1	$8.2 - 4.7$	**2**	$12.1 - 7.6$	**3**	$16 - 3.4$	**4**	$8.3 - 5.65$	**5**	$6.1 - 2.25$
6	$2.5 - 0.42$	**7**	$16 \div 1.25$	**8**	$10.5 \div 4.2$	**9**	$11.52 \div 2.4$	**10**	$28.34 \div 6.5$
11	$0.189 \div 0.06$	**12**	$0.84 \div 0.08$						

11 FRACTIONS

11.1 Understanding and representing fractions
(including halves and quarters)

The simplest kind of fraction refers to one given part of a whole quantity.

Look at the circles below:

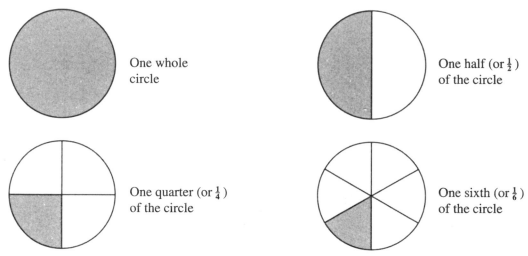

One whole circle

One half (or $\frac{1}{2}$) of the circle

One quarter (or $\frac{1}{4}$) of the circle

One sixth (or $\frac{1}{6}$) of the circle

Exercise 11A

For questions 1–4 state in words and write as a fraction the part of the diagram which is shaded.

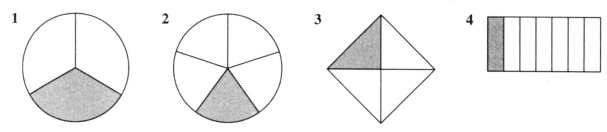

For questions 5–8 copy the diagram and illustrate the fraction given by shading.

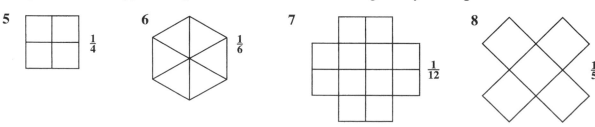

Fractions can also refer to more than one part of a whole quantity.

Look at the rectangles below:

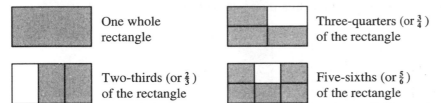

One whole
rectangle

Three-quarters (or $\frac{3}{4}$)
of the rectangle

Two-thirds (or $\frac{2}{3}$)
of the rectangle

Five-sixths (or $\frac{5}{6}$)
of the rectangle

Exercise 11B

For questions 1–6 state in words and write as a fraction the part of the
diagram which is shaded.

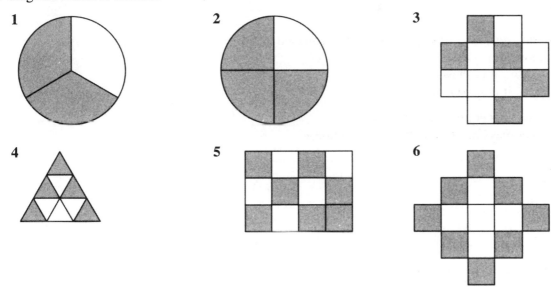

For questions 7–12 copy the diagram and illustrate the fraction given by shading.

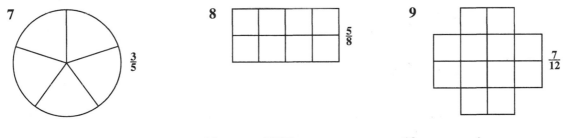

7 $\frac{3}{5}$

8 $\frac{5}{8}$

9 $\frac{7}{12}$

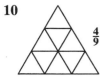

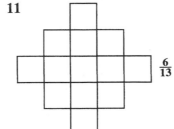

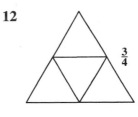

10 $\frac{4}{9}$

11 $\frac{6}{13}$

12 $\frac{3}{4}$

11.2 The idea of equivalent fractions

The diagrams below show three different ways of shading the same part of a square.

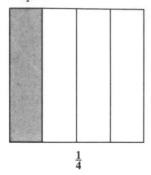

$\frac{1}{4}$

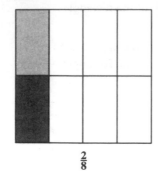

$\frac{2}{8}$

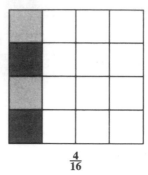

$\frac{4}{16}$

In each of the squares above **one quarter** has been shaded in.
In the first square this is shown as $\frac{1}{4}$.
In the second square it is shown as $\frac{2}{8}$.
In the third square it is shown as $\frac{4}{16}$.

$\frac{1}{4}$, $\frac{2}{8}$ and $\frac{4}{16}$ are therefore equivalent fractions.
They are different ways of writing the same fraction.

Example 1

Copy and complete:

a **i** $\dfrac{1}{4} = \dfrac{?}{20}$ **ii** $\dfrac{1}{4} = \dfrac{?}{24}$

b **i** $\dfrac{3}{4} = \dfrac{6}{?}$ **ii** $\dfrac{3}{4} = \dfrac{30}{?}$

a **i** $\dfrac{1}{4} = \dfrac{1 \times 5}{4 \times 5} = \dfrac{5}{20}$ **ii** $\dfrac{1}{4} = \dfrac{1 \times 6}{4 \times 6} = \dfrac{6}{24}$

b **i** $\dfrac{3}{4} = \dfrac{3 \times 2}{4 \times 2} = \dfrac{6}{8}$ **ii** $\dfrac{3}{4} = \dfrac{3 \times 10}{4 \times 10} = \dfrac{30}{40}$

Note in each of the above the numerator and denominator of the fraction (the upper and lower figures) are both multiplied by the same number.

Exercise 11C

Copy and complete each of the following.

1 **a** $\dfrac{1}{3} = \dfrac{?}{6}$ **b** $\dfrac{1}{3} = \dfrac{?}{9}$ **c** $\dfrac{1}{3} = \dfrac{?}{15}$ **d** $\dfrac{1}{3} = \dfrac{?}{24}$ **e** $\dfrac{1}{3} = \dfrac{?}{30}$

2 **a** $\dfrac{1}{12} = \dfrac{?}{36}$ **b** $\dfrac{1}{12} = \dfrac{?}{60}$ **c** $\dfrac{1}{12} = \dfrac{?}{72}$ **d** $\dfrac{1}{12} = \dfrac{?}{108}$ **e** $\dfrac{1}{12} = \dfrac{?}{120}$

3 **a** $\dfrac{5}{8} = \dfrac{?}{24}$ **b** $\dfrac{5}{8} = \dfrac{?}{40}$ **c** $\dfrac{5}{8} = \dfrac{?}{48}$ **d** $\dfrac{5}{8} = \dfrac{?}{56}$ **e** $\dfrac{5}{8} = \dfrac{?}{72}$

4 **a** $\dfrac{2}{9} = \dfrac{?}{27}$ **b** $\dfrac{2}{9} = \dfrac{?}{45}$ **c** $\dfrac{2}{9} = \dfrac{?}{63}$ **d** $\dfrac{2}{9} = \dfrac{?}{72}$ **e** $\dfrac{2}{9} = \dfrac{?}{90}$

5 $\dfrac{4}{9} = \dfrac{?}{18} = \dfrac{?}{45} = \dfrac{?}{54} = \dfrac{?}{81} = \dfrac{?}{90}$ **6** $\dfrac{5}{12} = \dfrac{15}{?} = \dfrac{20}{?} = \dfrac{30}{?} = \dfrac{35}{?} = \dfrac{40}{?}$

Example 2

Copy and complete:

a $\dfrac{5}{10} = \dfrac{?}{2}$ **b** $\dfrac{14}{21} = \dfrac{?}{3}$

a $\dfrac{5}{10} = \dfrac{5 \div 5}{10 \div 5} = \dfrac{1}{2}$ **b** $\dfrac{14}{21} = \dfrac{14 \div 7}{21 \div 7} = \dfrac{2}{3}$

Note in each example both the numerator and the denominator are divided by the same figure.

Exercise 11D

Copy and complete the following.

1 $\dfrac{6}{20} = \dfrac{?}{10}$ **2** $\dfrac{14}{20} = \dfrac{?}{10}$ **3** $\dfrac{12}{14} = \dfrac{?}{7}$ **4** $\dfrac{10}{12} = \dfrac{?}{6}$ **5** $\dfrac{15}{50} = \dfrac{?}{10}$

6 $\dfrac{15}{25} = \dfrac{?}{5}$ **7** $\dfrac{10}{25} = \dfrac{?}{5}$ **8** $\dfrac{18}{60} = \dfrac{?}{10}$ **9** $\dfrac{6}{60} = \dfrac{?}{10}$ **10** $\dfrac{6}{12} = \dfrac{?}{2}$

Example 3

Copy and complete:

a $\dfrac{6}{24} = \dfrac{1}{?}$ **b** $\dfrac{24}{27} = \dfrac{8}{?}$

a $\dfrac{6}{24} = \dfrac{6 \div 6}{24 \div 6} = \dfrac{1}{4}$ **b** $\dfrac{24}{27} = \dfrac{24 \div 3}{27 \div 3} = \dfrac{8}{9}$

Note again that in each example the numerator and denominator are divided by the same figure.

Exercise 11E

1 $\dfrac{8}{18} = \dfrac{4}{?}$ 2 $\dfrac{10}{18} = \dfrac{5}{?}$ 3 $\dfrac{10}{14} = \dfrac{5}{?}$ 4 $\dfrac{6}{14} = \dfrac{3}{?}$ 5 $\dfrac{6}{8} = \dfrac{3}{?}$

6 $\dfrac{4}{6} = \dfrac{2}{?}$ 7 $\dfrac{18}{30} = \dfrac{3}{?}$ 8 $\dfrac{24}{30} = \dfrac{4}{?}$ 9 $\dfrac{6}{30} = \dfrac{1}{?}$ 10 $\dfrac{8}{40} = \dfrac{1}{?}$

11 $\dfrac{8}{16} = \dfrac{1}{?}$ 12 $\dfrac{8}{80} = \dfrac{1}{?}$

Example 4

'Cancel' these fractions to their lowest terms and find the 'odd answer out'.

a $\dfrac{48}{60}$ b $\dfrac{35}{40}$ c $\dfrac{36}{45}$

a $\dfrac{48}{60} = \dfrac{4}{5}$ (The numerator and denominator are both divided by 12.)

b $\dfrac{35}{40} = \dfrac{7}{8}$ (The numerator and denominator are both divided by 5.)

c $\dfrac{36}{45} = \dfrac{4}{5}$ (The numerator and denominator are both divided by 9.)

The 'odd answer out' is **b**.

Exercise 11F

For each of the following cancel the fractions and find the answer which is different.

1 a $\dfrac{24}{36}$ b $\dfrac{20}{32}$ c $\dfrac{30}{48}$ 2 a $\dfrac{27}{36}$ b $\dfrac{28}{35}$ c $\dfrac{24}{32}$

3 a $\dfrac{30}{36}$ b $\dfrac{42}{48}$ c $\dfrac{35}{42}$ 4 a $\dfrac{14}{35}$ b $\dfrac{15}{40}$ c $\dfrac{12}{32}$

5 a $\dfrac{36}{45}$ b $\dfrac{40}{48}$ c $\dfrac{24}{30}$ 6 a $\dfrac{28}{42}$ b $\dfrac{18}{27}$ c $\dfrac{21}{35}$

Exercise 11G

Reduce each of the following to its lowest terms.

1 $\dfrac{14}{20}$ 2 $\dfrac{18}{20}$ 3 $\dfrac{8}{10}$ 4 $\dfrac{14}{16}$ 5 $\dfrac{2}{6}$

6 $\dfrac{3}{15}$ 7 $\dfrac{12}{15}$ 8 $\dfrac{12}{16}$ 9 $\dfrac{20}{24}$ 10 $\dfrac{16}{20}$

Example 5

A set of equivalent fractions is shown below.

$$\frac{3}{4} \qquad \frac{6}{8} \qquad \frac{9}{12} \qquad \frac{12}{16}$$

Find the next five fractions in the sequence.

The numerators (the upper figures) are the multiples of 3, so the next five numerators are:

    15   18   21   24 and 27

The denominators (the lower figures) are the multiples of 4, so the next five denominators are:

    20   24   28   32 and 36

The next five fractions are therefore:

$$\frac{15}{20} \qquad \frac{18}{24} \qquad \frac{21}{28} \qquad \frac{24}{32} \quad \text{and} \quad \frac{27}{36}$$

Exercise 11H

Find the next five fractions in the sequence for each of the following.

1   $\dfrac{3}{10}, \dfrac{6}{20}, \dfrac{9}{30}, \dfrac{12}{40}$ 2 $\dfrac{7}{10}, \dfrac{14}{20}, \dfrac{21}{30}, \dfrac{28}{40}$ 3 $\dfrac{4}{5}, \dfrac{8}{10}, \dfrac{12}{15}, \dfrac{16}{20}$

4   $\dfrac{3}{4}, \dfrac{6}{8}, \dfrac{9}{12}, \dfrac{12}{16}$ 5 $\dfrac{5}{6}, \dfrac{10}{12}, \dfrac{15}{18}, \dfrac{20}{24}$ 6 $\dfrac{1}{4}, \dfrac{2}{8}, \dfrac{3}{12}, \dfrac{4}{16}$

Example 6

A set of equivalent fractions is shown below.

$$\frac{20}{30} \qquad \frac{18}{27} \qquad \frac{16}{24} \qquad \frac{14}{21}$$

Find the remaining terms in the sequence until the simplest of the equivalent fractions is found.

The numerators are descending multiples of 2, so the remaining numerators are:

    12   10   8   6   4 and 2

The denominators are descending multiples of 3, so the remaining denominators are:

    18   15   12   9   6 and 3

$\frac{2}{3}$ is therefore the simplest of the equivalent fractions.

Exercise 11J

For each of the following find the remaining terms in the sequence until the simplest of the equivalent fractions is found.

1   $\dfrac{50}{80}, \dfrac{45}{72}, \dfrac{40}{64}, \dfrac{35}{56}$ 2 $\dfrac{30}{80}, \dfrac{27}{72}, \dfrac{24}{64}, \dfrac{21}{56}$

3   $\dfrac{70}{100}, \dfrac{63}{90}, \dfrac{56}{80}, \dfrac{49}{70}$ 4 $\dfrac{20}{30}, \dfrac{18}{27}, \dfrac{16}{24}, \dfrac{14}{21}$

5   $\dfrac{10}{60}, \dfrac{9}{54}, \dfrac{8}{48}, \dfrac{7}{42}$ 6 $\dfrac{10}{40}, \dfrac{9}{36}, \dfrac{8}{32}, \dfrac{7}{28}$

Example 7

Find the simplest fraction which is equivalent to $\frac{18}{30}$ and write down two other equivalent fractions.

$$\frac{18}{30} = \frac{18 \div 6}{30 \div 6} = \frac{3}{5}$$

For two other equivalent fractions any two (except $\frac{3}{5}$ and $\frac{18}{30}$) may be chosen from the sequence:

$$\frac{6}{10} \qquad \frac{9}{15} \qquad \frac{12}{20} \qquad \frac{15}{25}$$

Note   the numerators are the multiples of 3 and the denominators are the multiples of 5.

Exercise 11K

For each of the following reduce the fraction to its lowest terms and write down two other equivalent fractions.

1   $\dfrac{6}{10}$ 2 $\dfrac{6}{16}$ 3 $\dfrac{10}{12}$

4   $\dfrac{15}{18}$ 5 $\dfrac{21}{24}$ 6 $\dfrac{3}{30}$

7   $\dfrac{12}{20}$ 8 $\dfrac{20}{28}$ 9 $\dfrac{12}{16}$

10   $\dfrac{45}{54}$

11.3 Addition and subtraction of fractions

We can use equivalent fractions to enable us to add or subtract fractions of different types.

Example 8

Evaluate: **a** $\frac{1}{2} + \frac{1}{4}$ **b** $\frac{1}{3} + \frac{8}{15}$

a

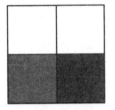

$$\frac{1}{2} \left(\text{or } \frac{2}{4} \right) \qquad + \qquad \frac{1}{4} \qquad = \qquad \frac{3}{4}$$

$$\frac{1}{2} + \frac{1}{4} = \frac{2}{4} + \frac{1}{4} = \frac{3}{4}$$

b

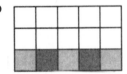 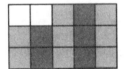

$$\frac{1}{3} \left(\text{or } \frac{5}{15} \right) \qquad + \qquad \frac{8}{15} \qquad = \qquad \frac{13}{15}$$

$$\frac{1}{3} + \frac{8}{15} = \frac{5}{15} + \frac{8}{15} = \frac{13}{15}$$

Exercise 11L

Copy and complete each of the following.

1 $\frac{1}{5} + \frac{9}{20} = \frac{?}{20} + \frac{9}{20} = \frac{?}{20}$

2 $\frac{1}{5} + \frac{13}{20} = \frac{?}{20} + \frac{13}{20} = \frac{?}{20}$

3 $\frac{2}{5} + \frac{9}{20} = \frac{?}{20} + \frac{9}{20} = \frac{?}{20}$

4 $\frac{2}{5} + \frac{3}{25} = \frac{?}{25} + \frac{3}{25} = \frac{?}{25}$

5 $\frac{2}{5} + \frac{8}{25} = \frac{?}{25} + \frac{8}{25} = \frac{?}{25}$

6 $\frac{3}{5} + \frac{6}{25} = \frac{?}{25} + \frac{6}{25} = \frac{?}{25}$

Exercise 11M

Evaluate each of the following.

1 $\dfrac{4}{5} + \dfrac{1}{15}$ **2** $\dfrac{4}{5} + \dfrac{2}{15}$ **3** $\dfrac{1}{3} + \dfrac{4}{9}$ **4** $\dfrac{1}{3} + \dfrac{5}{9}$

5 $\dfrac{3}{10} + \dfrac{3}{20}$ **6** $\dfrac{7}{10} + \dfrac{3}{20}$ **7** $\dfrac{1}{5} + \dfrac{7}{10}$ **8** $\dfrac{1}{5} + \dfrac{1}{10}$

9 $\dfrac{1}{4} + \dfrac{3}{8}$ **10** $\dfrac{1}{4} + \dfrac{5}{8}$ **11** $\dfrac{1}{3} + \dfrac{1}{12}$ **12** $\dfrac{2}{3} + \dfrac{4}{15}$

Example 9

Evaluate:

a $\dfrac{1}{2} - \dfrac{1}{4}$ **b** $\dfrac{2}{3} - \dfrac{7}{12}$

a

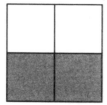

$\dfrac{1}{2}$ (or $\dfrac{2}{4}$) $-$ 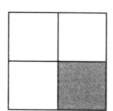 $\dfrac{1}{4}$ $=$ 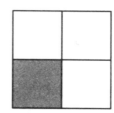 $\dfrac{1}{4}$

$$\dfrac{1}{2} - \dfrac{1}{4} = \dfrac{2}{4} - \dfrac{1}{4} = \dfrac{1}{4}$$

b

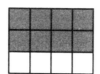   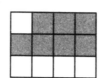

$\dfrac{2}{3}$ (or $\dfrac{8}{12}$) $-$ $\dfrac{7}{12}$ $=$ $\dfrac{1}{12}$

$$\dfrac{2}{3} - \dfrac{7}{12} = \dfrac{8}{12} - \dfrac{7}{12} = \dfrac{1}{12}$$

Exercise 11N

Copy and complete each of the following.

1 $\dfrac{4}{5} - \dfrac{9}{20} = \dfrac{?}{20} - \dfrac{9}{20} = \dfrac{?}{20}$ **2** $\dfrac{4}{5} - \dfrac{13}{20} = \dfrac{?}{20} - \dfrac{13}{20} = \dfrac{?}{20}$ **3** $\dfrac{3}{5} - \dfrac{9}{20} = \dfrac{?}{20} - \dfrac{9}{20} = \dfrac{?}{20}$

4 $\dfrac{1}{5} - \dfrac{3}{25} = \dfrac{?}{25} - \dfrac{3}{25} = \dfrac{?}{25}$ **5** $\dfrac{4}{5} - \dfrac{3}{25} = \dfrac{?}{25} - \dfrac{3}{25} = \dfrac{?}{25}$ **6** $\dfrac{4}{5} - \dfrac{11}{25} = \dfrac{?}{25} - \dfrac{11}{25} = \dfrac{?}{25}$

Exercise 11P

Evaluate each of the following.

1 $\dfrac{9}{10} - \dfrac{1}{20}$ **2** $\dfrac{7}{10} - \dfrac{11}{20}$ **3** $\dfrac{3}{5} - \dfrac{3}{10}$ **4** $\dfrac{1}{5} - \dfrac{1}{10}$ **5** $\dfrac{3}{4} - \dfrac{5}{8}$ **6** $\dfrac{3}{4} - \dfrac{3}{8}$

7 $\dfrac{1}{6} - \dfrac{1}{12}$ **8** $\dfrac{4}{5} - \dfrac{8}{15}$ **9** $\dfrac{2}{3} - \dfrac{4}{9}$ **10** $\dfrac{2}{3} - \dfrac{5}{9}$ **11** $\dfrac{1}{3} - \dfrac{4}{15}$ **12** $\dfrac{2}{3} - \dfrac{8}{15}$

Example 10

Evaluate: **a** $\dfrac{1}{3} + \dfrac{1}{6}$ **b** $\dfrac{1}{6} + \dfrac{5}{18}$ and in each case simplify your answer.

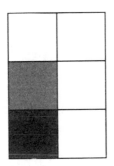   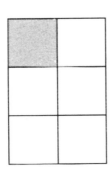   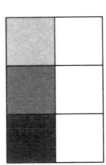

$\dfrac{1}{3}$ (or $\dfrac{2}{6}$)   + $\dfrac{1}{6}$ = $\dfrac{3}{6}$ (or $\dfrac{1}{2}$)

a $\dfrac{1}{3} + \dfrac{1}{6} = \dfrac{2}{6} + \dfrac{1}{6} = \dfrac{3}{6} = \dfrac{1}{2}$ **b** $\dfrac{1}{6} + \dfrac{5}{18} = \dfrac{3}{18} + \dfrac{5}{18} = \dfrac{8}{18} = \dfrac{4}{9}$

Exercise 11Q

Work out each of the following and simplify your answer.

1 $\dfrac{1}{4} + \dfrac{7}{12}$ **2** $\dfrac{3}{4} + \dfrac{1}{12}$ **3** $\dfrac{1}{6} + \dfrac{1}{18}$ **4** $\dfrac{5}{6} + \dfrac{1}{18}$ **5** $\dfrac{1}{3} + \dfrac{4}{15}$ **6** $\dfrac{2}{3} + \dfrac{2}{15}$

7 $\dfrac{1}{3} + \dfrac{5}{12}$ **8** $\dfrac{1}{4} + \dfrac{7}{20}$ **9** $\dfrac{2}{5} + \dfrac{7}{20}$ **10** $\dfrac{1}{10} + \dfrac{13}{20}$ **11** $\dfrac{2}{5} + \dfrac{4}{15}$ **12** $\dfrac{2}{5} + \dfrac{1}{10}$

Example 11

Evaluate: **a** $\dfrac{1}{2} - \dfrac{1}{10}$ **b** $\dfrac{5}{6} - \dfrac{5}{18}$ and simplify your answers.

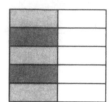

$\dfrac{1}{2}$ (or $\dfrac{5}{10}$) $-$ $\dfrac{1}{10}$ $=$ $\dfrac{4}{10}$ (or $\dfrac{2}{5}$)

a $\dfrac{1}{2} - \dfrac{1}{10} = \dfrac{5}{10} - \dfrac{1}{10} = \dfrac{4}{10} = \dfrac{2}{5}$ **b** $\dfrac{5}{6} - \dfrac{5}{18} = \dfrac{15}{18} - \dfrac{5}{18} = \dfrac{10}{18} = \dfrac{5}{9}$

Exercise 11R

Work out each of the following and simplify your answer.

1 $\dfrac{1}{4} - \dfrac{1}{12}$ **2** $\dfrac{3}{4} - \dfrac{7}{12}$ **3** $\dfrac{1}{2} - \dfrac{3}{10}$ **4** $\dfrac{2}{3} - \dfrac{1}{15}$ **5** $\dfrac{1}{3} - \dfrac{2}{15}$ **6** $\dfrac{2}{3} - \dfrac{5}{12}$

7 $\dfrac{3}{4} - \dfrac{7}{20}$ **8** $\dfrac{3}{4} - \dfrac{11}{20}$ **9** $\dfrac{3}{10} - \dfrac{1}{20}$ **10** $\dfrac{4}{5} - \dfrac{11}{20}$ **11** $\dfrac{2}{5} - \dfrac{1}{15}$ **12** $\dfrac{4}{5} - \dfrac{3}{10}$

Example 12

Evaluate: $\dfrac{3}{4} + \dfrac{1}{6}$

$\dfrac{3}{4} + \dfrac{1}{6} = \dfrac{9}{12} + \dfrac{2}{12} = \dfrac{11}{12}$

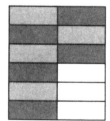 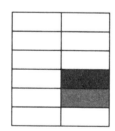 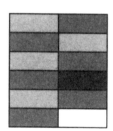

$\dfrac{3}{4}$ (or $\dfrac{9}{12}$) $+$ $\dfrac{1}{6}$ (or $\dfrac{2}{12}$) $=$ $\dfrac{11}{12}$

Example 13

Evaluate: $\dfrac{1}{4} - \dfrac{1}{6}$

$$\dfrac{1}{4} - \dfrac{1}{6} = \dfrac{3}{12} - \dfrac{2}{12} = \dfrac{1}{12}$$

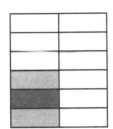 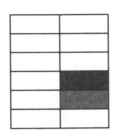 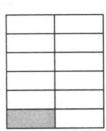

$$\dfrac{1}{4} \ \left(\text{or } \dfrac{3}{12}\right) \qquad - \qquad \dfrac{1}{6} \ \left(\text{or } \dfrac{2}{12}\right) \qquad = \qquad \dfrac{1}{12}$$

Exercise 11S

Evaluate each of the following.

1 $\dfrac{5}{8} + \dfrac{1}{10}$ **2** $\dfrac{1}{8} + \dfrac{7}{12}$ **3** $\dfrac{1}{4} + \dfrac{3}{10}$ **4** $\dfrac{1}{4} + \dfrac{1}{6}$ **5** $\dfrac{1}{6} + \dfrac{7}{10}$ **6** $\dfrac{1}{6} + \dfrac{1}{10}$

7 $\dfrac{1}{8} - \dfrac{1}{10}$ **8** $\dfrac{5}{8} - \dfrac{1}{12}$ **9** $\dfrac{1}{6} - \dfrac{1}{8}$ **10** $\dfrac{3}{4} - \dfrac{1}{6}$ **11** $\dfrac{1}{6} - \dfrac{1}{10}$ **12** $\dfrac{5}{6} - \dfrac{1}{10}$

11.4 Calculating fractions of quantities

Example 14

Hitesh has saved £36. He spends $\frac{1}{2}$ of it on a small radio, $\frac{1}{3}$ of it on an electronics kit, and $\frac{1}{6}$ of it on a new encyclopaedia.

How much does he spend on each?

His radio costs $\frac{1}{2}$ of £36 $= £36 \div 2 = £18$
His electronics kit costs $\frac{1}{3}$ of £36 $= £36 \div 3 = £12$
His encyclopaedia costs $\frac{1}{6}$ of £36 $= £36 \div 6 = £6$

…m London to Edinburgh is 630 kilometres.
  …from London to:
     …, which is $\frac{1}{2}$ of the way to Edinburgh
     …which is $\frac{1}{3}$ of the way to Edinburgh
     …rborough, which is $\frac{1}{5}$ of the way to Edinburgh
  d Sawtry, which is $\frac{1}{6}$ of the way to Edinburgh
  e Huntingdon, which is $\frac{1}{7}$ of the way to Edinburgh
  f Sandy, which is $\frac{1}{8}$ of the way to Edinburgh
  g Biggleswade, which is $\frac{1}{10}$ of the way to Edinburgh
  h Knebworth, which is $\frac{1}{15}$ of the way to Edinburgh.

2 Michelle's school is 960 metres along the road from her house.
   Find the distance from Michelle's house to:
   a the church, if it is $\frac{1}{2}$ of the distance to her school
   b the supermarket, if it is $\frac{1}{3}$ of the distance to her school
   c the library, if it is $\frac{1}{4}$ of the distance to her school
   d the pillar box, if it is $\frac{1}{5}$ of the distance to her school
   e the telephone kiosk, if it is $\frac{1}{6}$ of the distance to her school
   f the post office, if it is $\frac{1}{8}$ of the distance to her school
   g the park gates, if they are $\frac{1}{10}$ of the distance to her school
   h the fire station, if it is $\frac{1}{12}$ of the distance to her school
   i the newsagent's shop, if it is $\frac{1}{15}$ of the distance to her school
   j the greengrocer's shop, if it is $\frac{1}{16}$ of the distance to her school
   k the baker's shop, if it is $\frac{1}{20}$ of the distance to her school.

Example 15

Stickee's sugar is sold in three different sized packets: giant, large and small.

The giant pack contains 660 grams.

Find the weight of sugar in:
a the large sized packet if it contains $\frac{3}{4}$ as much as the giant packet
b the small sized packet if it contains $\frac{2}{5}$ as much as the giant packet.

a $\frac{1}{4}$ of 660 grams $= 660 \div 4$ grams $= 165$ grams
   so $\frac{3}{4}$ of 660 grams $= 165 \times 3$ grams $= 495$ grams
   So the weight of $\frac{3}{4}$ of 660 grams $= (660 \div 4) \times 3$ grams
$$= 165 \times 3 \text{ grams}$$
$$= 495 \text{ grams}$$
b $\frac{1}{5}$ of 660 grams $= 660 \div 5$ grams $= 132$ grams
   so $\frac{2}{5}$ of 660 grams $= 132 \times 2$ grams $= 264$ grams
   So the weight of $\frac{2}{5}$ of 660 grams $= (660 \div 5) \times 2$ grams
$$= 132 \times 2 \text{ grams}$$
$$= 264 \text{ grams}$$

Exercise 11U

1 The distance from London to Holyhead is 420 kilometres.
   Find the distance from London to:
   a Bangor, which is $\frac{9}{10}$ of the way to Holyhead
   b Chester, which is $\frac{7}{10}$ of the way to Holyhead
   c Rugby, which is $\frac{3}{10}$ of the way to Holyhead
   d Rhyl, which is $\frac{4}{5}$ of the way to Holyhead
   e Crewe, which is $\frac{3}{5}$ of the way to Holyhead
   f Tamworth, which is $\frac{2}{5}$ of the way to Holyhead
   g Colwyn Bay, which is $\frac{5}{6}$ of the way to Holyhead
   h Beeston Castle, which is $\frac{2}{3}$ of the way to Holyhead
   i Flint, which is $\frac{3}{4}$ of the way to Holyhead.

2 The distance from London to Shrewsbury is 240 kilometres.
   Find the distance from London to:
   a Cosford, which is $\frac{7}{8}$ of the way to Shrewsbury
   b Coventry, which is $\frac{5}{8}$ of the way to Shrewsbury
   c Castlethorpe, which is $\frac{3}{8}$ of the way to Shrewsbury
   d Blisworth, which is $\frac{5}{12}$ of the way to Shrewsbury
   e Brandon, which is $\frac{7}{12}$ of the way to Shrewsbury
   f Shifnal, which is $\frac{11}{12}$ of the way to Shrewsbury
   g Wolverhampton, which is $\frac{5}{6}$ of the way to Shrewsbury
   h Birmingham, which is $\frac{3}{4}$ of the way to Shrewsbury
   i Berkswell, which is $\frac{2}{3}$ of the way to Shrewsbury.

We have seen how to calculate fractions of a quantity, but a
calculator can make this task much easier. Look at the example below.

Example 16
Calculate $\frac{2}{5}$ of £80.

Press the calculator keys as shown:
[AC] [8] [0] [÷] [5] [×] [2] [=] 32
The answer is £32.

Alternatively:

Press the calculator keys as shown:
[AC] [2] [÷] [5] [×] [8] [0] [=] 32
The answer is £32.

Exercise 11V

Find the answer which is different for each of the following:

1 a $\frac{3}{25}$ of £52   b $\frac{4}{25}$ of £39   c $\frac{7}{25}$ of £23
2 a $\frac{9}{25}$ of £47   b $\frac{6}{25}$ of £68   c $\frac{8}{25}$ of £51
3 a $\frac{9}{40}$ of £26   b $\frac{7}{40}$ of £30   c $\frac{3}{40}$ of £70
4 a $\frac{5}{16}$ of £28   b $\frac{3}{16}$ of £44   c $\frac{7}{16}$ of £20
5 a $\frac{8}{15}$ of 210 metres   b $\frac{13}{15}$ of 135 metres   c $\frac{14}{15}$ of 120 metres
6 a $\frac{7}{30}$ of 390 metres   b $\frac{11}{30}$ of 270 metres   c $\frac{13}{30}$ of 210 metres
7 a $\frac{12}{25}$ of 21 metres   b $\frac{18}{25}$ of 14 metres   c $\frac{16}{25}$ of 17 metres
8 a $\frac{3}{4}$ of £3.40   b $\frac{5}{6}$ of £2.94   c $\frac{5}{8}$ of £4.08
9 a $\frac{7}{8}$ of £3.60   b $\frac{4}{5}$ of £3.90   c $\frac{2}{3}$ of £4.68

11.5   Expressing one quantity as a fraction of another

One quantity can be expressed as a fraction of another. Example 17 shows two simple cases of this.

Example 17

a Express £4 as a fraction of £20.
b Express 15 metres as a fraction of 50 metres.

a $\frac{4}{20} = \frac{1}{5}$ b $\frac{15}{50} = \frac{3}{10}$

Exercise 11W

Find the answer which is different for each of the following:

1 a £8 as a fraction of £40
   b £9 as a fraction of £60
   c £12 as a fraction of £80

2 a £12 as a fraction of £40
   b £8 as a fraction of £32
   c £9 as a fraction of £36

3 a 30 cm as a fraction of 50 cm
   b 26 cm as a fraction of 40 cm
   c 18 cm as a fraction of 30 cm

4 a 4 kg as a fraction of 64 kg
   b 9 kg as a fraction of 144 k
   c 12 kg as a fraction of 160 kg

5 a 28 g as a fraction of 160 g
   b 36 g as a fraction of 200 g
   c 21 g as a fraction of 120 g

6 a 18 km as a fraction of 36 km
   b 27 km as a fraction of 60 km
   c 36 km as a fraction of 80 km

Example 18

A Labrador bitch has 12 puppies in her litter and 8 of them are yellow.
What fraction of the puppies are yellow?

The fraction which are yellow = $\frac{8}{12} = \frac{2}{3}$

Exercise 11X

1 There are 20 girls in class 5A and one day 8 of them arrived late.
What fraction of the girls arrived late?

2 There are 20 eggs in a tray, but I drop the tray and 12 get broken.
What fraction of the eggs are broken?

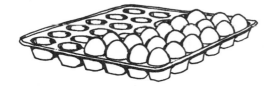

3 Anne took an English test which was marked out of 40.
She obtained 36 marks. What fraction of the total did she get?

4 There are 25 buses in a depot and 10 of them are being repaired.
What fraction of the buses are being repaired?

5 15 children are waiting for their school bus and 12 of them are boys.
What fraction of the children are boys?

6 There are 8 batteries in a portable TV set, but two of them are flat.
What fraction of the batteries are flat?

7 There are 20 boys in class 4C at Highfield School. 12 of them have dark hair, 6 of them have fair hair and 2 of them have ginger hair.
Express these figures as fractions of the total.

8 There are 20 girls in class 5B at Westmead School. 8 of them walk to school, 7 of them cycle to school and 5 travel to school by bus.
Express these figures as fractions of the total.

11.6 Converting fraction to decimals and vice versa

Example 19

Convert each fraction to its decimal equivalent.

a $\dfrac{3}{4}$ **b** $\dfrac{2}{5}$ **c** $\dfrac{3}{50}$

a $\dfrac{3}{4} = 3 \div 4 = 0.75$ (**Note** $\dfrac{3}{4} = \dfrac{3 \times 25}{4 \times 25} = \dfrac{75}{100}$)

b $\dfrac{2}{5} = 2 \div 5 = 0.4$ (**Note** $\dfrac{2}{5} = \dfrac{2 \times 2}{5 \times 2} = \dfrac{4}{10}$)

c $\dfrac{3}{50} = 3 \div 50 = 0.06$ (**Note** $\dfrac{3}{50} = \dfrac{3 \times 2}{50 \times 2} = \dfrac{6}{100}$)

Exercise 11Y

Convert each fraction to its decimal equivalent. (You may use your calculator.)

1 $\dfrac{31}{40}$ 2 $\dfrac{3}{16}$ 3 $\dfrac{5}{8}$ 4 $\dfrac{1}{8}$ 5 $\dfrac{29}{50}$ 6 $\dfrac{3}{10}$

7 $\dfrac{4}{5}$ 8 $\dfrac{8}{125}$ 9 $\dfrac{3}{250}$ 10 $\dfrac{9}{200}$ 11 $\dfrac{1}{625}$ 12 $\dfrac{1}{50}$

Exercise 11Z

For each of the following change the fractions to decimals and find the answer which is different.

1 a $\dfrac{35}{40}$ b $\dfrac{51}{60}$ c $\dfrac{85}{100}$ 2 a $\dfrac{45}{60}$ b $\dfrac{42}{50}$ c $\dfrac{60}{80}$

3 a $\dfrac{56}{80}$ b $\dfrac{34}{50}$ c $\dfrac{51}{75}$ 4 a $\dfrac{48}{150}$ b $\dfrac{52}{160}$ c $\dfrac{39}{120}$

In order to change a decimal to a fraction the place value of each figure must be considered.

Example 20

Convert each decimal to its fraction equivalent.

a 0.16   **b** 0.03   **c** 0.006

a $0.16 = \dfrac{1}{10} + \dfrac{6}{100} = \dfrac{10}{100} + \dfrac{6}{100} = \dfrac{16}{100} = \dfrac{4}{25}$

b $0.03 = \dfrac{0}{10} + \dfrac{3}{100} = \dfrac{3}{100}$

c $0.006 = \dfrac{0}{10} + \dfrac{0}{100} + \dfrac{6}{1000} = \dfrac{6}{1000} = \dfrac{3}{500}$

Exercise 11AA

Convert each decimal to its fraction equivalent.

1 0.54	2 0.38	3 0.94	4 0.14	5 0.92
6 0.475	7 0.575	8 0.525	9 0.925	10 0.014
11 0.018	12 0.024	13 0.032	14 0.002	

It is possible to change a decimal to a fraction by remembering the following rule:

'Place a 1 under the decimal point and then a 0 under every figure which follows it.'

Look at the example below.

Example 21

Change to a fraction   **a** 0.21   **b** 0.04

a $0.21 = \dfrac{21}{100}$ **b** $0.04 = \dfrac{4}{100} = \dfrac{1}{25}$

Exercise 11BB

Change each of the following to a fraction.

1 0.57	**2** 0.63	**3** 0.48	**4** 0.72	**5** 0.51
6 0.625	**7** 0.975	**8** 0.325	**9** 0.045	**10** 0.085

11.7 Using fractions in simple situations

Example 22

There are 300 boys at Westmead School. $\frac{1}{3}$ of them are in North House, $\frac{2}{5}$ of them are in Town House and $\frac{4}{15}$ of them are in South House.

Calculate the number of boys in each of the three houses.

The number in North House $= \frac{1}{3}$ of 300 = 100.
The number in Town House $= \frac{2}{5}$ of 300 = 120.
The number in South House $= \frac{4}{15}$ of 300 = 80.

Exercise 11CC

1 There are 250 girls at Eastgate School and they are given three sports options. $\frac{1}{2}$ choose netball, $\frac{3}{10}$ choose hockey and $\frac{1}{5}$ choose lacrosse.
Find the number of girls who choose each of the three sports.

2 There are 240 boys at Eastgate School and they are given three craft options. $\frac{2}{5}$ choose woodwork, $\frac{7}{20}$ choose metalwork and $\frac{1}{4}$ choose pottery.
Find the number of boys who choose each of the three crafts.

3 There are 60 loaves on a bakery shelf. $\frac{2}{5}$ of them are large white, $\frac{3}{10}$ of them are small white, $\frac{1}{4}$ of them are large brown and $\frac{1}{20}$ of them are small brown.
Find the number of loaves of each kind.

4 There are 1260 people who live in a small village and at an election they vote as follows:
$\frac{1}{3}$ vote Conservative, $\frac{3}{10}$ vote Labour, $\frac{1}{5}$ vote Liberal Democrat and $\frac{1}{6}$ do not vote.
Convert these fractions to actual numbers.

Fractions are often used to describe how a quantity increases or decreases.

Example 23

This year the number of pupils at Hay Bank School is 800. Next year the total is expected to rise by one fifth.

How many pupils are expected next year?

The expected increase is $\frac{1}{5}$ of $800 = \frac{1}{5} \times 800 = 160$.

Therefore the number of pupils expected next year $= 800 + 160 = 960$.

Exercise 11DD

1 There were 18 pupils in Class 2B. One day, however, some new pupils arrived and the class had one ninth as many pupils again. How many pupils are there in the class now?

2 Last year Peter was 150 cm tall, but he is now one tenth as tall again. How tall is he now?

3 The standard class rail fare from London to Glasgow is £64, but the first class fare is half as much again. What is the first class fare?

4 Last year a certain kind of television cost £300, but now it costs $\frac{1}{20}$ as much again. How much does it cost now?

5 A certain model of car costs £9600, but the de luxe version costs $\frac{3}{10}$ as much again. What is the price if the de luxe version?

6 Blackpool Tower is 165 metres tall. The Eiffel Tower, however, is $\frac{4}{5}$ as tall again. What is the height of the Eiffel Tower?

Example 24

This year the number of pupils at Sunny Hill School is 900. Next year the total is expected to fall by one twelfth.

How many pupils are expected next year?

The expected decrease is: $\frac{1}{12}$ of $900 = \frac{1}{12} \times 900 = 75$.

The number of pupils expected next year is: $900 - 75 = 825$.

Exercise 11EE

1 Mr Evans has 32 litres in his car's petrol tank. He drives to London and uses one eighth of this petrol up. How many litres are left in the tank?

2 Josiah has 12 litres of paint in a tin. He paints a fence and uses one third of the paint up. How many litres are left in the tin?

3 There are 90 cars in a car park one morning, but by midday one fifteenth of them have gone. If no more cars have arrived how many remain in the car park?

4 Mr Broome has a piece of skirting board which is 225 cm long. In order to make it fit he has to cut one ninth of it off. What length does he actually use?

5 The normal train fair from London to Aberdeen is £80, but a 'saver' ticket reduces the fare by three twentieths. How much is the 'saver' fare?

6 One week 4500 people go to a football ground to see a match, but for the next match the attendance is down by a fraction of $\frac{3}{50}$. What is the attendance at the second match?

Example 25

a This year my weekly pay is £160. I am told it is going to increase by £40 per week.
Express this increase as a fraction of my current pay.

b If instead my pay actually decreases by £8 per week, express this decrease as a fraction of my current pay.

a £40 as a fraction of £160 $= \frac{40}{160} = \frac{1}{4}$

b £8 as a fraction of £160 $= \frac{8}{160} = \frac{1}{20}$

Exercise 11FF

For questions 1–5 express the increase as a fraction of the original number or quantity.

1 At midday there were 28 buses in a depot, but by the time that the depot had closed in the evening 7 more had arrived.

2 Last month Ayo's puppy was 40 cm long, but it is now 16 cm longer.

3 A train was carrying 300 passengers, but after stopping at a station it was carrying 15 more.

4 Last year Mr Patel earned £225 per week, but he now earns £36 per week more.

5 A paperback copy of a certain book costs £7.50 (750p), whereas a hardback copy costs £3 (300p) more.

For questions 6–10 express the decrease as a fraction of the original number or quantity.

6 Mr Jones sees a second-hand car for sale at £5400, but he actually pays £270 less because he forfeits the guarantee.

7 The train fare from London to Inverness is £90, but it is possible to travel for £6 less by making an advanced booking.

8 Candace sees a chair for sale at £45 (4500p) but the shop sells it to her for £1.80 (180p) less because it is slightly scratched.

9 Shani sees a book for sale at £10.80 (1080p) but the shop sells it to her for £1.62 (162p) less because it is shop-soiled.

10 Marcus weighed 72 kg, but after going on a training course he lost 4.5 kg.

12 PERCENTAGES

12.1 Understanding and representing percentages

At Willow Bank school there are 100 pupils: 53 boys and 47 girls.

$\frac{53}{100}$ of the pupils are boys and $\frac{47}{100}$ of the pupils are girls.

We can also say that:
53 per cent (53%) of the pupils are boys, and
47 per cent (47%) of the pupils are girls.

The term 'per cent' means 'out of one hundred'.

Example 1

Write this fraction as a percentage: $\frac{9}{100}$

$\frac{9}{100} = 9\%$

$\frac{9}{100}$ or 9% is represented on the square.
9 squares out of 100 have been shaded.

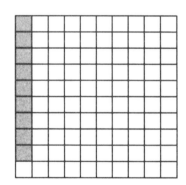

Example 2

Write this percentage as a fraction: 31%
$31\% = \frac{31}{100}$

31% or $\frac{31}{100}$ is represented on the square.
31 squares out of 100 have been shaded.

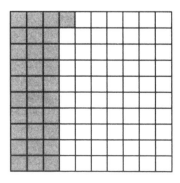

Exercise 12A

Write down the percentage which is represented by the shading in each of
the following squares.

1

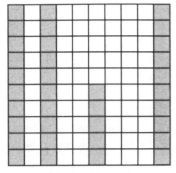

2

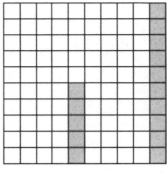

3

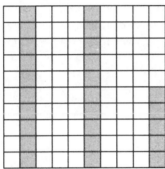

4

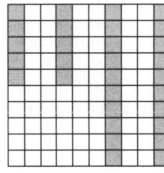

5

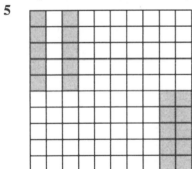

6

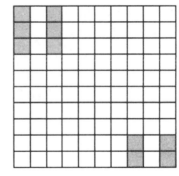

Ask your tutor for four photocopies of the grid illustrated and illustrate
each of the following percentages by marking the appropriate number of
squares.

7   40%   **8**   60%
9   50%   **10** 45%

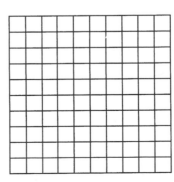

Exercise 12B

1 Write these fractions as percentages.

   a $\dfrac{97}{100}$ b $\dfrac{77}{100}$ c $\dfrac{57}{100}$ d $\dfrac{49}{100}$ e $\dfrac{17}{100}$ f $\dfrac{3}{100}$

2 Write these percentages as fractions.
   a 93%   b 73%   c 47%   d 31%   e 23%   f 7%

3 There are 100 bags of sugar on a supermarket shelf. 81 of them
   contain brown sugar and 19 of them contain white sugar.
   a What fraction of the bags contain brown sugar?   b Write your answer to **a** as a percentage.
   c What fraction of the bags contain white sugar?   d Write your answer to **c** as a percentage.

4 There are 100 dwellings in Park Avenue. 87 of them are houses and 13 of them are bungalows.
   a What fraction of the dwellings are houses?   b Write your answer to **a** as a percentage.
   c What fraction of the dwellings are bungalows?   d Write your answer to **c** as a percentage.

12.2   Calculating percentages of quantities

Example 3

There are 30 chocolates in a box and 20% of them are wrapped. Find
the number of wrapped chocolates.

$$\begin{aligned}
\text{The number of wrapped chocolates} &= 20\% \text{ of } 30 \\
&= \tfrac{20}{100} \text{ of } 30 \\
&= \tfrac{2}{10} \times 30 \\
&= 30 \div 10 \times 2 \\
&= 3 \times 2 \\
&= 6
\end{aligned}$$

Exercise 12C

1 There are 20 girls in Class 3B and 40% of
   them have blonde hair.
   Find the number of girls with blonde hair.

2 There are 30 bungalows in Rose Avenue
   and 70% of them have garages.
   Find the number of bungalows with
   garages.

3 There are 90 pupils at a nursery school.
   50% of them are four years old, 30% of
   them are three years old and 20% of them
   are two years old.
   Find the number who are:
   a four years old,
   b three years old,
   c two years old.

Example 4

Find 20% of £40.

$$20\% \text{ of } £40 = \tfrac{20}{100} \text{ of } £40$$
$$= \tfrac{2}{10} \times £40$$
$$= £40 \div 10 \times 2$$
$$= £4 \times 2$$
$$= £8$$

Exercise 12D

Find each of the following.

1	70% of £80	**2**	90% of £50	**3**	80% of £40	**4**	50% of £70
5	20% of 90 m	**6**	30% of 70 m	**7**	40% of 80 m	**8**	60% of 20 m

Example 5

Find 50% of 3 metres.

$$50\% \text{ of } 3 \text{ m} = 50\% \text{ of } 300 \text{ cm}$$
$$= \tfrac{50}{100} \text{ of } 300 \text{ cm}$$
$$= \tfrac{5}{10} \times 300 \text{ cm}$$
$$= 300 \div 10 \times 5 \text{ cm}$$
$$= 30 \times 5 \text{ cm}$$
$$= 150 \text{ cm, or } 1.50 \text{ cm, or } 1 \text{ m } 50 \text{ cm}$$

Exercise 12E

Find each of the following.

1	40% of £8	**2**	30% of £5	**3**	20% of £9	**4**	70% of £8
5	30% of £2	**6**	60% of 4 m	**7**	80% of 7 m	**8**	90% of 4 m

Example 6

Calculate 56% of 15 centimetres.

Press the calculator keys as shown: `AC` `1` `5` `÷` `1` `0` `0` `×` `5` `6` `=` `84`
The answer is 8.4 cm or 8 cm 4 mm.

Or alternatively:

Press the calculator keys as shown: `AC` `5` `6` `÷` `1` `0` `0` `×` `1` `5` `=` `84`
The answer is 8.4 cm or 8 cm 4 mm.

Exercise 12F

Use your calculator to find the answer which is different for each of the following.

1   **a** 30% of £250   **b** 25% of £280   **c** 20% of £375
2   **a** 52% of £150   **b** 64% of £125   **c** 60% of £130
3   **a** 15% of £80   **b** 16% of £75   **c** 20% of £70
4   **a** 84% of £19   **b** 54% of £24   **c** 72% of £18
5   **a** 95% of £64   **b** 92% of £65   **c** 80% of £76
6   **a** 8% of 450 mm   **b** 5% of 720 mm   **c** 7% of 500 mm

12.3   Expressing one quantity as a percentage of another

One quantity can be expressed as a percentage of another. Example 7 shows four simple examples of this.

Example 7

Find each of the following:

a 1 as a percentage of 5   **b** 5 as a percentage of 20
c 20 as a percentage of 50   **d** 7 as a percentage of 40

a '1 out of 5' $= \frac{1}{5} = \frac{20}{100} = 20\%$ (**Note** $\frac{20}{100} = 0.20$)
b '5 out of 20' $= \frac{5}{20} = \frac{25}{100} = 25\%$ (**Note** $\frac{25}{100} = 0.25$)
c '20 out of 50' $= \frac{20}{50} = \frac{40}{100} = 40\%$ (**Note** $\frac{40}{100} = 0.40$)
d '7 out of 40' $= \frac{7}{40} = \frac{175}{1000} = \frac{17.5}{100} = 17.5\%$ (**Note** $\frac{7}{40} = 0.175$)

Exercise 12G

Find the 'odd answer out' (you may use your calculator if you wish):

1   **a** £36 as a percentage of £240
     b £27 as a percentage of £180
     c £40 as a percentage of £250

2   **a** £54 as a percentage of £225
     b £45 as a percentage of £180
     c £48 as a percentage of £192

3   **a** £42 as a percentage of £120
     b £48 as a percentage of £150
     c £56 as a percentage of £160

4   **a** 72 m as a percentage of 150 m
     b 81 m as a percentage of 180 m
     c 99 m as a percentage of 220 m

5   **a** 135 m as a percentage of 250 m
     b 132 m as a percentage of 240 m
     c 165 m as a percentage of 300 m

6   **a** 75 ml as a percentage of 1500 ml
     b 35 ml as a percentage of 700 ml
     c 72 ml as a percentage of 1200 ml

Example 8

A Labrador bitch has 10 puppies in her litter and 7 of them are yellow. What percentage of the litter are yellow?

The percentage of puppies which are yellow

$$= \tfrac{7}{10} \; = \tfrac{70}{100} \; = 70\%$$

Exercise 12H

For each of the following questions express each given number as a percentage of the total.

1   There are 25 boys in Class 3A. 10 are in North House, 8 are in Town House and 7 are in South House.

2   There are 20 girls in Class 4C and all choose a music option. 10 sing in the choir, 6 play the piano and 4 play the violin.

3   60 people are travelling on a bus. 12 of them are women, 18 of them are girls, 21 of them are men and 9 of them are boys.

4   One day a vending machine sold 120 hot drinks: 24 cups of coffee, 36 cups of tea, 42 cups of hot chocolate and 18 cups of Bovril.

12.4   Converting percentages to decimals and vice versa

At the beginning of this chapter we saw that a percentage is a fraction where the denominator (the number you divide by) is 100.

For example, 17% can be written as $\tfrac{17}{100}$. In the same way the decimal 0.17 can also be written as $\tfrac{17}{100}$, so we can think of decimals and percentages as different ways of showing the same fraction.

The simplest way of converting a percentage to a decimal is to divide the percentage figure by 100.

Example 9

Convert each percentage to its decimal equivalent.

a 45%   **b** 2%   **c** 95.5%

a $45\% = 45 \div 100 = 0.45$ **b** $2\% = 2 \div 100 = 0.02$ **c** $95.5\% = 95.5 \div 100 = 0.955$

Exercise 12J

Convert each percentage to its decimal equivalent.

1 28%	2 37%	3 42%	4 53%	5 94%	6 16%
7 40%	8 10%	9 2%	10 5%	11 12.5%	12 72.5%

Example 10

Convert each decimal to its percentage equivalent.

a 0.21   **b** 0.50   **c** 0.03   **d** 0.7   **e** 0.125

a $0.21 = \frac{21}{100} = 21\%$ **b** $0.50 = \frac{50}{100} = 50\%$ **c** $0.03 = \frac{3}{100} = 3\%$

d $0.7 = \frac{7}{10} = \frac{70}{100} = 70\%$ **e** $0.125 = \frac{12.5}{100} = \frac{12.5}{100}$ 12.5%

Exercise 12K

Convert each decimal to its percentage equivalent.

1 0.29	**2** 0.38	**3** 0.47	**4** 0.58	**5** 0.63	**6** 0.81	**7** 0.17
8 0.8	**9** 0.2	**10** 0.03	**11** 0.07	**12** 0.405	**13** 0.095	**14** 0.015

12.5 Using percentages in simple situations

Example 11

On a bank holiday weekend an ice cream man sold 750 cornets. He sold 36% of them on Saturday, 24% of them on Sunday and 40% of them on Monday.
Find the number of cornets he sold on each of the three days.

The number he sold on Saturday = 36% of 750 = (36 ÷ 100) × 750 = 270.
The number he sold on Sunday   = 24% of 750 = (24 ÷ 100) × 750 = 180.
The number he sold on Monday = 40% of 750 = (40 ÷ 100) × 750 = 300.

Exercise 12L

For each question below convert the percentages to actual figures.

1 There are 60 jars of jam on a supermarket shelf. 35% of them contain strawberry jam, 25% of them contain raspberry jam, 30% of them contain plum jam and 10% of them contain blackberry jam.

2 240 people work at a certain factory. 15% of them walk to work, 10% of them cycle, 25% of them come by bus, 20% of them come by train and 30% of them come by car.

3 An ice-cream cart sells four flavours of ice-cream, and one day 600 cornets were sold. 44% of them were vanilla-flavoured, 30% of them were strawberry-flavoured, 18% of them were chocolate-flavoured and 8% of them were coffee-flavoured.

4 One day 1500 trains departed from Embankment Station in London. 35% of them were Bakerloo Line trains, 25% of them were Northern Line trains, 24% of them were District Line trains, and 16% of them were Circle Line trains.

Example 12

A sales representative earns £240 per week. He expects his earnings to increase by 10%. What will his new weekly wage be?

AVERAGE PAY
UP 10%

The increase is 10% of £240 = $\frac{10}{100} \times$ £240 = £24.   Therefore his new wage = £240 + £24 = £264.

Exercise 12M

For each of the following find: **a** the actual increase   **b** the new amount or quantity.

1   Mr Khan earns £250 per week, but he gets a rise of 6%.

2   The bus fare from my house to the town centre is 75p, but the bus company imposes a 4% rise.

3   One week a car salesman sold 50 cars, but the following week he sold 12% more.

4   Easter Sunday was a wet day and an ice-cream man sold only 150 cornets. Easter Monday, however, was a much better day and he sold 60% more.

Example 13

A sales representative earns £250 per week, but owing to a trade recession her earnings drop by 6%. What will her new weekly wage be?

The decrease is   6% of £250 = $\frac{6}{100} \times$ £250 = £15.   So her new wage is   £250 − £15 = £235.

Exercise 12N

For each of the following, find: **a** the actual decrease   **b** the new amount or quantity.

1   Last year Mr Thuo bought a house for £50 000, but it is now worth 4% less.

2   A train was carrying 250 passengers, but after calling at a station it was carrying 12% fewer.

3   There were 240 holidaymakers at a coach station, but after one coach had departed there were 20% fewer.

4   Marcus bought a word processor for £360, but after two years he sold it for 45% less.

Example 14

a This year my weekly pay is £160. I am told it is going to increase by £40 per week.
   Express the increase as a percentage of my current pay.

b If instead my pay actually decreases by £8 per week, express this decrease as a percentage of my current pay.

a £40 as a fraction of £160 = $\frac{40}{160} = \frac{1}{4}$ or 0.25, and 0.25 = 25%. So my expected increase is 25%.

b £8 as a fraction of £160 = $\frac{8}{160} = \frac{1}{20}$ or 0.05, and 0.05 = 5%. So my pay decrease is 5%.

Exercise 12P

For questions 1–3 express the increase as a percentage of the original number or quantity.

1 A standard sized lemonade can contains 250 millilitres of lemonade, but a larger can contains 75 millilitres more.

2 The standard class rail fare from London to Birmingham is £38, but the first class fare is £19 more.

3 An athlete's weight was 75 kg, but after an injury he was unable to train and his weight increased by 4.5 kg.

For questions 4–6 express the decrease as a percentage of the original number or quantity.

4 When I fill my petrol tank it contains 40 litres, but after I have driven to London it contains 8 litres less.

5 The normal price of a certain television is £250, but a dealer sold one to Tara for £30 less because he was overstocked.

6 A battery is marked '9 volts', but it is rather old and the actual voltage that it supplies to a torch bulb is 1.8 volts less.

Exercise 12Q

1 Express the shaded part of the diagram as: **i** a fraction **ii** a percentage **iii** a decimal of the whole.

a   **b**   **c**   **d**

2 Mr Fit walks 3 miles to the bus stop and then travels 9 miles by bus to get to work.
Express the distance he walks as: **a** a fraction **b** a percentage **c** a decimal of his whole journey.

3 Copy and complete the following table to give each quantity in its fractional, decimal and percentage form.

	Fraction	Decimal	Percentage
a	$\frac{23}{100}$		
b		0.87	
c			35%

	Fraction	Decimal	Percentage
d	$\frac{3}{10}$		
e		0.8	
f			40%

Sales discounts

> **Example 15**
> Which is the better discount: '$\frac{1}{20}$ off' or '6% off'?
>
> $\frac{1}{20} = \frac{5}{100} = 0.05$, and $0.05 = 5\%$. 6% is a bigger price reduction.

Exercise 12R

For each of the following find which is the better discount.

1 $\frac{1}{20}$ off or 4% off   **2** $\frac{1}{25}$ off or 5% off   **3** $\frac{1}{4}$ off or 30% off   **4** $\frac{2}{5}$ off or 35% off

5 $\frac{3}{10}$ off or 25% off   **6** $\frac{1}{8}$ off or 10% off   **7** $\frac{1}{10}$ off or $7\frac{1}{2}\%$ off   **8** $\frac{1}{5}$ off or $17\frac{1}{2}\%$ off

> **Example 16**
> The catalogue price of a television set is £300.
>
> There are two discount offers: '$\frac{1}{4}$ off' or '20% off'.
> Which is the better discount offer and by how much?
>
> $\frac{1}{4}$ of £300 $= \frac{1}{4} \times$ £300 $=$ £300 $\div 4 =$ £75
> 20% of £300 $= \frac{20}{100} \times$ £300 $=$ £20 $\div 100 \times 300 =$ £60
>
> Therefore '$\frac{1}{4}$ off' is the better discount by £15.

Exercise 12S

For each of the following find which is the better discount offer and by how much.

	Article for sale	Catalogue price	First discount	Second discount
1	Keyboard	£180	$\frac{1}{3}$	40%
2	Washing machine	£450	$\frac{1}{3}$	30%
3	Lawn mower	£150	$\frac{1}{5}$	16%
4	Bicycle	£150	$\frac{1}{6}$	20%
5	Microwave cooker	£240	$\frac{1}{8}$	15%
6	Word processor	£300	$\frac{1}{4}$	20%
7	Cabinet	£600	$\frac{1}{12}$	$7\frac{1}{2}\%$
8	Sewing machine	£120	$\frac{1}{6}$	$12\frac{1}{2}\%$

VAT

Value added tax (or VAT) is charged as a tax when many things are purchased. The current rate is 17.5% of the exclusive price.

Example 17

a The price of a radio (exclusive of VAT) is £16.40.
  Find: **i** the VAT charged **ii** the inclusive price.

  i VAT charged = 17.5% of £16.40 = (17.5 ÷ 100) × £16.40 = £2.87.
  ii Inclusive price = £16.40 + £2.87 = £19.27.

b Jean buys a doll's pram and the inclusive price is £75.20.
  Find: **i** the exclusive price **ii** the VAT charged.

  i The inclusive price is the exclusive price + $17\frac{1}{2}$% of the exclusive price (i.e. 117.5%).
  The exclusive price can be found by dividing the inclusive price by 1.175, so:

  Exclusive price = £75.20 ÷ 1.175 = £64.

  ii VAT charged = 17.5% of £64 = £11.20.
  (Check: £64 + £11.20 = £75.20)

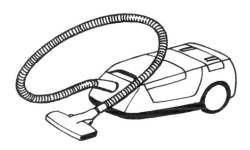

Exercise 12T

For questions 1–6 find: **a** the VAT charged
b the inclusive price.

For questions 7–12 find: **a** the exclusive price
b the VAT charged.

	Article for sale	Exclusive price
1	Television	£280
2	Electric cooker	£320
3	Electric drill	£108
4	Piano	£2500
5	Toaster	£56
6	Bathroom cabinet	£24.80

	Article for sale	Inclusive price
7	Cupboard	£211.50
8	Vacuum cleaner	£126.90
9	Dog kennel	£41.36
10	Kitchen stool	£15.04
11	Dressing table	£423
12	Greenhouse	£470

Simple interest

Interest is charged on unpaid debts or paid on invested money.
Simple interest is charged or paid as a fixed percentage of the principal
each year.

Example 18

Find: **a** the yearly interest   **b** the total interest
c the total repayable if Candace borrows £300 for 3 years at an
annual interest rate of 11%.

a Yearly interest = 11% of £300 = £33.
b Total interest = 3 × £33 = £99.
c Total repayable = £300 + £99 = £399.

Exercise 12U

For questions 1–5 find: **a** the yearly interest
b the total interest   **c** the total amount
repayable.

	Money borrowed	Yearly interest rate	Time
1	£400	15%	3 years
2	£150	16%	2 years
3	£750	10%	4 years
4	£300	20%	1 year 6 months
5	£900	12%	2 years 6 months

For questions 6–10 find: **a** the yearly interest
b the total interest   **c** the final vaue of the
depositor's savings.

	Money invested	Yearly interest rate	Time
6	£60	8%	3 years
7	£140	6%	4 years
8	£204	$7\frac{1}{2}$%	4 years
9	£720	$4\frac{1}{2}$%	2 years
10	£420	4%	1 year 6 months

13 RATIO AND SCALE

13.1 The idea of ratio and scales

One way of describing a mixture is to use a ratio. When mixing mortar for bricklaying one part of cement is used for every three parts of sand. We therefore say that the cement and sand are mixed in the ratio 1 : 3. For a weaker mix the ratio might be 1 : 4. In this case for every one part of cement, four parts of sand are used.

Example 1

A bricklayer using a 1 : 3 mortar mix has 4 bags of cement. How many equivalent sized bags of sand will he need?

The ratio 1 : 3 means that for every one bag of cement three bags of sand are required. So for 4 bags of cement, 4×3 or 12 bags of sand are required.

Exercise 13A

1 Orange squash has to be mixed with water in the ratio 1 : 7.
   If 30 grams of squash are poured out, how many grams of water must be mixed with it?

2 Concentrated sulphuric acid has to be mixed with water in the ratio 1 : 10 in order to make battery acid. If 25 grams of concentrated acid are to be used, how many grams of water must be added?

3 Mary has a cat and a dog and the ratio of their weights is 1 : 9. If her cat weighs 5 kg, what does her dog weigh?

4 On a bus one day the ratio of standing to seated passengers was 1 : 11.
   If 6 passengers were standing, how many were seated?

5 At North Lane School the ratio of left-handed to right-handed pupils is 1 : 15. If there are 36 left-handed pupils, how many right-handed pupils are there?

Example 2

A bricklayer using a 1 : 4 mortar mix has 20 bags of sand. How many equivalent sized bags of cement will he require?

The ratio 1 : 4 means that for every one bag of cement 4 bags of sand are required.

Therefore the number of bags of cement required
   $= \frac{1}{4} \times 20 \quad = 5$ bags

Exercise 13B

1 At a filling station on a certain day diesel and petrol vehicles arrive to refuel in the ratio of 1:8.
If 120 petrol vehicles arrive, how many diesel vehicles arrive?

2 One day a cafe sold cups of coffee and cups of tea in the ratio 1:2. If they sold 130 teas, how many coffees did they sell?

3 On a train the ratio of first class passengers to standard class passengers is 1:7. If there are 112 standard class passengers, how many first class passengers are there?

4 On a ship the ratio of crew members to passengers is 1:15. If there are 540 passengers, how many crew members are there?

5 One day the coffee machine in a canteen sold cups of black coffee and cups of white coffee in the ratio 1:12. If 156 cups of white coffee were sold, how many cups of black coffee were sold?

Example 3

A cake mixture requires 1 pound (lb) of currants for every 6 pounds of flour. How many pounds of currants are required for

a a large cake which uses 12 lb of flour

b a small cake which uses 3 lb of flour?

a Weight of currants required $= \frac{1}{6} \times 12$ lb $= 2$ lb

b Weight of currants required $= \frac{1}{6} \times 3$ lb $= 0.5$ lb (or $\frac{1}{2}$ lb).

Exercise 13C

1 For a baby's feeding bottle powdered milk must be mixed with warm water in the ratio 1:8. How many grams of milk are required for each of the following masses of water?

a 160 grams   **b** 120 grams
c 200 grams   **d** 140 grams
e 60 grams

2 In order to make vinegar a chemist must mix glacial ethanoic acid with water in the ratio 1:20.
How many grams of acid must be dissolved in each of the following masses of water?

a 100 grams   **b** 140 grams
c 75 grams   **d** 50 grams
e 15 grams

3 To make a lather I must mix liquid soap with water in the ratio 1:100.
Find the mass of soap which I must mix with each of the following masses of water.

a 15 kg   **b** 12 kg
c 10 kg   **d** 8 kg
e 3 kg

4 Grouting cement powder has to be mixed with water in the ratio 1:3. Find the mass of cement powder which has to be mixed with each of the following masses of water.

a 24 grams   **b** 15 grams
c 10.5 grams   **d** 4.5 grams
e 16.5 grams

Equivalent ratios

The ratio $1:3$ can be rewritten as the ratio $4:12$ and vice versa. Here each quantity is simply multiplied by 4. In the same way the ratio $3:18$ can be rewritten as the ratio $1:6$. Here each quantity is simply divided by 3.

Example 4

Fill in the missing number for each of the following.

a $1:3$ is the same ratio as $2:?$ **b** $1:4$ is the same ratio as $?:24$

c $5:20$ is the same ratio as $1:?$

a $1:3$ is the same ratio as $2:6$.   **b** $1:4$ is the same ratio as $6:24$.

   (Each quantity is multiplied by 2.)   (Each quantity is multiplied by 6.)

c $5:20$ is the same ratio as $1:4$.

   (Each quantity is divided by 5.)

Exercise 13D

Fill in the missing number for each of the following.

1 $1:4 = 4:? = 6:? = 8:? = 9:?$ **2** $1:9 = 4:? = 6:? = 8:? = 9:?$

3 $1:20 = 2:? = 3:? = 5:? = 7:?$ **4** $1:3 = ?:6 = ?:9 = ?:30 = ?:36$

5 $1:8 = ?:80 = ?:32 = ?:48 = ?:64$ **6** $1:7 = ?:28 = ?:56 = ?:63 = ?:70$

Example 5

On a bus there are 24 seats upstairs and 27 seats downstairs. Find the respective ratio in its simplest form.

The ratio is $24:27 = \frac{24}{27} = \frac{8}{9} = 8:9$.

Exercise 13E

For each of the following find the respective ratio in its simplest form.

1   On a camp site there are 12 caravans and 15 tents.

2   9 girls went to the keep fit club wearing skirts and 15 went wearing trousers.

3   At Anne's school there are 8 men teachers and 12 women teachers.

4   At High Park School 15 fourth-year girls chose netball and 20 chose hockey.

5   At Holly Hill School 15 second-year girls chose athletics and 35 chose tennis.

6   At Greenmead School 12 fifth-year boys said they supported United and 18 said they supported Rovers.

7   One morning a postman delivered 42 first-class letters and 48 second-class letters.

8   In South Avenue 32 houses have oil-fired central heating and 40 have gas-fired central heating.

Sharing in a given ratio

Example 6

Share 39 marbles between William and Robert in the ratio 5:8.

As 5 and 8 add to give 13, one share = 39 ÷ 13 = 3.

Therefore William's share = 5 × 3 = 15
and Robert's share = 8 × 3 = 24.

Exercise 13F

1 Share £42 between Jean and Barbara in the ratio 2:5.

2 Share 132 kg of compost between two gardeners in the ratio 2:9.

3 Share 480 grams of nuts between Anne and Margaret in the ratio 3:5.

4 A piece of curtain rail of length 195 cm is cut into two parts in the ratio 3:10.

5 154 grams of iron sulphide is to be made from sulphur powder and iron filings in the ratio 4:7.

6 6.5 metres of clothes line is to be cut into two parts in the ratio 4:9.

7 A boarding kennels centre accommodates 60 dogs at one particular time and the ratio of bitches to male dogs is 5:7.

8 Share 85 metres of knitting wool between Susan and Pauline in the ratio 5:12.

9 900 kg of grit for a road is made by mixing salt and shingle in the ratio 1:5.

10 120 millilitres of ink is distributed between a small bottle and a large bottle in the ratio 1:4.

Example 7

A carton containing 180 millilitres (ml) of orange juice costs 24p.
How many millilitres will there be in a carton which costs:
a 16p   **b** 36p?

a 180 millilitres must be proportionally changed by the ratio 16:24.
Therefore the contents = $(180 \times \frac{16}{24})$ ml = (180 × 16) ÷ 24 ml = 120 ml.
b 180 millilitres must be proportionally changed by the ratio 36:24.
Therefore the contents = $(180 \times \frac{36}{24})$ ml = (180 × 36) ÷ 24 ml = 270 ml.

Example 8

A can containing 250 millilitres of lemonade costs 30p.
What is the price of a can which contains
a 150 millilitres **b** 400 millilitres?

a 30p must be proportionally changed by the ratio 150 : 250.
Therefore the cost = $(30 \times \frac{150}{250})$p = $(30 \times 150) \div 250$p = 18p.
b 30p must be proportionally changed by the ratio 400 : 250.
Therefore the cost = $(30 \times \frac{400}{250})$p = $(30 \times 400) \div 250$p = 48p.

Exercise 13G

1 Peter lives 12 km from his school and it takes him 30 minutes to cycle this distance. How far, therefore, could he cycle in each of the following times?
a 5 minutes **b** 20 minutes
c 25 minutes **d** 40 minutes
e 45 minutes **f** 55 minutes
g 1 hour 15 minutes (75 minutes)

2 175 kilograms of potatoes exactly fill 7 sacks.
How many kilograms would exactly fill:
a 2 sacks **b** 3 sacks **c** 5 sacks
d 9 sacks **e** 12 sacks **f** 14 sacks
g 15 sacks?

3 One type of telephone call costs £2.40 (240p) for 10 minutes if it is made at peak rate time and the charge increases in proportion to the number of minutes. What would be the cost of a call lasting:
a 2 minutes
b 3 minutes
c 8 minutes
d 9 minutes
e 12 minutes
f 15 minutes
g 16 minutes
h 25 minutes?

4 200 grams of fruity sweets cost 80p.
How many grams could be bought for:
a 30p **b** 50p **c** 60p **d** £1.20
e £1.50 **f** £1.80 **g** £2?

5 At Refill's garage (with knockdown prices!) 12 litres of petrol costs £4.
How many litres could be bought for:
a £1.50 **b** 2.50 **c** £3.50
d £4.50 **e** £6 **f** £9
g £7.50 **h** £10.50?

6 Steady Sue only ever cycles at one speed. She lives 15 km from her school and it takes her 40 minutes to cycle this distance. How long would it take her to cycle to each of the following places?
a the golf course, which is 6 km from her house
b the tennis courts, which are 9 km from her house
c the youth club, which is 13.5 km from her house
d her grandmother's house, which is 18 km from her own
e her uncle's house, which is 21 km from her own
f her friend's house, which is 22.5 km from her own
g her married sister's house, which is 27 km from her own.

13.2   Measuring lengths in scale drawings, maps and plans

The scale of a map is often described by using a ratio. If a map has a scale of 1 : 100 it means that every length of 1 unit on the map represents a length of 100 units on the ground. If the scale of a model is described as 1 : 32 it means that every one unit of length on the model represents 32 units of length on the actual object.

Example 9

The map on the right shows four places in a village and the roads which connect them, and the scale of the map is 1 : 5000. For each case below find:

i the distance between the two places on the map by measuring

ii the real distance between the two places in centimetres

iii the real distance between the two places in metres.

a The station and the Grand Hotel.

b The station and the post office.

c The station and the church.

d The Grand Hotel and the post office.

e The post office and the church.

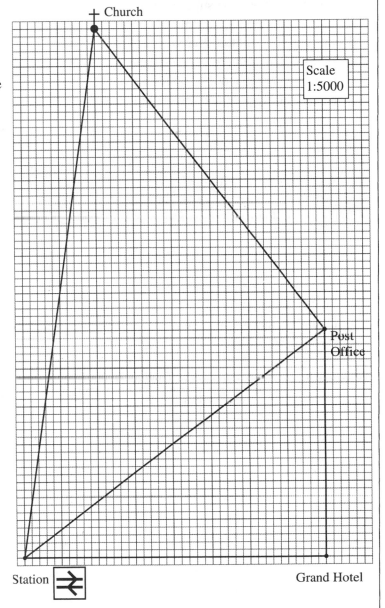

a i 8 cm
   ii 8 × 5000 cm = 40 000 cm
   iii 40 000 ÷ 100 m = 400 m

b i 10 cm
   ii 10 × 5000 cm = 50 000 cm
   iii 50 000 ÷ 100 m = 500 m

c i 14 cm
   ii 14 × 5000 cm = 70 000 cm
   iii 70 000 ÷ 100 m = 700 m

d i 6 cm
   ii 6 × 5000 cm = 30 000 cm
   iii 30 000 ÷ 100 m = 300 m

e i 10 cm
   ii 10 × 5000 cm = 50 000 cm
   iii 50 000 ÷ 100 m = 500 m

Exercise 13H

Questions 1–3 show maps of where John, Jane and Susan live. For all parts of each question find:

i   the distance between the two places on the map in centimetres by measuring
ii the real distance between the two places in centimetres
iii the real distance between the two places in metres.

1 a John's house and John's school
  b John's house and the supermarket
  c John's house and the swimming pool
  d John's house and the church
  e John's school and the supermarket
  f the supermarket and the swimming pool
  g the swimming pool and the church

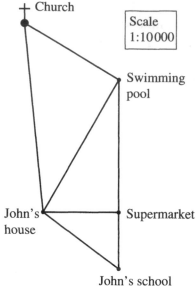

2 a Jane's house and the village hall   **b** Jane's house and the church
  c Jane's house and the post office   **d** Jane's house and the sports centre
  e the village hall and the church   **f** the church and the post office
  g the post office and the sports centre

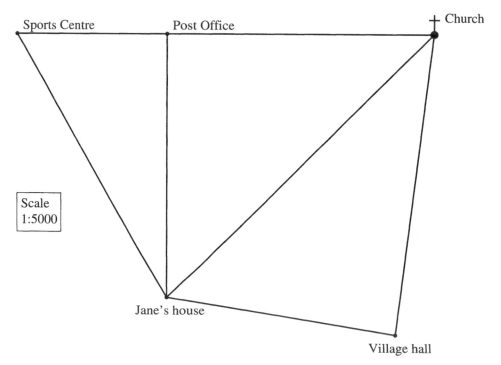

3 **a** Susan's house and the railway station
  b Susan's house and the telephone kiosk
  c Susan's house and the letter box
  d Susan's house and the church
  e the railway station and the telephone kiosk
  f the telephone kiosk and the letter box
  g the letter box and the church

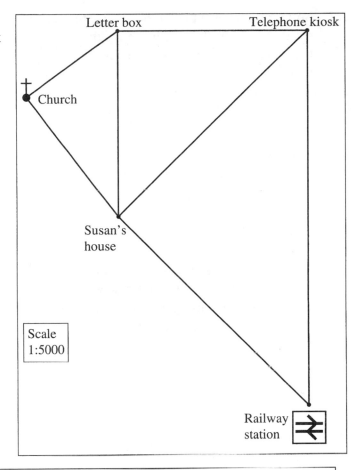

Example 10

A model of a car is constructed using a scale of $1:20$.
If the length of the real car is 6 metres, what is the length of the model?

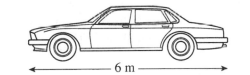

The length of the real car = 6 metres
$$= 6 \times 100 \text{ centimetres}$$
$$= 600 \text{ centimetres}$$
Therefore the length of the model $= \frac{1}{20} \times 600$ cm
$$= 30 \text{ cm}$$

Exercise 13J

1 A model of a railway locomotive is to be constructed using a scale of $1:80$.
  If the length of the real locomotive is 20 metres, what will the length of the model be?

2 A model of a yacht is constructed using a scale of $1:35$.
  If the length of the real yacht is 14 metres, what is the length of the model?

(continued)

3 Susan is drawing a plan of her bedroom using a scale of 1:25. If the length and width of her bedroom are 6 metres and 5 metres, how long will they each be on her drawing?

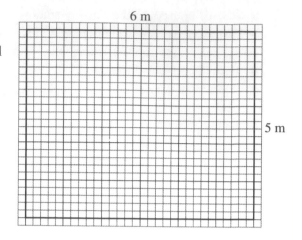

4 James has a dog kennel whose dimensions are 80 cm, 180 cm and 100 cm. He decides to make a smaller replica for his cat using a scale of 1:4. What will the dimensions of the replica be?

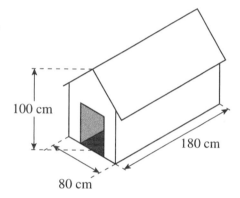

Example 11

The model of the car shown on the right has a bonnet of length 10 cm. What is the length of the bonnet on the original car? (The scale is 1:20.)

The length of the bonnet on the original car
= (10 × 20) cm = 200 cm or 0.2 m.

Exercise 13K

1 A toy lorry has a length of 25 cm and it is built to a scale of 1:60. What is the length of the real lorry?

2 A model ship has a length of 75 cm and it is built to a scale of 1:120. What is the length of the real ship?

3 Mark is drawing a plan of a gate which he has to make and he is using a scale of 1 : 10. If the dimensions of the gate on his plan are 30 cm and 10 cm, what will the dimensions of the real gate be?

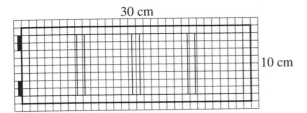

30 cm

10 cm

4 Kate is drawing a plan of the swimming pool at her school and she is using a scale of 1 : 90.
If the dimensions of the pool on her plan are 30 cm and 20 cm, what are the dimensions of the real pool?

5 Peter, Jane and Anne have heights of 10 cm, 9 cm and 7 cm on a photograph. If the scale of the photograph is 1 : 16, what are their real heights?

Example 12

On a model of a house the height of the door is 4 cm, whereas on the actual house it is 200 cm. What is the scale of the model?

4 cm on the model represents 200 cm on the actual house, therefore the ratio is 4 : 200.

4 : 200 can be simplified to 1 : 50 by dividing both quantities by 4.

Therefore the scale of the model is 1 : 50.

Exercise 13L

1 A doll's pram has a length of 60 cm. It is a replica of a real pram of length 180 cm.
To what scale was the doll's pram?

2 Paul has a toy saw of length 19 cm in his carpenter's set and it is a replica of a real one of length 76 cm.
To what scale was the toy one made?

3 The porch on a doll's house is 15 cm high and the doll's house is a model of a real house with a porch 3 m (300 cm) high.
To what scale was the doll's house built?

4 Janet has a model of Nelson's Column which is 14 cm high.
If the height of the real column is 56 m, what is the scale of the model?

5 At a tourist information office there is a model of the Humber Bridge which has a main span dimension of 28 cm.
If the main span dimension on the real bridge is 1400 m, what is the scale of the model?

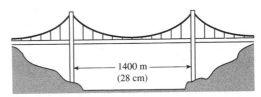

1400 m
(28 cm)

13.3 Producing scale drawings for maps and plans

A builder works from the plan of a house which has been drawn by the architect. The architect had to produce a scale drawing of the house, so that he could convey his ideas to the builder in a way which would enable the builder to copy them exactly.

Example 13

The lounge of a house is a rectangle which measures 6 metres by 3 metres.

Draw a plan of this rectangle using a scale where 1 cm is used to represent 1 m.

Using a piece of 1 cm squared paper:
i   Draw a line AB 6 cm (i.e. 6 squares) long.
ii Draw lines AD and BC, each 3 cm
    (i.e. 3 squares) long at right angles to AB.
iii Join the points D and C which should be 6 cm
    (i.e. 6 squares) apart.

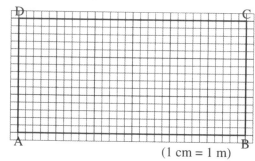

(1 cm = 1 m)

The rectangle ABCD is the required scale drawing of the lounge.

Exercise 13M

Draw a plan of each of the following rectangles or squares by using a scale where 1 cm is used to represent 1 m.

1 a kitchen which measures 5 metres by 4 metres
2 the bedroom of a house which measures 4 metres by 3 metres
3 a garage which measures 7 metres by 4 metres

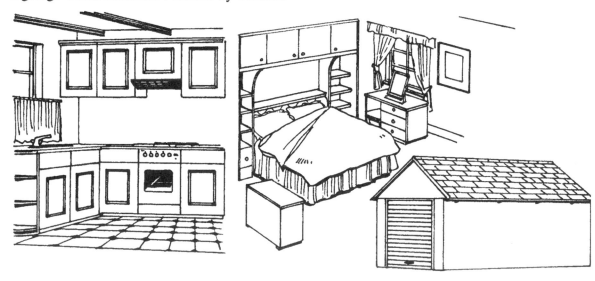

Example 14

A football pitch is a rectangle which measures 100 metres by 50 metres.

Draw a plan of this pitch using a scale where 1 cm is used to represent 20 metres.

Using a piece of 1 cm squared paper, we must first calculate the lengths for the scale drawing.

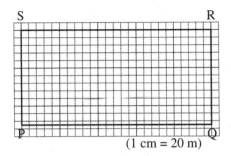

(1 cm = 20 m)

If 20 metres is represented by 1 cm, then 100 metres will be represented by $\frac{100}{20} \times 1$ cm or 5 cm and 50 metres will be represented by $\frac{50}{20} \times 1$ cm or 2.5 cm.

i   Draw a line PQ 5 cm (i.e. 5 squares) long to represent the length of the football pitch.

ii Draw lines PS and QR, each 2.5 cm (i.e. $2\frac{1}{2}$ squares) long at right angles to PQ.

iii Join the points S and R which should be 5 cm (i.e. 5 squares) apart.

Exercise 13N

Draw a plan of each of the following rectangles by using a scale where 1 cm is used to represent 20 metres.

1   a garage forecourt which measures 80 metres by 60 metres
2   a school playground which measures 120 metres by 80 metres
3   a rugby pitch which measures 110 metres by 60 metres

Draw a plan of each of the following rectangles by using a scale where 1 cm is used to represent 10 metres.

4   an ice rink which measures 40 metres by 30 metres
5   a swimming pool which measures 50 metres by 35 metres
6   a gymnasium which measures 45 metres by 30 metres

Example 15

A kitchen is 5 metres long and 3 metres wide at one end but only 2 metres wide at the other end, as shown in the sketch.

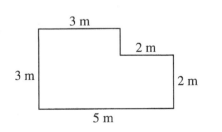

Draw a plan of the kitchen using a scale where 2 cm is used to represent 1 metre.

If 1 m is represented by 2 cm:

then 2 m is represented by 2×2 cm = 4 cm

and 3 m is represented by 3×2 cm = 6 cm

and 5 m is represented by 5×2 cm = 10 cm.

On a piece of 1 cm squared paper:

i Draw a line AB, 10 cm long (i.e. 10 squares long) to represent the 5 m length of the kitchen.

ii Draw a line BC, 4 cm long (i.e. 4 squares long) to represent the 2 m width.

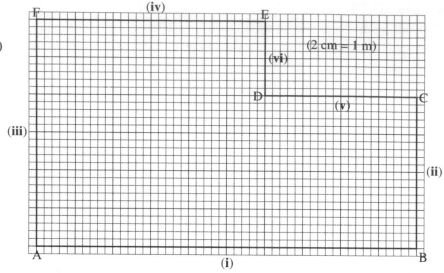

iii Draw a line AF, 6 cm long (i.e. 6 squares long) to represent the 3 m width.

iv Draw a line FE, 6 cm long (i.e. 6 squares long) to represent part of the far side.

v Draw a line CD, 4 cm long (i.e. 4 squares long) to represent the other part of the far side.

vi Join DE which should be 2 cm long (i.e. 2 squares long).

(Do not forget to put the scale on your drawing.)

Exercise 13P

Draw a plan of each of the following by using a scale where 1 cm represents 1 m.

1 a dining room

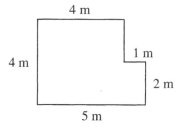

2 a back garden

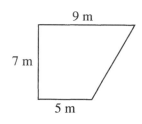

For each of the following draw a plan by using a scale where 1 cm = 5 m.

3 a harbour

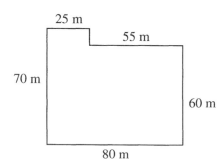

4 a recreation ground

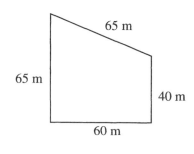

14 TEMPERATURE

14.1 Understanding positive and negative units of temperature and reading thermometers

When measuring temperatures we usually describe temperatures above the freezing point (0 °Celsius, 0 °C) as positive and temperatures below the freezing point as negative.

Five temperatures are shown, ranging from a warm day to an extremely cold day.

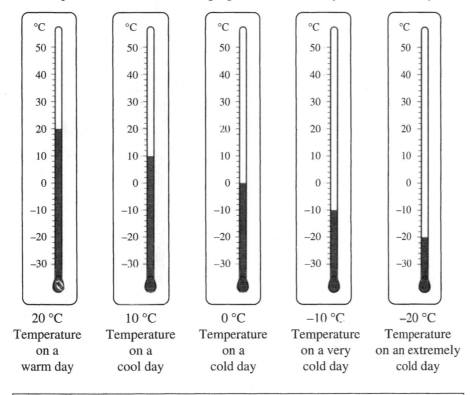

20 °C	10 °C	0 °C	−10 °C	−20 °C
Temperature on a warm day	Temperature on a cool day	Temperature on a cold day	Temperature on a very cold day	Temperature on an extremely cold day

Example 1

a Put the following temperatures in order from warmest to coldest
   10 °C, −40 °C, 30 °C, −50 °C, 40 °C and −20 °C

b Put the following temperatures in order from coldest to warmest.
   50 °C, −10 °C, 30 °C, −30 °C, 20 °C and −40 °C

a The order from warmest to coldest is:
   40 °C, 30 °C, 10 °C, −20 °C, −40 °C and −50 °C.

b The order from coldest to warmest:
   −40 °C, −30 °C, −10 °C, 20 °C, 30 °C and 50 °C.

Exercise 14A

For questions 1–4 put the temperatures in order from warmest to coldest.

1   30°C, –50°C, 10°C, –10°C, 40°C, –20°C

2   30°C, –20°C, 40°C, –50°C, 50°C, –10°C

3   10°C, –40°C, 30°C, –30°C, 50°C, –20°C

4   10°C, –10°C, 20°C, –40°C, 50°C, –30°C

For questions 6–10 put the temperatures in order from coldest to warmest.

5   –20°C, 20°C, –30°C, 10°C, –40°C, 50°C

6   –20°C, 10°C, –30°C, 40°C, –40°C, 50°C

7   –10°C, 50°C, –20°C, 10°C, –40°C, 30°C

8   –10°C, 30°C, –20°C, 50°C, –40°C, 40°C

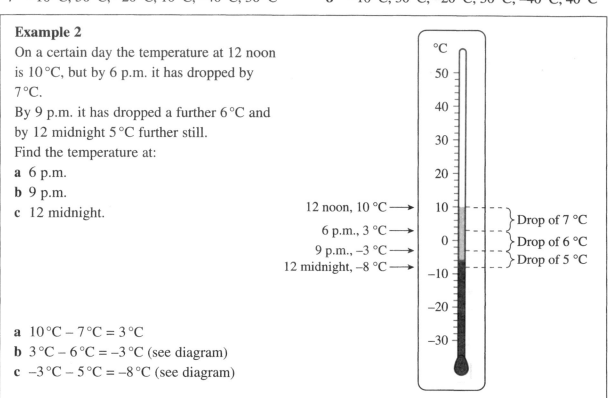

Example 2

On a certain day the temperature at 12 noon is 10°C, but by 6 p.m. it has dropped by 7°C.

By 9 p.m. it has dropped a further 6°C and by 12 midnight 5°C further still.

Find the temperature at:

a 6 p.m.

b 9 p.m.

c 12 midnight.

12 noon, 10 °C ⟶
6 p.m., 3 °C ⟶
9 p.m., –3 °C ⟶
12 midnight, –8 °C ⟶

Drop of 7 °C
Drop of 6 °C
Drop of 5 °C

a 10°C – 7°C = 3°C

b 3°C – 6°C = –3°C (see diagram)

c –3°C – 5°C = –8°C (see diagram)

Exercise 14B

1   The table below shows how the temperature dropped between 12 noon and 6 p.m. on five days during a certain week in April. Copy and complete the table.

Day	Temperature at 12 noon	Drop in temperature	Temperature at 6 p.m.
Monday	15°C	5°C	
Tuesday	17°C	6°C	
Wednesday	13°C	8°C	
Thursday	12°C	9°C	
Friday	11°C	7°C	

2 The table below shows how the temperature dropped between 12 noon and 6 p.m. on five days during a certain week in January. Copy and complete the table.

Day	Temperature at 12 noon	Drop in temperature	Temperature at 6 p.m.
Monday	7 °C	9 °C	
Tuesday	6 °C	9 °C	
Wednesday	6 °C	8 °C	
Thursday	5 °C	9 °C	
Friday	5 °C	8 °C	

3 The table below shows how the temperature rose between 6 a.m. and 12 noon on five days during a certain week in December. Copy and complete the table.

Day	Temperature at 6 a.m.	Rise in temperature	Temperature at 12 noon
Monday	−4 °C	6 °C	
Tuesday	−5 °C	6 °C	
Wednesday	−7 °C	9 °C	
Thursday	−6 °C	8 °C	
Friday	−6 °C	7 °C	

4 The table below shows how the temperature rose between 6 a.m. and 12 noon on five days during a certain week in January. Copy and complete the table.

Day	Temperature at 6 a.m.	Rise in temperature	Temperature at 12 noon
Monday	−5 °C	2 °C	
Tuesday	−7 °C	2 °C	
Wednesday	−9 °C	2 °C	
Thursday	−8 °C	2 °C	
Friday	−8 °C	1 °C	

14.2 Calculating temperature differences

Example 3

The temperature at 12 noon is 5 °C, but by
6 p.m. it has dropped to –1 °C, and by 9 p.m.
has dropped further to –6 °C.

Find the drop in temperature between:
a 12 noon and 6 p.m.
b 6 p.m. and 9 p.m.

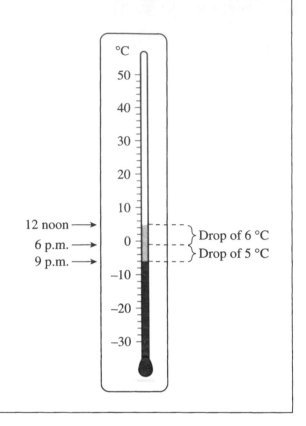

a Drop in temperature
$= 5\,°C - (-1\,°C)$
$= 5\,°C + 1\,°C$
$= 6\,°C$ (see diagram)
b Drop in temperatuare $= -1\,°C - (-6\,°C)$
$= -1\,°C + 6\,°C$
$= 5\,°C$ (see diagram)

Exercise 14C

1   The table below shows how the temperature dropped between
12 noon and 6 p.m. on five days during a certain week in February.
Copy and complete the table.

Day	Temperature at 12 noon	Drop in temperature	Temperature at 6 p.m.
Monday	5 °C		–3 °C
Tuesday	6 °C		–4 °C
Wednesday	7 °C		–2 °C
Thursday	6 °C		–5 °C
Friday	8 °C		–2 °C

2 The table below shows how the temperature dropped between 6 p.m. and 12 midnight at the same place as for the details in question 1 and over the same period. Copy and complete the table.

Day	Temperature at 6 p.m.	Drop in temperature	Temperature at 12 midnight
Monday	3 °C		–7 °C
Tuesday	4 °C		–9 °C
Wednesday	2 °C		–5 °C
Thursday	5 °C		–7 °C
Friday	2 °C		–6 °C

Example 4

When I woke up early this morning the temperature was –4 °C, but by lunch time it had risen to 11 °C and by tea time it had dropped again to –2 °C. Find each of the following:

a the rise in temperature between early morning and lunch time

b the fall in temperature between lunch time and tea time

c the net change in temperature between early morning and tea time.

a The rise in temperature
= 11 °C – (–4 °C) = 11 °C + 4 °C = 15 °C

b The fall in temperature
= 11 °C – (–2 °C) = 11 °C + 2 °C = 13 °C

c The net change in temperature
= –2 °C – (–4 °C) = –2 °C + 4 °C = 2 °C

Exercise 14D

1 The table below shows how the temperature varied between early morning, lunch time and tea time on five days during a certain week in February. Copy and complete the table.

Day	Temperature at 6 a.m.	Rise during the morning	Temperature at 12 noon	Fall during the afternoon	Temperature at 6 p.m.	Net rise between 6 a.m. and 6 p.m.
Monday	–5 °C		7 °C		–3 °C	
Tuesday	–4 °C		9 °C		–2 °C	
Wednesday	–3 °C		8 °C		–1 °C	
Thursday	–6 °C		4 °C		–2 °C	
Friday	–2 °C		10 °C		4 °C	

14.3   Converting between Celsius and Fahrenheit temperatures

Just as we have both metric and imperial units for measuring length, area, volume and mass, etc., so we have two different systems of units for temperature.

The Celsius (or Centigrade) scale has taken the temperature at which water freezes to be 0 °C and the temperature at which water boils to be 100 °C. Temperatures below this freezing point are negative temperatures and clearly there can be temperatures well above 100 °C.

On the Fahrenheit scale the temperature for freezing water is 32 °F and the temperature for boiling water is 212 °F.

Sometimes we need to convert a Celsius temperature to a Fahrenheit temperature or vice versa. This can be done in two ways, either by using a formula, or by using a conversion graph.

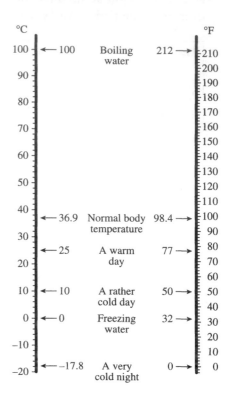

Formula for converting Celsius to Fahrenheit
Take the temperature in Celsius, multiply this by 9, divide the result by 5 and then add 32 to the final result.

Example 5
Convert the following temperatures from Celsius to Fahrenheit:
a 10 °C   **b** 25 °C   **c** 100 °C

a $10 \times 9 = 90$ $90 \div 5 = 18$ $18 + 32 = 50$ So 10 °C = 50 °F.
b $25 \times 9 = 225$ $225 \div 5 = 45$ $45 + 32 = 77$ So 25 °C = 77 °F.
c $100 \times 9 = 900$ $900 \div 5 = 180$ $180 + 32 = 212$ So 100 °C = 212 °F.

Exercise 14E

Convert each of the following temperatures from Celsius to Fahrenheit.

1 55 °C	**2** 75 °C	**3** 35 °C	**4** 95 °C	**5** 5 °C	**6** 12.5 °C
7 18.5 °C	**8** 22.5 °C	**9** −5 °C	**10** −15 °C	**11** −2.5 °C	**12** −10.5 °C

Formula for converting Fahrenheit to Celsius
Take the temperature in Fahrenheit, from this subtract 32, multiply the result by 5 and then divide the final result by 9.

Example 6

Convert the following temperatures from Fahrenheit to Celsius:

a 50 °F   **b** 77 °F   **c** 212 °F

a 50 − 32 = 18   18 × 5 = 90   90 ÷ 9 = 10   So 50 °F = 10 °C.
b 77 − 32 = 45   45 × 5 = 225   225 ÷ 9 = 25   So 77 °F = 25 °C.
c 212 − 32 = 180   180 × 5 = 900   900 ÷ 9 = 100   So 212 °F = 100 °C.

Exercise 14F

Convert each of the following temperatures from Fahrenheit to Celsius.

1 59 °F	**2** 149 °F	**3** 185 °F	**4** 113 °F	**5** 221 °F	**6** 50.9 °F
7 61.7 °F	**8** 56.3 °F	**9** 14 °F	**10** −12.5 °F	**11** −7.5 °F	**12** −4.5 °F

Conversion graph

We can use the standard temperatures for freezing and boiling water to draw a conversion graph, so that other conversions can be found quickly. First the point corresponding to 32 °F and 0 °C is marked. Then the point corresponding to 212 °F and 100 °C is marked. These two points are then joined with a straight line.

Example 7

Use the conversion graph to convert
a 50 °F to Celsius
b 40 °C to Fahrenheit.

a To convert 50 °F to Celsius, look for 50 on the Fahrenheit axis, go up the dotted line and then read across to the Celsius axis, so 50 °F = 10 °C.
b To convert 40 °C to Fahrenheit, look for 40 on the Celsius axis, go across the dotted line and then read down to the Fahrenheit axis, so 40 °C = 104 °F.

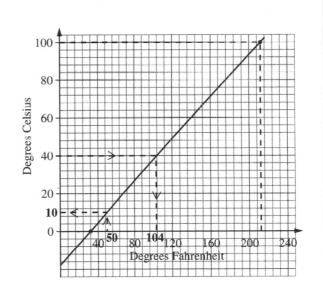

Exercise 14G

Use the graph to convert the °F to °C and the °C to °F.

1 68 °F   **2** 158 °F   **3** 140 °F   **4** 194 °F   **5** 30 °C   **6** 50 °C   **7** 80 °C   **8** −10 °C

15 USING YOUR CALCULATOR (3)
(OTHER FEATURES INCLUDING THE MEMORY KEYS)

15.1 The idea of negative numbers and use of the +/– key

Bank balances

A negative balance or overdraft of £100 is often shown as –£100.

Example 1

Put the following in order of preference for the balance in your bank account.

£200, a credit of £300, an overdraft of £100, £50,
an overdraft of £300, –£50, a credit of £150, –£250,
an overdraft of £75

The order of preference is:

£300 (credit), £200, £150 (credit), £50, –£50, £75 (overdraft),
£100 (overdraft), –£250, £300 (overdraft)

Exercise 15A

Put in order of preference for the balance in your bank account:

1   £200, –£150, £100, –£200, £300 (credit), £250 (overdraft), £250 (credit), £50 (overdraft)
2   £200, –£200, £100, –£100, £150 (credit), £250 (overdraft), £300 (credit), £150 (overdraft)
3   £300, –£200, £250, –£250, £50 (credit), £50 (overdraft), £150 (credit), £150 (overdraft)
4   £150, –£50, £300, –£300, £100 (credit), £200 (overdraft), £250 (credit), £250 (overdraft)
5   £250 (credit), £50 (overdraft), £200 (credit), £100 (overdraft), £50, –£200, £300, –£150
6   £100 (credit), £150 (overdraft), £50 (credit), £200 (overdraft), £150, –£300, £250, –£100

Example 2
a   Keeley Simpson has an overdraft of £75 on her bank account and
    she pays in £90.
    What is her balance now?
b   Andrew Saunders also has an overdraft of £75 on his bank account
    and he pays in £50.
    What is his balance now?

a Her new balance is −£75 + £90 = £15.
   She is now £15 in credit.
b His new balance is −£75 + £50 = −£25.
   He now has an overdraft of £25.

Exercise 15B

All of the people in the table below have a bank overdraft and they each
pay some money in.

Copy and complete the table and state clearly whether each new balance is
in credit or an overdraft.

	Account holder	Initial balance	Money paid in	New balance
1	Candace Gray	−£125	£135	
2	Josiah Johnson	−£125	£170	
3	Jodie Allum	−£135	£155	
4	Deena Reid	−£135	£115	
5	Bobbie Mack	−£120	£100	
6	Rita Woolley	−£120	£80	
7	Sharon Bailey	−£145	£170	
8	Janet Varley	−£145	£195	
9	Laura Betts	−£110	£115	
10	Hilda Brown	−£105	£75	
11	Colin Dodgson	−£115	£95	
12	Robert Greenacre	−£115	£105	

Example 3
a Mr Ahmed has an overdraft of £100. How much must he pay into his account if his new
   balance is to be £200 (credit)?
b Mrs Davies has an overdraft of £200. How much must she pay into her account if she is to
   reduce her overdraft to £50?

a Amount paid in is £200 − (−£100) = £200 + £100 = £300
b Amount paid in is −£50 − (−£200) = −£50 + £200 = £150

(**Note**   taking away a minus amount is the same as adding the positive amount.)

Exercise 15C

All of the people in the table below have a bank overdraft, but they each
pay some money in. Copy and complete the table.

	Account holder	Initial balance	Money paid in	New balance
1	Joan Yates	£100 (overdraft)		£75 (credit)
2	Jean Travis	£100 (overdraft)		£25 (credit)
3	Helen Cross	£150 (overdraft)		£50 (credit)
4	Bob Read	£150 (overdraft)		£100 (credit)
5	Harry Brown	£125 (overdraft)		£25 (credit)
6	Chris Norris	£100 (overdraft)		£25 (overdraft)
7	Beatrice Potts	£100 (overdraft)		£75 (overdraft)
8	Anne Bond	£150 (overdraft)		£50 (overdraft)
9	Ella Foster	£150 (overdraft)		£75 (overdraft)
10	Elaine Orry	£125 (overdraft)		£25 (overdraft)

All of the people in the table below have a bank overdraft, but they each
make two in-payments. Copy and complete the table.

	Account holder	Initial balance	First payment	Balance after payment	Second payment	Balance after payment	Net improvement to balance
11	Shani	£80 (o/d)		£30 (o/d)		£30 (cr)	
12	Jisanne	£95 (o/d)		£60 (o/d)		£15 (cr)	
13	Kanika	£70 (o/d)		£20 (o/d)		£20 (cr)	
14	Eshe	£35 (o/d)		£20 (o/d)		£35 (cr)	
15	Marcus	£100 (o/d)		£35 (o/d)		£15 (cr)	

Using your calculator with negative numbers (+/− key)
Many calculators have a +/− key. This changes the sign of any number
entered. For example if you enter a figure 5 and then press the +/− key, −5
appears on the calculator display. If you then press the +/− key again the
− sign disappears and 5 is again shown on the display. If your calculator has
this key then you can use it for calculations involving negative numbers.

Example 4
Use your calculator to find:

a $7 + (-4)$ **b** $7 - (-4)$ **c** $-7 + (-4)$ **d** $-7 - (-4)$

(Press the keys in the given sequence. Remember that **AC** is the 'all clear' key, and that you press the **+/−** key **after** entering a number to change its sign.)

a **AC** **7** **+** **4** **+/−** **=** $\exists$

b **AC** **7** **−** **4** **+/−** **=** 11

c **AC** **7** **+/−** **+** **4** **+/−** **=** -11

d **AC** **7** **+/−** **−** **4** **+/−** **=** $-\exists$

(**Note**   some calculators show −3 as 3− or show the − sign at the left-hand end of the display.)

Exercise 15D

(**Note**   if your calculator does not have a **+/−** key you cannot use it for this exercise.)

Use your calculator to evaluate each of the following.

1 **a** 8 + (−5)   **b** 8 + (−2)   **c** 5 + (−12)   **d** 4 + (−10)
2 **a** −5 + (−2)   **b** −9 + (−3)   **c** −6 + (−4)   **d** −8 + (−1)
3 **a** 6 − (−4)   **b** 7 − (−2)   **c** 9 − (−5)   **d** 8 − (−6)
4 **a** −2 − (−5)   **b** −4 − (−7)   **c** −5 − (−1)   **d** −9 − (−4)

5 The following all have bank overdrafts, but they each pay some money in. Use your calculator to find the new balance for each case.
  a Ronnie: £105 (overdraft) but £140 paid in
  b Charmaine: £125 (overdraft), but £150 paid in
  c Zoey: £115 (overdraft), but £160 paid in

6 The following all have bank overdrafts, but although they pay some money in they only reduce their overdrafts. Use your calculator to find the new balance for each case.
  a Peter: £95 (overdraft), but £70 paid in
  b Matthew: £100 (overdraft), but £55 paid in
  c Joanna: £110 (overdraft), but £95 paid in

15.2   The idea of square roots and use of the **√** key

When we find the area of a square of side length 4 cm, we multiply the length (4 cm) by the width (4 cm) to give a result of 16 square centimetres which is abbreviated as 16 cm^2.

When we multiply a number by itself, therefore, the result is called the square of the original number. 4 × 4 = 16, so 16 is called the square of 4.

In the same way we say that the square of 3 is 3 × 3 = 9, or that 3^2 = 9. We also say that 3 is the **square root** of 9, which we can write using the square root sign as √9 = 3. Similarly we can write √16 as equal to 4, which is read as 'the square root of 16 is 4'.

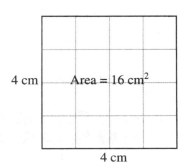

4 cm   Area = 16 cm^2

4 cm

Example 5

Find the square root of: **a** 16   **b** 36   **c** 3600

a √16 = 4 because 4 × 4 = 16   **b** √36 = 6 because 6 × 6 = 36
c √3600 = 60 because 60 × 60 = 3600

Exercise 15E

Find the square root of each of the following.

1	49	**2**	25	**3**	81	**4**	4	**5**	100	**6**	400
7	900	**8**	2500	**9**	4900	**10**	6400	**11**	10 000	**12**	90 000

If your calculator has a ☐√ key then you can use it to find square roots.

Example 6

Use your calculator to evaluate √441

Press your calculator keys in this sequence: [4] [4] [1] [√]   ⸑ !   so √441 = 21.

Exercise 15F

Use your calculator to evaluate each of the following.

1	√169	**2**	√225	**3**	√196	**4**	√625	**5**	√1764	**6**	√1936
7	√6.76	**8**	√7.29	**9**	√12.96	**10**	√15.21	**11**	√0.81	**12**	√0.04

15.3   Use of the [%] key

Many calculators have a [%] key, but this does not always work as you
might expect it to, so do beware. In fact it is often much simpler to find 5%
of something by multiplying by 5 and then dividing by 100.

Example 7

Use your calculator to find: **a** 5% of 200   **b** 17½% of 50

Press your calculator keys in the given sequence.

a [AC] [2] [0] [0] [×] [5] [%] [=]   ! 0
b [AC] [5] [0] [×] [1] [7] [.] [5] [%] [=]   8·⁊5

Note   that you may not have to press the [=] key at the end of the sequence to get these answers.

If your calculator does not have a ▮%▮ key or gives different answers for the above questions you will have to use the method explained before Example 7 for the next two exercises. (See also Example 6 on page 131.)

Exercise 15G

For questions 1–3 use your calculator to find the answer which is different.

1   **a** 30% of 80   **b** 28% of 75   **c** 25% of 96
2   **a** 24% of 225 cm   **b** 18% of 300 cm   **c** 20% of 280 cm
3   **a** $12\frac{1}{2}$% of 120 kg   **b** $7\frac{1}{2}$% of 240 kg   **c** $4\frac{1}{2}$% of 400 kg

For questions 4–8 use your calculator to convert each of the percentages to actual figures.

4   Ayo studies mathematics, physics and chemistry and he has 20 textbooks. 45% of them are mathematics books, 25% of them are physics books and 30% of them are chemistry books.

5   Anish spent £40 on a day out. He spent 30% of the money on train fares, 35% of it on going to a football match, 15% of it on going to a restaurant and 20% of it on going to a theatre.

6   A football club unfortunately went out of business after 30 years. They had made a profit for only 40% of the time, broken even for only 15% of the time and had lost money for 45% of the time.

7   There are 125 trees along a very long avenue. 16% of them are oak, 24% of them are beech, 32% of them are poplar and 28% of them are larch.

8   There are 600 pupils at Highfield Secondary School. 20% of them are in year seven, 15% of them are in year eight, 25% of them are in year nine, $17\frac{1}{2}$% of them are in year ten and $22\frac{1}{2}$% of them are in year eleven.

Example 8

Use your calculator to find:

a 200 + 5% of 200 (or 105% of 200)

b 50 + $17\frac{1}{2}$% of 50 (or $117\frac{1}{2}$% of 50)

Press your calculator keys in the given sequence. You may not need to press the ▮=▮ key to get these results, as in Example 7.

a [AC] [2] [0] [0] [×] [1] [0] [5] [%] [=] 210

b [AC] [5] [0] [×] [1] [1] [7] [.] [5] [%] [=] 58.75

Exercise 15H

Use your calculator to evaluate each of the following.

1   200 + 15% of 200 (or 115% of 200)
2   250 + 12% of 250   3   150 + 18% of 150   4   £125 + 16% of £125
5   £175 + 8% of £175   6   £160 + 5% of £160   7   120 m + $7\frac{1}{2}$% of 120 m

(continued)

8   Find the new price for each of the following.
    a The train fare from London to Newcastle was £60 but there was an increase of 5%.
    b My council tax was £75 per month but it has gone up by 8%.
    c A private school's fees were £750 per term but they have increased by 6%.
    d A certain model of car was priced at £7250 but the price increased by 4%.

9   Find the inclusive price of each of the following if Value Added Tax (VAT) is charged at $17\frac{1}{2}$%.
    a a large electric fan of exclusive price £120
    b a dining room suite of exclusive price £440
    c a clothes drier of exclusive price £280
    d a video camera of exclusive price £720

10 A large youth club had a membership of 150 boys and 160 girls, but the numbers increased by 8% and 5% respectively. Find the new number for each.

Example 9

Use your calculator to express 60 as a percentage of 75.

Press the keys in the given sequence. (Check to see whether you need the ▬ key.)

AC **6** **0** **÷** **7** **5** **%** **=** 80

(If your calculator does not have a **%** key, divide 60 by 75 and then multiply by 100.)

Exercise 15J

For questions 1–4 use your calculator to find the answer which is different.

1   **a** 420 as a percentage of 600
    b 465 as a percentage of 620
    c 405 as a percentage of 540

2   **a** £168 as a percentage of £480
    b £175 as a percentage of £500
    c £162 as a percentage of £450

3   **a** 42 m as a percentage of 240 m
    b 72 m as a percentage of 320 m
    c 99 m as a percentage of 440 m

4   **a** 12 cm as a percentage of 160 cm
    b 13.5 cm as a percentage of 180 cm
    c 18.9 cm as a percentage of 420 cm

For questions 5–7 use your calculator to express each of the figures as a percentage of the total.

5   60 people are waiting in a queue at a railway station ticket office. 27 of them pay in cash, 18 pay by cheque and 15 pay by credit card.

6   There are 75 people at an open air swimming pool. 42 of them are swimming, 18 of them are paddling and 15 of them are sun bathing.

7   125 children are watching a play in a school hall. 45 of them are standing at the back, 65 of them are seated in the middle and 15 of them are sitting on the floor at the front.

15.4 The idea of memory and use of ⊞ⁿ⁺ ⊟ⁿ⁻ and ᴹᴿᶜ (or ᴿᶜᴹ/ᴹᴿ) keys

Often it is helpful to store the result of a calculation which you may want to use later. Many calculators have a memory and a key for adding a number into the memory, M+, a key for subtracting a number from the memory, M−, and a key for recalling and clearing the contents of the memory, MRC (or RCM or MR) (R stands for recall, C stands for clear.)

Example 10

Find the cost of buying 2 shirts at £14.50 each and 3 ties at £7.99 each.

To do this calculation we need to find $2 \times £14.50$ and remember the result, then find $3 \times £7.99$ and finally add the two results together. If your calculator has memory keys as described above the sequence of key presses would be as follows, giving the result of £52.97.

$$\boxed{AC}\ \boxed{1}\ \boxed{4}\ \boxed{\cdot}\ \boxed{5}\ \boxed{\times}\ \boxed{2}\ \boxed{=}\ \boxed{M+}$$
$$\boxed{7}\ \boxed{\cdot}\ \boxed{9}\ \boxed{9}\ \boxed{\times}\ \boxed{3}\ \boxed{=}\ \boxed{M+}\ \boxed{MRC}\quad 52.97$$

The first time the M+ key is pressed the $14.5 \times 2 = 29$ is added to the memory. The second time the M+ key is pressed the $7.99 \times 3 = 23.97$ is added to the memory. The MRC key recalls the current contents of the memory, i.e. 52.97, so the total bill is £52.97.

Usually a small 'M' appears on the display to show that there is something in the memory. If the MRC is pressed again, 52.97 will remain displayed but the small 'M' will disappear, showing that the memory has been cleared.

Example 11

Use your calculator to find

a $7 \times 8 - 5 \times 6$ **b** $7 \times 8 + 6 \times 5 + 4 \times 3$

$$\boxed{AC}\ \boxed{7}\ \boxed{\times}\ \boxed{8}\ \boxed{=}\ \boxed{M+}\ \boxed{5}\ \boxed{\times}\ \boxed{6}\ \boxed{=}\ \boxed{M-}\ \boxed{MRC}\quad 26$$

So $7 \times 8 - 5 \times 6 = 26$. Here 56 is added to the memory using M+ and then 30 is subtracted from the memory using M−.

$$\boxed{MRC}\ \boxed{AC}\ \boxed{7}\ \boxed{\times}\ \boxed{8}\ \boxed{=}\ \boxed{M+}\ \boxed{6}\ \boxed{\times}\ \boxed{5}\ \boxed{=}\ \boxed{M+}\ \boxed{4}\ \boxed{\times}\ \boxed{3}\ \boxed{=}\ \boxed{M+}\ \boxed{MRC}\ \boxed{MRC}\quad 98$$

So $7 \times 8 + 5 \times 6 + 4 \times 3 = 98$. Here the MRC key is pressed initially to clear the memory, and pressed twice at the end to leave the memory clear after the calculation.

Do not forget to make sure that both the memory and the calculator are clear before starting a new calculation.

Exercise 15K

Use your calculator and its memory keys to work out each of the following.
1   $18 \times 4 + 13 \times 5$ 2 $16 \times 15 + 20 \times 3$ 3 $12 \times 9 + 15 \times 4$

4   For a school trip to a theatre 9 adult tickets at £5 each are required for the teachers and 65 children's tickets at £3 each for the pupils. Find the total cost.
5   The supervisor at a children's playgroup buys 28 pens at 15p each and 16 pencils at 5p each. Find how much she spends in: **a** pence   **b** pounds.
6   A man who owns some boarding kennels buys 16 bags of dog food which contain 15 kg each and 30 others which contain 12 kg each. How many kilograms does he buy altogether?

7   $10 \times 3 + 12 \times 2 + 9 \times 4$ 8 $15 \times 6 + 8 \times 7 + 13 \times 8$

9   Deena goes to an ice-cream cart and buys 4 cornets at 60p each, 2 choc ices at 75p each and 3 lollies at 70p each. Find how much she spends in: **a** pence   **b** pounds.
10   Marcus buys all of his paper for studying at once. He buys 4 pads of lined paper with 120 sheets in each, 3 pads of plain paper with 80 sheets in each and 2 pads of graph paper with 60 sheets in each. How many sheets of paper does he buy altogether?

11   $25 \times 5 - 13 \times 8$ 12 $76 \times 3 - 24 \times 6$ 13 $96 \times 4 - 16 \times 9$

14   A freight lift stops at a certain floor and 5 crates of weight 36 kg each are loaded on, but 4 others of weight 35 kg each are taken off. Find the extra weight in the cage.
15   Candace has 4 large packets of soap powder which each contain 1350 grams. Shani has 6 medium packets of the same powder which each contain 895 grams.
Find how many more grams of powder Candace has.

15.5   Using a calculator for shopping and other general purposes

Example 12

Find the total bill for five articles costing £2.43, £3.57, 97p, £4.99 and £8.00.

[MRC] [AC] [2] [·] [4] [3] [M+] [3] [·] [5] [7] [M+] [0] [·] [9] [7] [M+] [4] [·] [9] [9] [M+] [8] [·] [0] [0] [M+] [MRC] 19.96

So the total bill is £19.96.

Note   using the memory like this leaves the calculator free for you to do other calculations which do not use the memory.

Example 15L

For each question find the amount shown by the display when the [MRC] key is pressed if each person records everything in a calculator memory. Remember to press the [MRC] key a second time to clear the memory before doing the next question.

1   Anne goes shopping and spends: £28.26 in a supermarket, £10.37 at a greengrocer's shop, £15.21 at a hardware shop and £1.56 at a newsagent's shop.

2   Nicola goes to a DIY store and spends: £40.24 on paint, £10.16 on brushes, £30.22 on wallpaper and £5.18 on wallpaper paste.

3   Suzanne travels from Bury to Upminster and her costs are:
Tram fare from Bury to Manchester £3.20
Train fare from Manchester to London £35.15
Lunch on the train £6.90
Train fare from London to Upminster £4.75

4   A company representative has to fill his car's petrol tank four times during a certain week and the amounts he pays are: £15.31, £16.72, £17.05 and £15.92.

Example 13

a Find the cost of buying 3 towels at £5.95 each and 2 flannels at £2.95 each.

b If I were given an 8% discount on the total bill, what would this discount be?

c After the discount what would I actually have to pay?

a [MRC] [AC] [5] [•] [9] [5] [×] [3] [=] [M+] [2] [•] [9] [5] [×] [2] [=]
[M+] [MRC] `23.75`
So the total cost is £23.75.

b Now press
[×] [8] [%] `1.90` so the 8% discount is £1.90.

c Now press
[M-] [MRC] `21.85` so the actual price is £21.85 after the discount has been subtracted.

Exercise 15M

For each of the following find: **a** the total bill   **b** the amount of discount offered   **c** the actual amount payable.

1   Charmaine went to a market hall to buy some things for her new house:
a carpet (£250.75), some curtains (£73.15), some floor tiles (£46.30) and some wall tiles (£49.80).
She was given an 8% discount on the total.

2   Eshe buys 4 cardigans at £7.25 each and 2 blouses at £1.90 each, and she is given a 5% discount on the total.

3   Kanika bought some electrical appliances: a television (£350.45), a video (£270.20), a computer (£108.15), and a word processor (£371.20).
She was given a 12% discount on the total.

4   Natalie buys 3 pullovers at £4.95 each and 2 skirts at £3.95 each, and she is given an 8% discount on the total.

5   Afiya buys 3 pairs of shoes at £14.95 a pair and 2 pairs of socks at £2.20 a pair, and she is given a 4% discount on the total.

16 AREA

16.1 Understanding units of area in the metric and imperial systems

Areas using centimetre squares

On page 88 we called the distance around the edge of a shape its perimeter. The shapes below have the same perimeter (20 cm), but they clearly cover different amounts of surface.

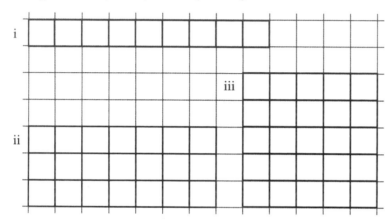

The amount of surface that a shape covers is called the area of the shape. We usually measure the area of a shape in square units, for example the square centimetre.

We say that a 1 cm square, i.e.

has an area of 1 square centimetre, which is written as 1 cm^2.

The first shape is covered by nine 1 cm squares and has an area of 9 square centimetres (or 9 cm^2).

The second shape is covered by twenty-one 1 cm squares and has an area of 21 square centimetres (or 21 cm^2).

The third shape has an area of 25 square centimetres (or 25 cm^2).

Example 1

Each of the shapes below is covered by 1 cm squares (slightly reduced).
Write down the area of each.

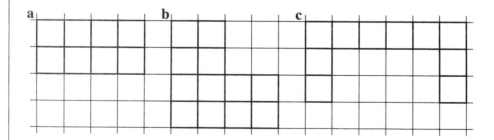

a The shape is covered by eight 1 cm squares, so its area is 8 square centimetres (or 8 cm^2).
b The shape is covered by twelve 1 cm squares, so its area is 12 square centimetres (or 12 cm^2).
c The shape has an area of 10 square centimetre (or 10 cm^2).

Exercise 16A

Find the area of each of the following by counting the number of 1 cm squares.

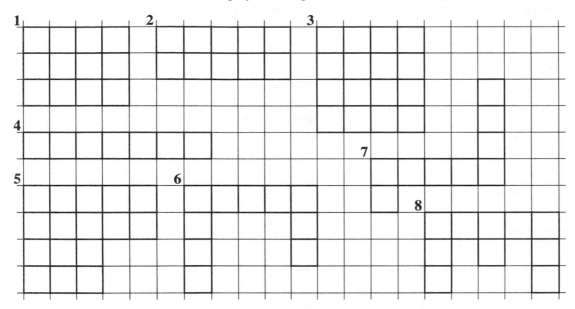

We can also find the area of more complicated shapes providing that we can put them on a grid of 1 cm squares.

Example 2

Find the area of the shapes.

a Shape **a** can be covered by 6 whole 1 cm squares and 4 half 1 cm squares (×).

So its area is:
$(6 + 4 \times \frac{1}{2})$ cm^2 =
$(6 + 2)$ cm^2 = 8 cm^2

b Shape **b** can be covered by 4 whole 1 cm squares and nearly whole 1 cm squares (●). If we count as one those part squares which are clearly more than a half square and ignore those part squares which are clearly less than a half square, we can say that the area of the circle is approximately:

$(4 + 8)$ cm^2 = 12 cm^2

Exercise 16B

Find the area of each of the following.
(For the circles count only the part squares which are marked with a dot.)

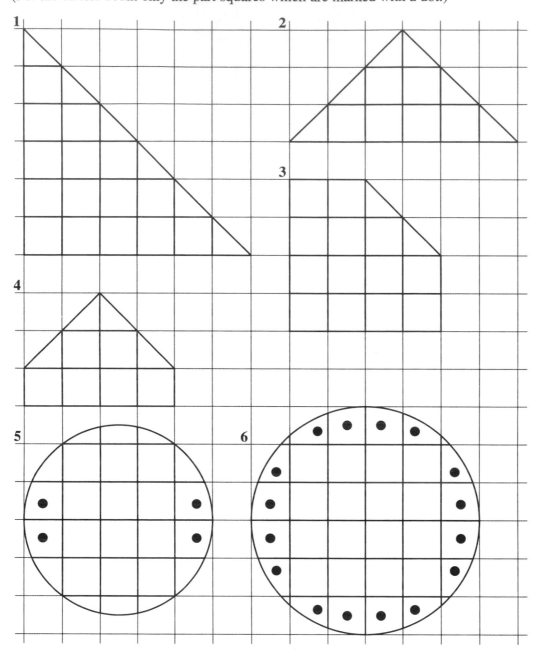

Areas using metre squares and millimetre squares

So far we have used 1 cm squares as our unit for measuring areas. This is fine for the shapes above, but would be very tedious for large areas such as football fields or very small areas such as postage stamps. For large areas we can use 1 metre squares and for small areas 1 millimetre squares.

Example 3

Find the area for each of the shapes below:

a Garden (metre squares)   **b** Patio (metre squares)   **c** Postage stamp (millimetre squares)

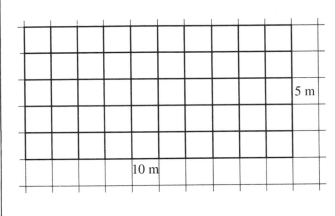

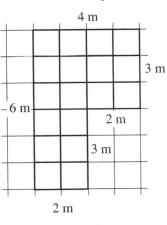

a The shape can be covered by 50 one-metre squares, so its area is 50 square metres (or 50 m²). Note that $10 \times 5 = 50$ if you think that there are too many squares to count.

b The shape can be covered by 18 one-metre squares, so its area is 18 square metres (or 18 m²).

c The shape can be covered by 150 one-millimetre squares, so its area is 150 square millimetres (or 150 mm²). Note that $15 \times 10 = 150$ if you think that there are too many squares to count.

Exercise 16C

Find the area of each of the following.

1 Yard (metre squares)

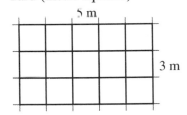

2 Living room floor (metre squares)

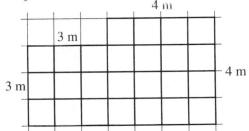

3 Concrete path around three sides of a pond (metre squares)

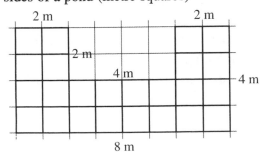

4 Price tag (millimetre squares)

5 Rectangular badge (millimetre squares)

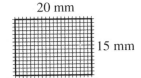

Areas using imperial units

We can also measure areas by using imperial units such as square inches, square feet or square yards.

Example 4

Find the area of each shape.

a Photograph (inch squares)

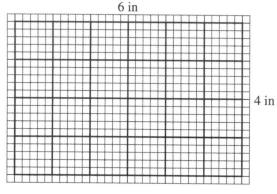

b Carpet (foot squares)

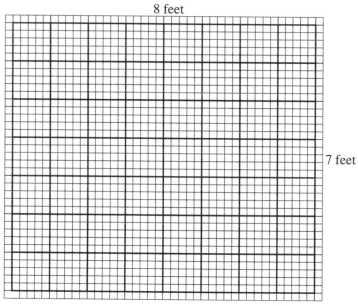

c Patio (yard squares)

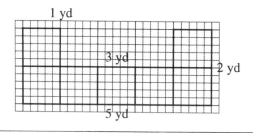

a Shape **a** has an area of 24 square inches (or 24 in^2).

b Shape **b** has an area of 56 square feet (or 56 ft^2).

c Shape **c** has an area of 7 square yards (or 7 yd^2).

Exercise 16D

Find the area of each of the following.

1 Large door mat (foot squares)

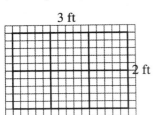

3 ft

2 ft

2 Large table in a conference room (foot squares)

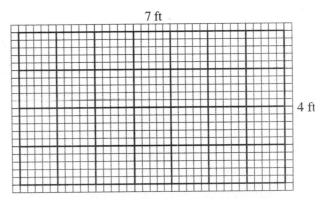

7 ft

4 ft

3 Table mat (inch squares)

8 in

6 in

4 Picture (inch squares)

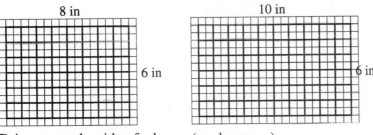

10 in

6 in

5 Window in a door (inch squares)

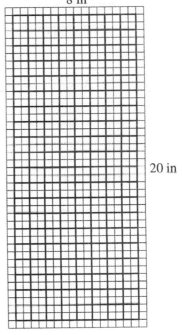

8 in

20 in

6 Driveway at the side of a house (yard squares)

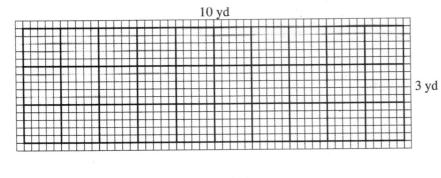

10 yd

3 yd

Very large areas

For very large areas such as fields the units of area we use are hectares in the metric system or acres in the imperial system.

One **hectare** is the area of a square which measures 100 m by 100 m or $10\,000$ m^2, and there are 100 hectares in a square kilometre.

One **acre** is equal to 4840 square yards. This area is equal to that of 10 squares which each measure 22 yards by 22 yards, and there are 640 acres in a square mile.

Example 5

Find the area of:

a the car park

b the cornfield.

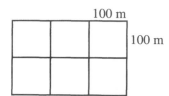

100 m

100 m

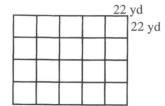

22 yd

22 yd

a Each 100 m by 100 m square is a hectare. Therefore the area of the car park is 6 hectares or 6 ha (ha is the abbreviation for hectares).

b The area is equal to that of 20 squares which measure 22 yd by 22 yd. The area is therefore equal to (20 ÷ 10) acres or 2 acres.

Exercise 16E

Find the area of each of the following.

1 A large harbour

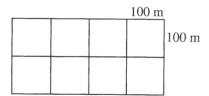

100 m

100 m

2 A pleasure park

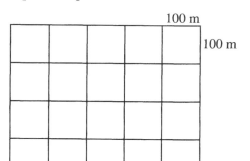

100 m

100 m

3 A reservoir

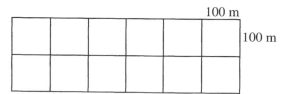

100 m

100 m

4 A barge dock on a canal

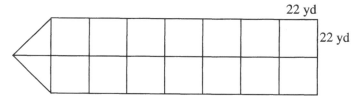

22 yd

22 yd

5 A railway station forecourt

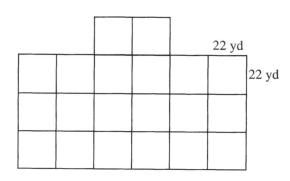

22 yd

22 yd

16.2 Finding areas of rectangles, triangles, circles and irregular shapes

Area of a rectangle

You probably noticed in the last section that there is a quick way of finding
the area of a rectangle. You simply multiply the length by the width.

Example 6

Find the area of each of these rectangles.

a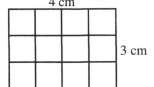

b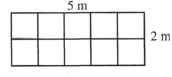

c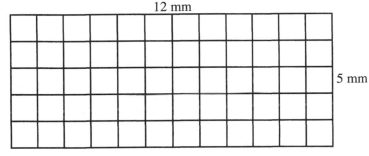

a The area of the rectangle is (4×3) cm^2 = 12 cm^2.
b The area of the rectangle is (5×2) m^2 = 10 m^2.
c The area of the rectangle is (12×5) mm^2 = 60 mm^2.

The formula for the area of a rectangle is therefore:

$$Area = Length \times Width$$

or $A = l \times w$

(using the letters l, w and A to stand for the length, width and area of the rectangle.)

Exercise 16F

For questions 1–3 find which rectangle has a different area from the other
two. You may use your calculator if you wish.

1 a 24 cm, 9 cm   **b** 27 cm, 8 cm   **c** 32 cm, 7 cm

(continued)

2 a

45cm

7 cm

b

65 cm

5 cm

c

35 cm

9 cm

3 a

9.5 m

1.6 m

b

9.6 m

1.5 m

c

4.5 m

3.2 m

Find the area of each of the following.

4

120 cm

Table top

75 cm

5

150 cm

Window pane

108 cm

6

37.5 m

Garage forecourt

9.6 m

7

1.75 m

Piece of shelving board

0.4 m

8

35mm

1230

16 mm   Calculator screen

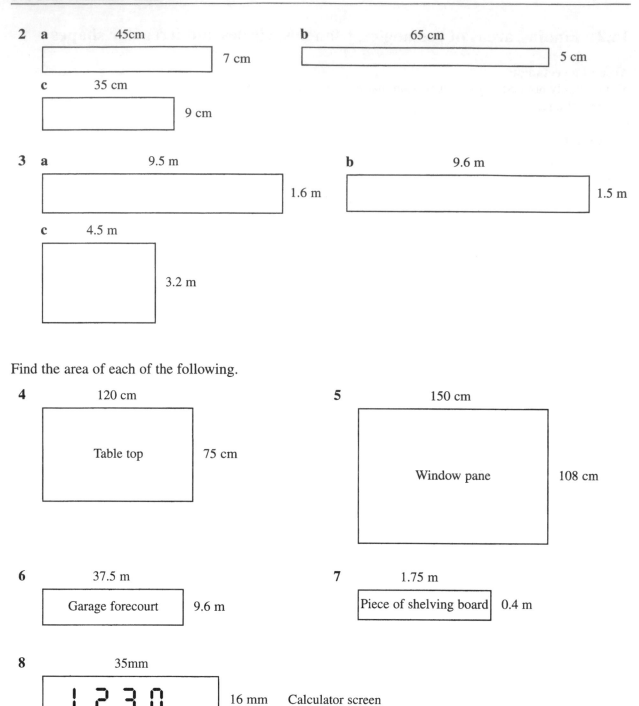

Area of a triangle

Example 7

Find the area of each of these triangles.

a 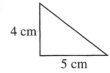   b   c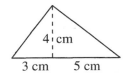

a We can think of the area of this triangle
as being half the area of a rectangle which
is 5 cm long and 4 cm wide.

The area of the rectangle is (5×4) cm^2 = 20 cm^2,
so the area of the triangle is $(20 \div 2)$ cm^2 = 10 cm^2

b The area of this triangle is half the area of a rectangle
whose dimensions are 4 cm by 3 cm.

The area of the rectangle is 12 cm^2,
so the area of the triangle is 6 cm^2.

c We can see from the diagram that the area of the
triangle is one half of the area of a rectangle
8 cm long and 4 cm high.

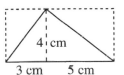

The area of the rectangle is (8×4) cm^2 or 32 cm^2,
so the area of the triangle is $(32 \div 2)$ cm^2 or 16 cm^2.

Using the above example we can derive a formula for finding
the area of a triangle.

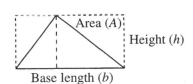

The area of a the complete triangle is $(b \times h)$, so the area A of the
triangle is one half of $(b \times h)$.

Therefore $A = \frac{1}{2} \times (b \times h)$.
The area of a triangle is found by multiplying the base length by the
height and then halving the result.

(The height of the triangle, which is the perpendicular height from the base
of the triangle is also called the **altitude** of the triangle.)

Exercise 16G

For questions 1–6 find the area of the triangle. You may use your calculator.

1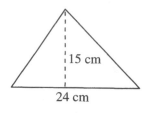
15 cm
24 cm

2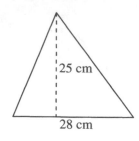
25 cm
28 cm

3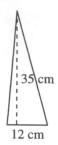
35 cm
12 cm

4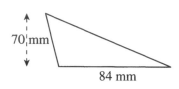
70 mm
84 mm

5
55 mm
32 mm

6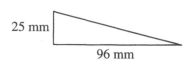
25 mm
96 mm

Find the area of each of the following.

7 The traffic island

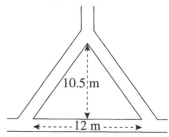
10.5 m
12 m

8 The corner flag on a football field

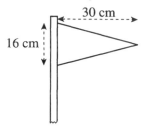
30 cm
16 cm

9 The 60° set square

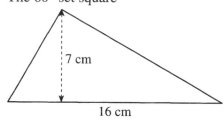
7 cm
16 cm

10 Mr Jones lives near a road junction and has two triangular gardens.
Find the area of each.

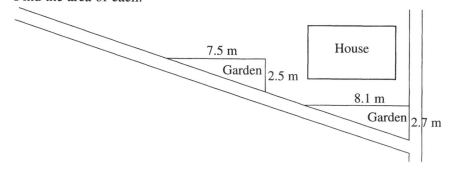
7.5 m
Garden 2.5 m
House
8.1 m
Garden 2.7 m

Area of a circle

If we look at the diagram opposite, we can see that the area of the circle lies somewhere between the area of the square outside, which is a 2 cm by 2 cm square of area 4 cm^2, and the area of the square inside which is 2 cm^2, because this is made up of four of the triangles illustrated which each have an area of $\frac{1}{2}$ cm^2. The area of the circle is therefore about 3 cm^2. We could find this area more accurately by covering the circle with 1 mm squares and counting them. This would probably give 3.14 cm^2 which is a better approximation.

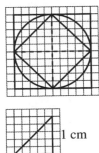

1 cm
1 cm

The ancient Greeks found that finding the exact area of a circle requires the use of a special number called 'pi'. Pi is a never-ending decimal which starts 3.14..., and the symbol π is used to denote this number.

The formula for the area A of a circle of radius r is:

$$A = \pi \times (radius)^2 \text{ or } \pi \times r^2$$

where π is the special number 3.14...

For most purposes taking $\pi = 3.14$ will give an accurate enough value for the area of a circle.

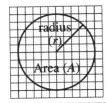
radius (r)
Area (A)

Example 8

Find the area of each circle. (Take π as 3.14.) You may use your calculator.

a

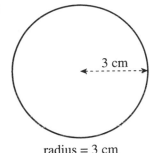

3 cm

radius = 3 cm

b

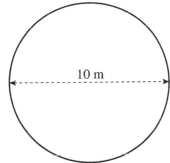

10 m

diameter = 10 m

a The area of circle **a** is $(\pi \times 3^2)$ cm^2 = $(\pi \times 9)$ cm^2 = (3.14×9) cm^2 = 28.26 cm^2.

b The diameter of circle **b** is 10 m, therefore its radius is 5 m.
The area of circle **b** is therefore $(\pi \times 5^2)$ cm^2 = $(\pi \times 25)$ cm^2 = (3.14×25) cm^2 = 78.5 m^2.

Exercise 16H

For questions 1–5 find the area of the circle from its radius. (Take $\pi = 3.14$.)

1 Radius = 2 cm   **2** Radius = 8 cm   **3** Radius = 15 cm

4 Radius = 2.5 m   **5** Radius = 4.5 m

(continued)

Find the area of each of the following.

6 A button

7 A door-bell button switch

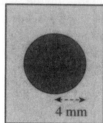

4 mm

8 A clock face

12 cm

9 A circular bread board

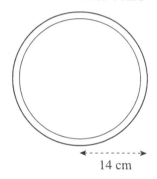

14 cm

10 A small roundabout at a road junction

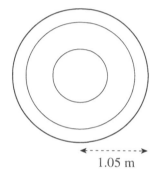

1.05 m

For questions 11–15 find the area of the circle from its diameter.
(Remember to find the radius first.)

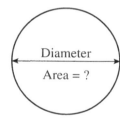

Diameter

Area = ?

11 Diameter = 8 cm
12 Diameter = 18 cm
13 Diameter = 50 m
14 Diameter = 7 m
15 Diameter = 15 mm

Area of an irregular shape

Example 9

Find the area of this shape.

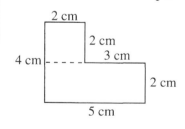

2 cm

2 cm

4 cm

3 cm

2 cm

5 cm

We can split the shape into two rectangles.

The area of the small rectangle (or square) is (2×2) cm^2 or 4 cm^2.

The area of the large rectangle is (5×2) cm^2 or 10 cm^2.

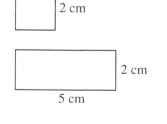

2 cm

2 cm

5 cm

2 cm

So the area of the shape is $(4 + 10)$ cm^2 or 14 cm^2.

Example 10

Find the area of this shape.

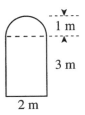

We can split the shape into a triangle and a rectangle.
The area of the triangle is $\frac{1}{2} \times (2 \times 5)$ cm^2 or $(\frac{1}{2} \times 10)$ cm^2 which is 5 cm^2.
The area of the rectangle is (3×5) cm^2 or 15 cm^2.
So the area of the shape is $(5 + 15)$ cm^2 = 20 cm^2.

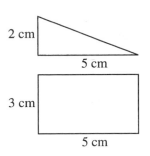

Example 11

Find the area of this shape.

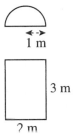

We can split the shape into a semicircle and a rectangle.
The area of the semicircle is $\frac{1}{2} \times (\pi \times 1^2)$ m^2 = $(\frac{1}{2} \times \pi)$ m^2 = $(\frac{1}{2} \times 3.14)$ m^2 = 1.57 m^2.
The area of the rectangle is (2×3) m^2 or 6 m^2.
So the area of the shape is $(1.57 + 6)$ m^2 = 7.57 m^2.

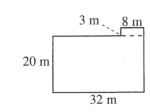

Exercise 16J

For questions 1–3 find the area of the shape. You may use your calculator.

1
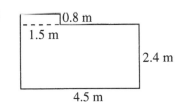

2
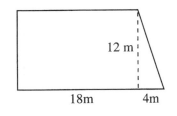

3
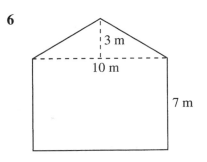

For questions 4–6 find the area of the shape.

4

5

6

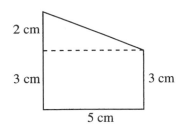

(continued)

For the questions 7–10 find the area of the shape. Take π = 3.14.

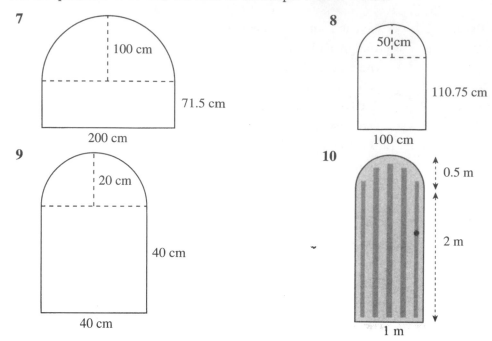

7 100 cm 71.5 cm 200 cm

8 50 cm 110.75 cm 100 cm

9 20 cm 40 cm 40 cm

10 0.5 m 2 m 1 m

16.3 Converting between units of area in the metric and imperial systems

Converting metric areas

In the metric system it is quite easy to change one unit of area to another.
For example, a one-centimetre square measures 10 mm by 10 mm.

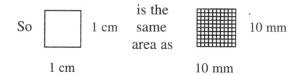

So 1 cm is the same area as 10 mm

1 cm   10 mm

The area of the first square is 1 cm^2, but using mm^2 we can see that its area is (10×10) mm^2 or 100 mm^2. So 1 cm^2 = 100 mm^2.

In the same way a one-metre square measures 100 cm by 100 cm or 1000 mm by 1000 mm.

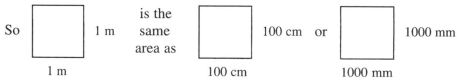

So 1 m is the same area as 100 cm or 1000 mm

1 m   100 cm   1000 mm

The area of 1 m^2 is therefore the same as (100×100) cm^2 or 10 000 cm^2 and (1000×1000) mm^2 or 1 000 000 mm^2 (i.e. one million square millimetres).

So 1 cm^2 = 100 mm^2 and 1 m^2 = 10 000 cm^2 or 1 000 000 mm^2.

Exercise 16K

Copy and complete the table below.

	Area (m²)	Area (cm²)	Area (mm²)
1	5	$5 \times 10\,000 =$	$5 \times 1\,000\,000 =$
2	1.5		
3		135\,000	
4		9800	
5			9\,500\,000
6			128\,000

Converting imperial areas

In the imperial system a one-yard square measures 3 ft by 3 ft.

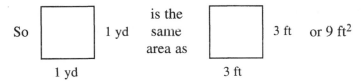

So ☐ 1 yd   is the same area as   ☐ 3 ft   or 9 ft²
   1 yd   3 ft

So 1 square yard = 9 square feet.

Also a one-foot square measures 12 in by 12 in.

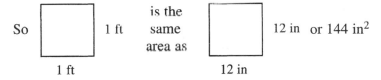

So ☐ 1 ft   is the same area as   ☐ 12 in   or 144 in²
   1 ft   12 in

So 1 square foot = 144 square inches.

Also 1 square yard = 9 square feet = (9×144) square inches or 1296 square inches.

Exercise 16L

Copy and complete the table below. (You may use your calculator.)

	Area (yd²)	Area (ft²)	Area (in²)
1	5	$5 \times 9 =$	$5 \times 9 \times 144 =$
2	10.5		
3		27	
4		58.5	
5			3240
6			17\,496

Changing metric areas to imperial areas and vice versa

We can also change metric area units to imperial ones and vice versa.

1 inch is approximately 2.54 cm.

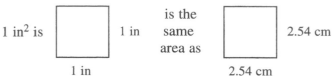

so 1 in² = (2.54 × 2.54) cm² ≈ 6.45 cm²
and 1 cm² is therefore equal to (1 ÷ 6.45) in² or 0.155 in².

1 foot is approximately 30.5 cm.

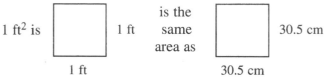

so 1 ft² = (30.5 × 30.5) cm² ≈ 930 cm²
and 1 cm² is therefore equal to (1 ÷ 930) ft² or 0.0011 ft².

1 yard is approximately 0.917 m.

so 1 yd² ≈ (0.917 × 0.917) m² ≈ 0.841 m²
and 1 m² is therefore equal to (1 ÷ 0.841) yd² or 1.19 yd².

1 acre is 4840 square yards which is (4840 × 0.841) m² or approximately 4070 m².
So 1 acre is approximately (4070 ÷ 10 000) hectares or 0.407 hectares,
and 1 hectare is therefore equal to (1 ÷ 0.407) acres or 2.46 hectares.

Exercise 16M

(You may use your calculator.)

1 Given that 1 in² = 6.45 cm², change to cm²:
    a 4 in²   **b** 18 in²   **c** 2.4 in²

2 Given that 1 cm² = 0.155 in², change to in²:
    a 40 cm²   **b** 54 cm²   **c** 36.4 cm²

3 Given that 1 ft² = 930 cm², change to cm²:
    a 5 ft²   **b** 3.5 ft²   **c** 0.6 ft²

4 Given that 1 cm² = 0.0011 ft², change to ft²:
    a 6400 cm²   **b** 9200 cm²   **c** 22 500 cm²

5 Given that 1 yd² = 0.841 m², change to m²:
    a 15 yd²   **b** 8 yd²   **c** 1.4 yd²

6 Given that 1 m² = 1.19 yd², change to yd²:
    a 7 m²   **b** 3 m²   **c** 7.6 m²

7 Given that 1 acre = 0.407 hectares, change to hectares:
    a 9 acres   **b** 14 acres   **c** 9.6 acres   **d** 6.5 acres

8 Given that 1 hectare = 2.46 acres, change to acres:
    a 15 hectares   **b** 35 hectares   **c** 12.5 hectares   **d** 4.5 hectares

17 CAPACITY AND VOLUME

17.1 Understanding units of capacity and volume in the metric and imperial systems

Volume using centimetre cubes

The volume of an object is the amount of space that the shape takes up. We usually measure the volume of a shape in cubic units, for example the cubic centimetre.

We say that a 1 cm cube has a volume of 1 cubic centimetre which is written as 1 cm^3.

Example 1

Each of the shapes below is made up of 1 cm cubes. Write down the volumes of each.

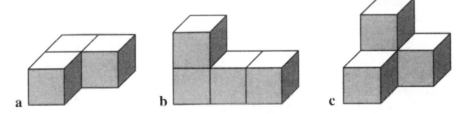

a   b   c

a The shape consists of three 1 cm cubes, so its volume is 3 cubic centimetres (or 3 cm^3).
b The shape consists of four 1 cm cubes, so its volume is 4 cubic centimetres (or 4 cm^3).
c The shape consists of four 1 cm cubes, so its volume is 4 cubic centimetres (or 4 cm^3).

Exercise 17A

Find the volume of each of the following shapes which are made from 1 cm cubes.

1

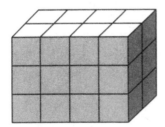

2

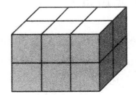

(continued)

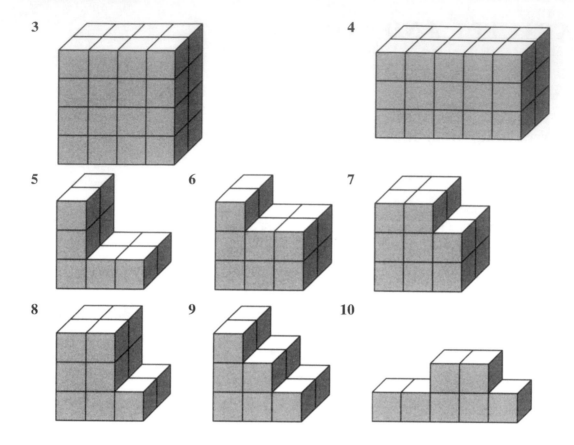

Volume using metre cubes and millimetre cubes
As with measuring areas, we may need a larger unit of volume (i.e. a
1 metre cube) or a smaller unit of volume (i.e. a 1 millimetre cube).

Example 2
Find the volume of each of the shapes below.

a (Metre cubes could be arranged like this to make a bench.)
The shape can be made from four metre cubes, so its volume
is 4 cubic metres (or 4 m³).

b (Metre cubes could be arranged like this to make a stage.)
The shape can be made from sixteen metre cubes, so its volume
is 16 cubic metres (or 16 m³).

c (The shape is made from millimetre cubes.)
The shape can be made from twenty-six millimetre cubes,
so its volume is 26 cubic millimetres (or 26 mm³).

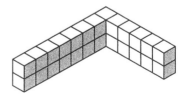

Exercise 17B

Find the volume of each of the following. (Each shape is made from metre cubes.)

1 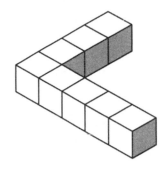   **2** 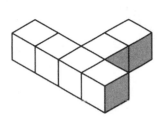   **3**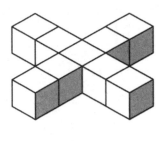

Find the volume of each of the following. (Each shape is made from millimetre cubes.)

4 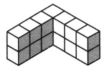   **5**   **6**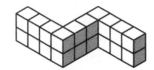

Volume using imperial units

We can also measure volumes by using imperial units such as cubic inches, cubic feet and cubic yards.

Example 3

Find the volume of each shape.

a (The shape is made from inch cubes.)

The shape can be made from six inch
cubes, so its volume is 6 cubic inches (or 6 in³).

b (The shape is made from foot cubes.)

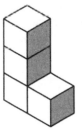

The shape can be made from four foot cubes, so its volume
is 4 cubic feet (or 4 ft³).

c (The shape is made from yard cubes.)

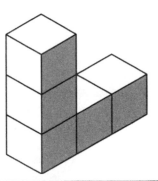

The shape can be made from five yard cubes,
so its volume is 5 cubic yards (or 5 yd³).

Exercise 17C

Find the volume of each of the following. (Each shape is made from inch cubes.)

1 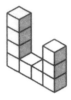   **2**   **3** 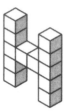   **4**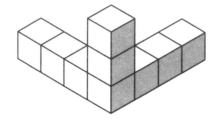

5 Find the volume of this shape which is made from foot cubes.

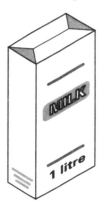

6 Find the volume of this shape which is made from yard cubes.

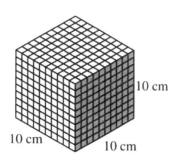

Capacity using litres

The capacity of a container is the amount of liquid it will hold.

We usually measure the capacity of a container in litres and l is used as the symbol for one litre.

A litre occupies the same space as a 10 centimetre cube, which itself occupies the same space as $10 \times 10 \times 10$ (or 1000) one centimetre cubes, so 1 litre equals 1000 cubic centimetres.

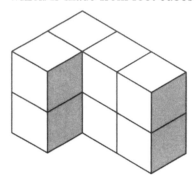

10 cm
10 cm   10 cm

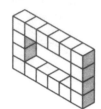

Example 4

Find the capacity of each of the following containers. (It will help if you find how many 10 centimetre cubes the container will hold and remember that 1000 cubic centimetres = 1 litre.)

a

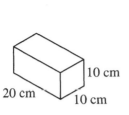

20 cm 10 cm 10 cm

b

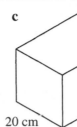

30 cm 10 cm 10 cm

c

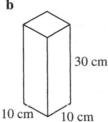

20 cm 20 cm 30 cm

a Shape **a** holds two 10 centimetre cubes, so it has a capacity of 2 litres (2 l).
b Shape **b** holds three 10 centimetre cubes, so it has a capacity of 3 litres (3 l).
c Shape **c** holds twelve 10 centimetre cubes, so it has a capacity of 12 litres (12 l).

Exercise 17D

Find the capacity, in litres, of each of the following containers.

1

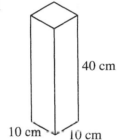

40 cm 10 cm 10 cm

2

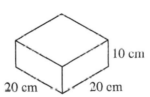

10 cm 20 cm 20 cm

3

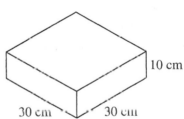

10 cm 30 cm 30 cm

4

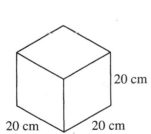

20 cm 20 cm 20 cm

5

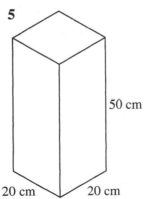

50 cm 20 cm 20 cm

6

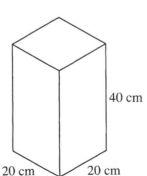

40 cm 20 cm 20 cm

Capacity using millilitres

In the section on length we saw that we could divide a metre into 100 parts each called a centimetre, or 1000 parts each called a millimetre. For smaller containers we need a measure of capacity which is much smaller than a litre, so we divide a litre into 1000 parts and each part is called a millilitre. (We use the symbol ml to stand for 1 millilitre.)

As there are 1000 cubic centimetres in a litre it follows that a millilitre has the same capacity as a 1 centimetre cube.

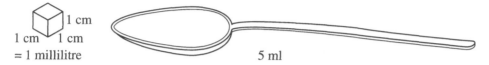

Smaller quantities, such as a dose of medicine, are measured in millilitres (ml).
A full teaspoon, for example, contains approximately 5 ml.

Example 5

Find the capacity of each of the following containers in millilitres. (It will help if you first find how many 1 cm cubes the container will hold.)

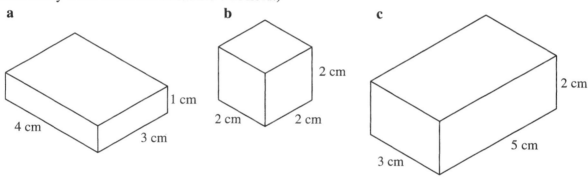

   a Shape **a** holds twelve 1 cm cubes, so it has a capacity of 12 millilitres (12 ml).
   b Shape **b** holds eight 1 cm cubes, so it has a capacity of 8 millilitres (8 ml).
   c Shape **c** holds thirty 1 cm cubes, so it has a capacity of 30 millilitres (30 ml).

Exercise 17E

Find the capacity in millilitres, of each of the following containers.

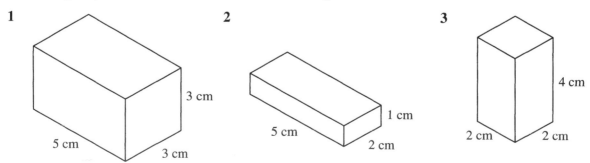

Capacity using imperial units

Although milk delivered by the milkman is often put in pint bottles and beer in pubs is sold in pints and half pints, all milk sold in supermarkets is now sold in litre and half-litre containers. In the same way, although petrol and diesel used to be sold in gallons it is now sold in litres instead.

The main imperial units used for capacity are pints, quarts and gallons:

    1 gallon = 8 pints   1 quart = 2 pints   1 gallon = 4 quarts

Two useful conversions are:

    1 gallon = 4.55 litres   1 litre = 1.76 pints

Unfortunately there are no simple conversions between imperial measures of capacity and their metric counterparts. This aspect will, however, be looked at on page 198.
The following relations are worth noting:

    1 gallon of pure water has a mass of about 10 pounds.   1 cubic foot = $6\frac{1}{4}$ gallons.

17.2 Finding volumes of cubes, cuboids, cylinders and composite shapes

Volume of a cuboid

You probably noticed in the last section that there is a quick way of finding the volume of a cuboid. (A cuboid is the name given to a rectangular box.) To find the volume you multiply the length by the width and then multiply by the height.

Example 6

Find the volume of each of these cuboids.

a

b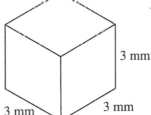

c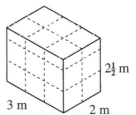

a The volume of the cuboid is $(4 \times 3 \times 2)$ cubic centimetres $= 24$ cm^3.

b The voume of the cube is $(3 \times 3 \times 3)$ cubic millimetres $= 27$ mm^3.

c The volume of the cuboid is $(3 \times 2 \times 2\frac{1}{2})$ cubic metres $= 15$ m^3.

Note the last answer can be found by counting the number of whole and half cubes. There are 12 whole cubes and 6 half cubes or 15 cubes altogether.

The formula for the volume of a cuboid is therefore:

    Volume = Length × Width × Height

or $V = l \times w \times h$ (where the letters l, w, h and V stand for the length, width, height and
                                      volume of the cuboid).

Exercise 17F

Copy and complete the table below.

	Length (l)	Width (w)	Height (h)	Volume of cuboid ($l \times w \times h$)
1	2 cm	3 cm	2 cm	
2	2 cm	4 cm	5 cm	
3	10 cm	3 cm	7 cm	
4	5 mm	2 mm	19 mm	
5	25 mm	40 mm	13 mm	
6	4 m	2.5 m	3 m	

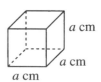

Volume of a cube

The volume of a cube of side length a cm is $(a \times a \times a)$ cm³ or a^3 cm³.

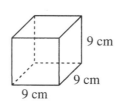

Example 7

Find the volume of a cube
whose side length is 9 cm.

Volume = $(9 \times 9 \times 9)$ cm³ = 729 cm³

Exercise 17G

Copy and complete the table below:

	Side length of cube	Volume of cube			Side length of cube	Volume of cube
1	8 cm			**5**	40 mm	
2	7 cm			**6**	50 mm	
3	12 cm			**7**	25 mm	
4	11 cm			**8**	15 m	

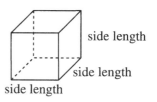

Example 8

Find the volume of a cuboid of
length 4 m, width 2.5 m and
height 1.05 m.

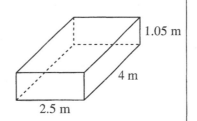

Volume = (4 × 2.5 × 1.05) m³ = 10.5 m³

Exercise 17H

For questions 1–5 copy and complete the table below and
state which cuboid has a different volume from the other two.

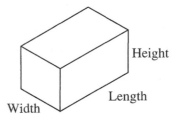

		Length	Width	Height	Volume
1	a	13 cm	11 cm	2 cm	
	b	12 cm	8 cm	3 cm	
	c	16 cm	9 cm	2 cm	
2	a	12 cm	9 cm	4 cm	
	b	15 cm	14 cm	2 cm	
	c	18 cm	6 cm	4 cm	
3	a	15 mm	8 mm	7 mm	
	b	14 mm	12 mm	5 mm	
	c	18 mm	9 mm	5 mm	

		Length	Width	Height	Volume
4	a	2.0 m	1.5 m	0.8 m	
	b	4.0 m	1.75 m	0.4 m	
	c	1.6 m	1.25 m	1.2 m	
5	a	2.5 m	2.0 m	0.7 m	
	b	3.0 m	1.5 m	0.8 m	
	c	4.0 m	1.2 m	0.75 m	
6	a	24.3 m	8.4 m	5.0 m	
	b	37.4 m	4.2 m	6.5 m	
	c	50.4 m	8.1 m	2.5 m	

Find the volume of each of the following.

7 A match box

30 mm 50 mm 12 mm

8 A brick

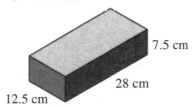

7.5 cm 28 cm 12.5 cm

9 A biscuit tin

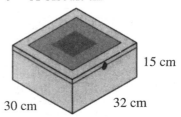

15 cm 30 cm 32 cm

Volume of a composite shape

Example 9

Find the volume of this shape.

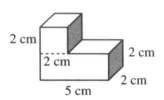

The shape can be divided into a cube and a cuboid.

Volume of cube = $(2 \times 2 \times 2)$ cm^3 = 8 cm^3.
Volume of cuboid = $(5 \times 2 \times 2)$ cm^3 = 20 cm^3.
Therefore total volume = $(8 + 20)$ cm^3 = 28 cm^3.

Exercise 17J

Find the volume of each of the following.

1

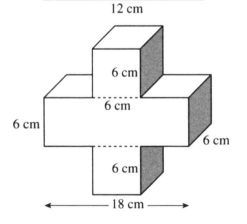

2

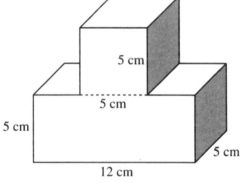

3

4

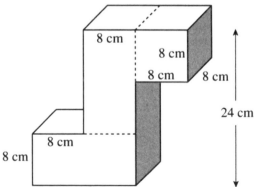

Volumes of cylinders

We saw on page 181 that the formula for the area A of a
circle of radius r is $A = \pi \times (\text{radius})^2$ or $A = \pi \times r^2$, where $\pi = 3.14$.

We can find the volume of a cylinder by thinking of it as a set of
circles stacked on top of each other. Provided that we know the
area of the circular base, we can find the volume of the cylinder
by multiplying the area of the base A by the height h.

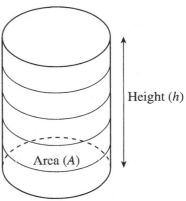

So the formula for the volume is:

$$\text{Volume} = A \times h$$

The area of the circular base of the
cylinder is $\pi \times r^2$, where r is the
radius of the base, so the full formula
for the volume of the cylinder is:

$$\text{Volume} = \pi \times r^2 \times h$$

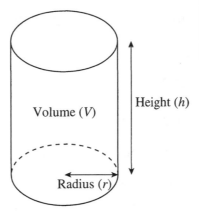

Example 10

Find the volume of a cylinder of
radius 10 cm and height 20 cm.
(Take $\pi = 3.14$.)

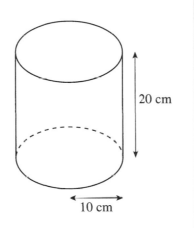

$$\begin{aligned}
\text{Volume} &= \pi \times (\text{Radius})^2 \times \text{Height} \\
&= \pi \times (10)^2 \times 20 \text{ cm}^3 \\
&= 3.14 \times 100 \times 20 \text{ cm}^3 \\
&= 6280 \text{ cm}^3
\end{aligned}$$

Exercise 17K

For questions 1–6 find the volume of the cylinder. (Take $\pi = 3.14$.)

1 Radius = 5 cm, height = 12 cm
2 Radius = 3 cm, height = 5 cm
3 Radius = 6 cm, height = 7.5 cm
4 Radius = 15 mm, height = 18 mm
5 Radius = 25 mm, height = 30 mm
6 Radius = 20 mm, height = 35 mm

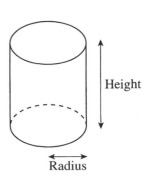

(continued)

Find the volume of each of the following. (Take $\pi = 3.14$.)

7   A tin of beans of radius 4 cm and height 12.5 cm
8   A waste paper bin of radius 12.5 cm and height 40 cm
9   An oil storage tank of radius 10 m and height 30 m
10 The spoil removed when boring a railway tunnel of radius 6 m and length 150 m

17.3   Converting between units of volume and capacity in the metric and imperial systems

Converting between metric volumes

1 cubic metre is a cube which measures 1 metre by 1 metre by 1 metre.

Since 1 metre = 100 centimetres, the cube also measures
100 cm by 100 cm by 100 cm,
so 1 cubic metre is the same as $(100 \times 100 \times 100)$ cubic centimetres, or:

$$1 \text{ m}^3 = 1\,000\,000 \text{ cm}^3 \text{ (or 1 million cm}^3\text{)}$$

Since 1 centimetre = 10 millimetres, 1 cubic centimetre is a cube which measures
10 mm $\times$ 10 mm $\times$ 10 mm,
so 1 cubic centimetre is the same as $(10 \times 10 \times 10)$ cubic millimetres or:

$$1 \text{ cm}^3 = 1000 \text{ mm}^3$$

So $1 \text{ m}^3 = 1\,000\,000 \text{ cm}^3 = 1\,000\,000\,000 \text{ mm}^3$ (or 1000 million mm^3)

Exercise 17L

Copy and complete the table below.

	Volume (m³)	Volume (cm³)	Volume (mm³)
1	5		
2	12		
3	1.5		
4	7.5		
5		4 000 000	

	Volume (m³)	Volume (cm³)	Volume (mm³)
6		7 000 000	
7		2 500 000	
8			6 000 000 000
9			13 000 000 000
10			4 500 000 000

Converting between imperial volumes

1 cubic yard is a cube which measures 3 ft by 3 ft by 3 ft.
So 1 cubic yard = $(3 \times 3 \times 3)$ cubic feet, or 1 yd^3 = 27 ft^3.

1 cubic foot is a cube which measures 12 in by 12 in by 12 in.
So 1 cubic foot = $(12 \times 12 \times 12)$ cubic inches, or 1 ft^3 = 1728 in^3.
So 1 yd^3 = 27 ft^3 = 27×1728 in^3 = 46 656 in^3.

Exercise 17M

Copy and complete the table below.

	Volume (yd³)	Volume (ft³)	Volume (in³)
1	60		
2	15		
3	8		
4		810	
5		2025	

	Volume (yd³)	Volume (ft³)	Volume (in³)
6		108	
7		81	
8			1 166 400
9			746 496
10			606 528

Converting metric capacities

1 litre = 1000 millilitres

Exercise 17N

Copy and complete the table below.

	Capacity (l)	Capacity (ml)
1	9	
2	5	
3	1.6	
4	2.1	
5	3.6	

	Capacity (l)	Capacity (ml)
6		7000
7		4000
8		1800
9		2400
10		3200

Converting imperial capacities

1 gallon = 4 quarts   1 quart = 2 pints   so 1 gallon = 8 pints

Exercise 17P

Copy and complete the table below.

	Capacity (gallons)	Capacity (quarts)	Capacity (pints)
1	5		
2	8		
3	15		
4	2.5		
5			32

	Capacity (gallons)	Capacity (quarts)	Capacity (pints)
6			132
7			84
8		24	
9		16	
10		34	

Converting capacities and volumes from metric units to imperial units and vice versa

---

Example 11

a A full carton contains 0.75 pints of orange juice.
Convert its capacity to litres, given that 1 pint = 0.6 litres.

b A full bottle contains 0.3 litres of vinegar.
Convert its capacity to pints, given that 1 litre = 1.75 pints.

a 0.75 pints = 0.75 × 0.6 litres = 0.45 litres

b 0.3 litres = 0.3 × 1.75 pints = 0.525 pints

Exercise 17Q

For questions 1–3 convert all capacities to litres, given that 1 pint = 0.6 litres.

1 Goodgrub's supermarket sells milk in cartons of four sizes:
0.8 pints, 1.5 pints, 2.5 pints and 4.0 pints.

2 Goodgrub's supermarket sells lemonade in bottles of four sizes:
0.4 pints, 0.6 pints, 1.4 pints and 2.4 pints.

3 Fixacar's garage sells engine oil in drums of four sizes:
0.9 pints, 1.6 pints, 2.6 pints and 3.2 pints.

For questions 4–6 convert all capacities to pints, given that 1 litre = 1.75 pints.

4 The Foodhall supermarket sells orange squash in bottles of four sizes:
0.8 litres, 1.2 litres, 2.0 litres and 2.8 litres.

5 The Foodhall supermarket sells cooking oil in bottles of four sizes:
0.4 litres, 0.6 litres, 1.4 litres and 1.8 litres.

6 The Foodhall supermarket sells liquid soap in plastic bottles of four sizes:
0.2 litres, 0.5 litres, 1.5 litres and 2.5 litres.

Example 12

a A large drum of paraffin is full and contains 15 gallons.
Convert this capacity to litres, given that 1 gallon = 4.5 litres.

b A lorry has a fuel tank which can hold 90 litres of diesel.
Convert this capacity to gallons, given that 1 litre = 0.22 gallons.

a 15 gallons = 15 × 4.5 litres = 67.5 litres

b 90 litres = 90 × 0.22 gallons = 19.8 gallons

Exercise 17R

1 There are six cars at Refill's garage. The amount of petrol that each driver buys for his or her car is shown below. Convert each amount to litres, given that 1 gallon = 4.5 litres.
First car, 4 gallons. Second car, 10 gallons. Third car, 6 gallons. Fourth car, 8 gallons. Fifth car, 12 gallons. Sixth car, 2 gallons.

2 There are six cars at Fulltank's garage. The amount of petrol that each driver buys for his or her car is shown below. Convert each amount to gallons given that 1 litre = 0.22 gallons.
First car, 15 litres. Second car, 20 litres. Third car, 35 litres. Fourth car, 50 litres. Fifth car, 60 litres. Sixth car, 45 litres.

Example 13

a A builders' merchant sells 3 cubic metres of sand. If $1 \text{ m}^3 = 1.3 \text{ yd}^3$, convert this volume to cubic yards.

b A builder requires 4 cubic yards of sand. Convert this volume to cubic metres, given that 1 cubic yard = 0.77 cubic metres.

a 1 cubic metre = 1.3 cubic yards, so 3 cubic metres = 3 × 1.3 or 3.9 cubic yards.

b 1 cubic yard = 0.77 cubic metres, so 4 cubic yards = 4 × 0.77 or 3.08 cubic metres.

Exercise 17S

For questions 1–5, use any of the following information:
$$1 \text{ m}^3 = 1.3 \text{ yd}^3 \qquad 1 \text{ yd}^3 = 27 \text{ ft}^3 \qquad 1 \text{ ft}^3 = 6.25 \text{ gallons}$$

For questions 1–3 convert the volume to: **a** cubic yards **b** cubic feet.
1 A gardener removes 7 m^3 of soil.
2 A beer cellar has 30 m^3 of storage space.
3 A warehouse has 40 000 m^3 of storage space.

For questions 4 and 5 convert the quantity to: **a** cubic yards **b** cubic feet **c** gallons.
4 A swimming pool can hold 720 m^3 of water.
5 A filling station has storage capacity for: **i** 200 m^3 of petrol **ii** 64 m^3 of diesel.

For questions 6–10, use any of the following information:
1 gallon = $\frac{4}{25}$ of a cubic foot   1 cubic foot = $\frac{1}{27}$ of a cubic yard
1 cubic yard = 0.77 cubic metres   1 cubic metre = 1000 litres

For questions 6–8 convert the volume to **a** cubic yards **b** cubic metres.
6 A removal van has 8370 cubic feet of storage space.
7 55 350 cubic feet of spoil are removed to bore a pedestrian subway.
8 A water tank in a loft has a volume of 6.75 cubic feet.

For questions 9 and 10 convert the quantity to: **a** cubic feet **b** cubic yards **c** cubic metres **d** litres.
9 A tanker can carry 16 875 gallons of petrol.
10 A railway locomotive has: **i** a fuel tank which holds 810 gallons of diesel **ii** a coolant system which is filled by 40.5 gallons of water.

18 MASS AND WEIGHT

18.1 Understanding units of mass and weight in the metric and imperial systems

Mass in the metric system

In the metric system the units of mass are directly related to the units of capacity. We use grams and kilograms where 1 kilogram = 1000 grams.

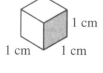

The mass of a litre of water is 1 kilogram, or 1 kg.
The mass of a millilitre of water is 1 gram, or 1 g.

As a millilitre of water takes up the space of a 1 cm cube, it follows that 1 cubic centimetre of water also has a mass of one gram.

For larger masses the unit used is 1 tonne which is 1000 kilograms.

Mass in the imperial system

The most commonly used units of mass in the imperial system are pounds (lb) and ounces (oz). For larger masses tons and sometimes stones (st) and hundredweights (cwt) are also used.

The table for these units is:

```
    16 ounces (oz) = 1 pound (lb)
    14 pounds (lb) = 1 stone (st)
     8 stones (st) or 112 pounds (lb) = 1 hundredweight (cwt)
    20 hundredweights (cwt) or 2240 pounds (lb) = 1 ton
```

18.2 Reading weighing scales

A bag of sugar weighs about 1 kilogram (kg) or 2 pounds (lb).

A small box of chocolates weighs about 200 grams (g) or 8 ounces (oz).

A bag of cement weighs about 25 kilograms (kg) or $\frac{1}{2}$ a hundredweight (cwt) = 56 lb or 4 stone.

A small car weighs about 1 metric tonne (1000 kg) or 1 ton (20 cwt).

A metric tonne is slightly smaller (2205 lb) than an imperial ton (2240 lb).

Most scales record the mass of the object being weighed and often the two words mass and weight are interchanged. Strictly speaking, however, whilst the mass of an object remains the same always, the reading on the scales may change according to where the object is being weighed. For example, a 1 kg bag of sugar weighed on a set of scales on earth would appear to have a mass of less than 1 kg if the same scales were used by an astronaut on the surface of the moon, because the weight would be less there due to the moon's gravity being only $\frac{1}{6}$ of the earth's gravity.

There are four types of weighing scale in common use.

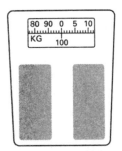

Bathroom scales

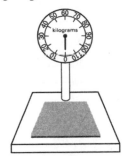

Hospital and wholesale shop scales

Kitchen scales

Digital scales

With the most recent digital (electronic) scales an object is weighed and the weight or mass is shown directly as a number on the display.

With many bathroom scales the weight or mass is shown with an arrow on a dial which has moved from a zero position. The arrow often points to a position between two numbers which are separated by ten divisions.

Example 1

What is the weight shown on this scale?

There are 10 divisions between 34 and 35 and the arrow points at the sixth line. So the scale reads 34.6 kg.

weight in kg

Example 2

What is the weight shown on this scale?

There are five divisions between 60 and 70 so each one represents 2 kg. The arrow points at the third line (i.e. 6 kg), so the scale reads 66 kg.

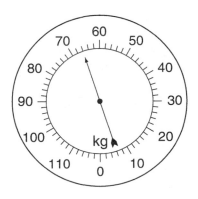

Example 3

What is the weight shown on this scale?

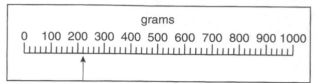

Each main division represents 100 grams or 0.1 kg. There are five divisions between 200 g and 300 g so each one represents 20 g. So the scale reads 220 g or 0.22 kg.

Exercise 18A

Write down the weight shown on each of the following scales.

1

2

3

4
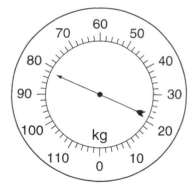

5

6
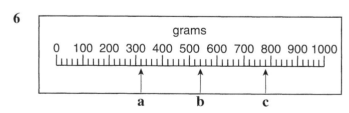

18.3   Converting between units of mass in the metric and imperial systems

Converting metric masses

1 kilogram (kg) = 1000 grams (g)   1 metric tonne = 1000 kilograms (kg)

So to convert kilograms to grams, or tonnes to kilograms, you must multiply by 1000.

To convert grams to kilograms, or kilograms to tonnes, you must divide by 1000.

Example 4

Convert: **a** 5 kilograms to grams   **b** 2000 kilograms to tonnes.

a 5 kilograms = 5 × 1000 grams = 5000 grams
b 2000 kilograms = 2000 ÷ 1000 tonnes = 2 tonnes

Exercise 18B

Copy and complete the table below.

	Tonnes	Kilograms	Grams
1	15		
2	2		
3	9		
4	20		
5		14 000	

	Tonnes	Kilograms	Grams
6		26 000	
7		6000	
8			16 000 000
9			25 000 000
10			7 000 000

Example 5

A bowl has a capacity of 11 000 millilitres. Find each of the
following.

a the capacity of the bowl in litres
b the mass of water which fills the bowl in kilograms
c the mass of water which fill the bowl in grams.

a 11 000 millilitres = 11 000 ÷ 1000 litres = 11 litres
b 11 kilograms, because 1 litre of water has a mass of 1 kilogram
c 11 000 grams, because 1 millilitre of water has a mass of 1 gram

---

Exercise 18C

Copy and complete the table below.

	Capacity of container (litres)	Capacity of container (millilitres)	Mass of water which fills the container (kilograms)	Mass of water which fills the container (grams)
1	8			
2	14			
3		4 000		
4		13 000		
5			23	
6			30	
7				19 000
8				42 000

Converting imperial masses

Example 6

Convert each of the following:

a 2 lb to ounces **b** 5 tons to hundredweight

c 28 lb to stone **d** 32 stone to hundredweight.

a There are 16 oz in 1 lb, so 2 lb = 2 × 16 oz = 32 oz.

b There are 20 cwt in 1 ton, so 5 tons = 5 × 20 cwt = 100 cwt.

c There are 14 lb in 1 stone, so 28 lb = 28 ÷ 14 st = 2 st.

d There are 8 stones in 1 cwt, so 32 st = 32 ÷ 8 cwt = 4 cwt.

Exercise 18D

Copy and complete the table below.

	Tons	Hundredweights	Stones	Pounds	Ounces
1	3				
2		80			
3			1120		
4				4480	
5					17 920

Converting metric masses to imperial masses and vice versa

Example 7

a Theo has a bag which contains 22 ounces of nuts.
Given that 1 ounce = 28 grams, convert this weight to grams.

b A block of ice cream in a cardboard packet weighs 425 grams.
Given that 1 gram = 0.04 (or $\frac{1}{25}$) ounces, convert this weight to ounces.

a 22 ounces = (22 × 28) grams = 616 grams
b 425 grams = (425 × 0.04) ounces = 17 ounces

Exercise 18E

For questions 1–6 convert the weight to grams, given that 1 ounce = 28 grams.

1 A lollipop has a weight of 2 ounces.
2 A jar contains 10 ounces of coffee.
3 A packet contains 12 ounces of sugar.
4 A plastic carton contains 18 ounces of margarine.
5 A packet contains 21 ounces of soap powder.
6 A plastic carton contains 30 ounces of ice cream.

For questions 7–12 convert the weight to ounces, given that 1 gram = 0.04 (or $\frac{1}{25}$) ounces.

7 A tube contains 125 grams of toothpaste.
8 A packet contains 175 grams of 'Wallfiller'.
9 A tin contains 275 grams of cocoa.
10 A packet contains 225 grams of grouting cement.
11 A drum contains 350 grams of salt.
12 A jar contains 500 grams of coffee.

Example 8

a A piano weighs 360 pounds (lb). Convert this weight to kilograms, given that 1 lb = 0.45 kg.

b A sack of potatoes weights 30 kg. Convert this weight to pounds, given that 1 kg = 2.2 lb.

a 360 lb = 360 × 0.45 kg = 162 kg   **b** 30 kg = 30 × 2.2 lb = 66 lb

---

Exercise 18F

In questions 1–6 the weights of the members of Peter's family and his pets are given in pounds.
Convert each of these weights to kilograms, given that 1 lb = 0.45 kg.

1 Peter's sister, 80 lb
2 Peter's dog, 40 lb
3 Peter's older brother, 160 lb
4 Peter's mother, 120 lb
5 Peter's father, 180 lb
6 Peter's younger brother, 60 lb

In questions 7–12 the weights of the members of Jane's family and her pets are given in kilograms.
Convert these weights to pounds, given that 1 kg = 2.2 lb.

7 Jane's baby brother, 15 kg
8 Jane's rabbit, 5 kg
9 Jane's older brother, 75 kg
10 Jane's younger sister, 35 kg
11 Jane's mother, 70 kg
12 Jane's father, 90 kg

19 ANGLES

19.1 Understanding angles as a fraction of a turn and units of degrees

An angle is the way we measure turn or change of direction.

When the wind changes, the weather vane turns to show
the new wind direction.

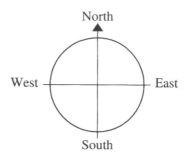

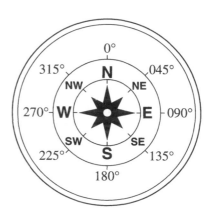

A complete turn is divided into 360 parts called degrees.
    1 complete turn = 360°
    1 half turn = 180°

Example 1

Find the number of degrees of turn when the wind changes in a clockwise direction:
a from N to E   **b** from NE to W   **c** from NW to SE.

a From N to E is a quarter turn.

So N to E = 90°

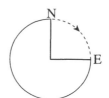

b NE to E = 45°
   E to W = 180°

   So NE to W = 45° + 180°
           = 225°

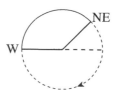

c This is a half turn.
   So NW to SE = 180°

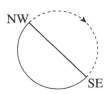

Exercise 19A

Find the number of degrees of turn when the wind changes in a clockwise direction.

1	from N to S	**2**	from S to W	**3**	from S to NW	**4**	from S to E
5	from NE to E	**6**	from NE to S	**7**	from NE to SW	**8**	from SE to N

Example 2

Find the size of the smaller angle between the hands of the clock
when the clock is showing the following times:

a 9 o'clock   **b** 1 o'clock   **c** 8 o'clock.

a The angle is 90°.

b The angle is one-third of 90° = 30°

c The angle = 90° + 30°
          = 120°

Exercise 19B

Find the size of the smaller angle between the hands of a clock when the
clock is showing the following times.

1	3 o'clock	**2**	11 o'clock	**3**	4 o'clock	**4**	10 o'clock
5	2 o'clock	**6**	6 o'clock	**7**	5 o'clock	**8**	7 o'clock

A quarter turn (90°) is called a **right angle**.

An angle that is less than 90° is called an **acute angle**.

An angle that is greater than 90° but less than 180° is called an **obtuse angle**.

A half turn (180°) is called a **straight angle** because it is a straight line.

An angle that is greater than 180° is called a **reflex angle**.

Example 3

This weighing machine at the Post Office can weigh up to 300 grams.

a Find the angle through which the pointer turns when weighing a letter of 50 g and state the type of angle.

b Find the angle through which the pointer turns when weighing a parcel of 150 g and state the type of angle.

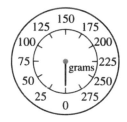

a The pointer moves from 0 to 50.

This is $\frac{50}{300}$ of a complete turn.

$\therefore$ angle $= \frac{50}{300} \times 360° = 60°$.

This is an acute angle.

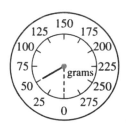

b The pointer moves from 0 to 150.

This is $\frac{150}{300}$ of a complete turn.

$\therefore$ angle $= \frac{150}{300} \times 360° = 180°$

This is a straight angle.

Exercise 19C

This weighing machine can weigh up to 120 kg.

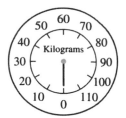

Peter weighs 60 kg.   Julie weighs 40 kg.
John weighs 30 kg.   Anne weighs 20 kg.
Julie's dog Patch weighs 10 kg.

Find the size of the angle through which the pointer turns when the following stand on the machine. State the type of angle.

1 Anne   **2** Patch   **3** John   **4** Julie   **5** Peter
6 Anne and Patch together   **7** John and Patch together
8 Julie and Patch together   **9** Julie and Anne together

Two angles whose sum is 90° are called **complementary** angles, e.g. 20° is the complement of 70°.

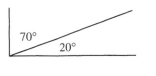

Two angles whose sum is 180° are called **supplementary** angles, e.g. 20° is the supplement of 160°.

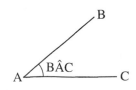

Exercise 19D

Find the complement of the following angles.

1 10°   **2** 30°   **3** 35°   **4** 12°
5 36°   **6** 72°   **7** 66°   **8** 27.5°

Find the supplement of the following angles.

9   30°   **10** 40°   **11** 90°   **12** 170°
13 5°   **14** 15°   **15** 155°   **16** 97.5°

Naming angles

If two straight lines AB and AC meet at A as shown they form an acute angle BAC which is written BÂC or CÂB.

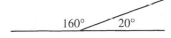

In the diagram, the two straight lines XY and XZ meet at X and form an obtuse angle YX̂Z or ZX̂Y.

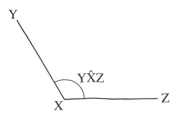

Example 4

Using three letters, name the angles marked a, b, c.

$a = \hat{QRS}$ (or $\hat{SRQ}$)
$b = \hat{PMS}$ (or $\hat{SMP}$)
$c = \hat{QPR}$ (or $\hat{RPQ}$)
    (or $\hat{QPM}$)
    (or $\hat{MPQ}$)

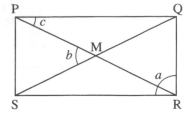

Exercise 19E

Using three letters, name the marked angle or angles in each of the following diagrams:

1

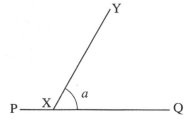

2

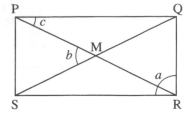

3

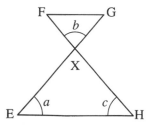

4

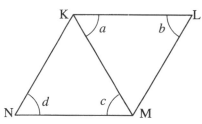

5

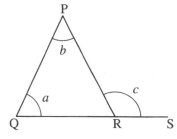

6

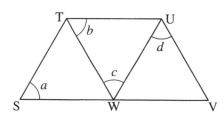

7

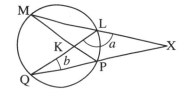

8

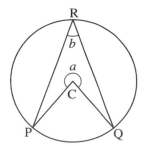

19.2   Using a protractor to measure and draw angles and triangles

Measuring angles

To measure an angle you need a protractor. The example below shows how to use one. AB shows the base line and O is the centre of the protractor.

Example 5

Measure the size of PÔR.

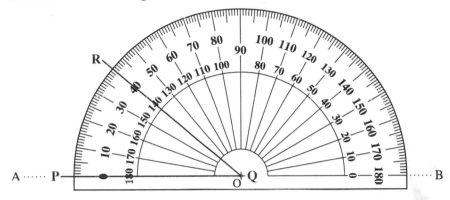

Place the protractor on the angle so that O is on Q as shown, and OA lies on QP.

Where the line QR cuts the scale, read off the angle on the scale starting from 0° at P.

PÔR = 40°.

Example 6

Measure the size of LM̂N.

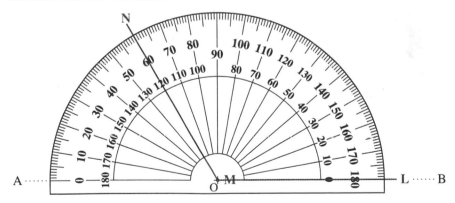

Place the protractor on on the angle so that O is on M as shown and OB lies on ML.

Where the line MN cuts the scale, read off the angle on the scale starting from 0° at L.

LM̂N = 120°.

Exercise 19F

1

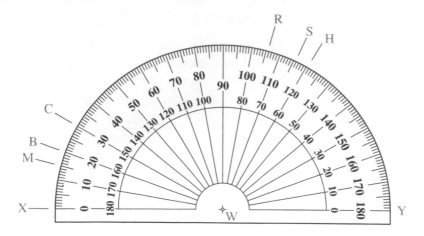

Find these angles on the diagram.

a XŴB	**b** XŴC	**c** XŴH	**d** XŴM	**e** XŴR	**f** XŴS
g YŴH	**h** YŴC	**i** YŴB	**j** YŴS	**k** YŴR	**l** YŴM

2

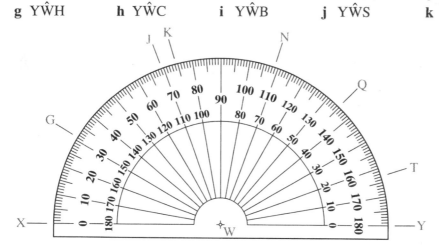

Find these angles on the diagram.

a XŴG	**b** XŴJ	**c** XŴK	**d** XŴN	**e** XŴQ	**f** XŴT
g YŴQ	**h** YŴN	**i** YŴK	**j** YŴJ	**k** YŴG	

Exercise 19G

With a protractor, measure each of the following angles.

1

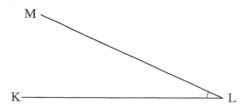

2

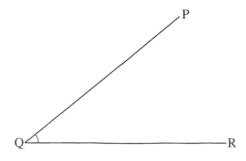

3

4

5

6

7

8

9

10

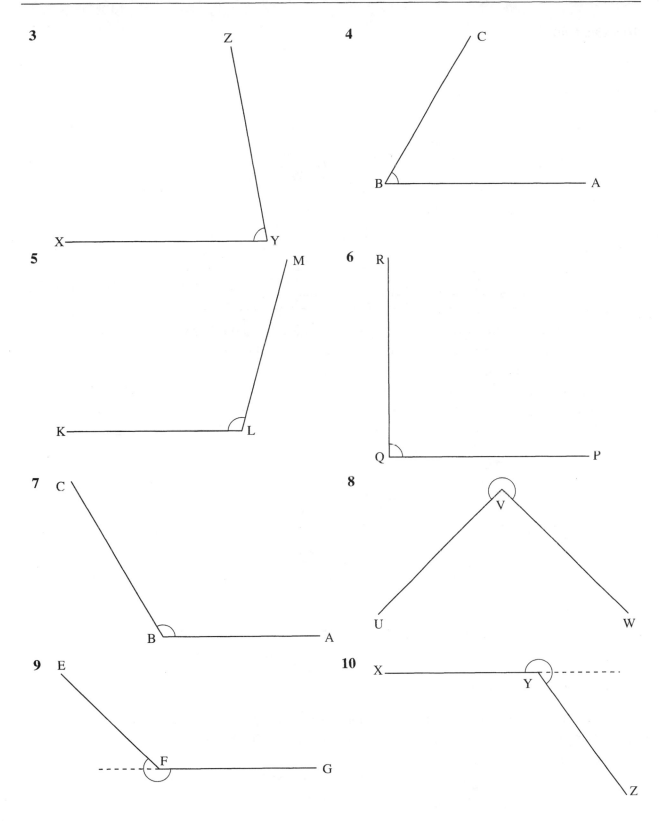

Drawing angles

Example 7

Using a protractor, draw **a** AB̂C = 50°   **b** XŶZ = 170°.

a

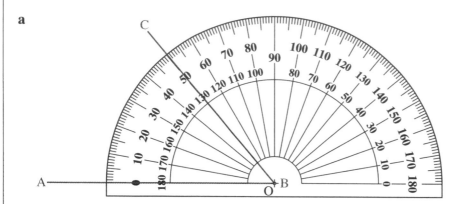

Draw the straight line AB. Make it 6 cm long to extend beyond the protractor.
Place the protractor on the paper with its base line on the line AB and
its centre point O on B as shown.
Mark the point C at 50° on the scale starting from 0° at A.
Join BC, and the angle 50° is now drawn complete.

b

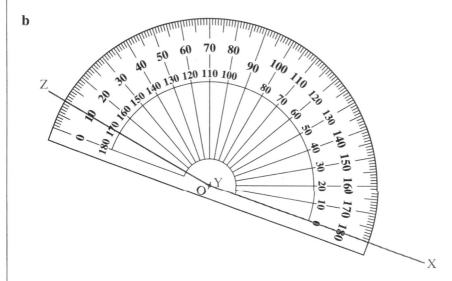

Draw the straight line XY. Make it 6 cm long to extend beyond the protractor.
Place the protractor on the paper with its base line on the line XY and
its centre point O on Y as shown.
Mark the point Z at 170° on the scale starting from 0° at X.
Join YZ and the angle of 170° is now drawn complete.

Exercise 19H

For each question, draw a line AB 6 cm long. Then draw the angle.

1   Draw A$\hat{\text{B}}$C equal to 60°.   2   Draw A$\hat{\text{B}}$C equal to 45°.
3   Draw B$\hat{\text{A}}$C equal to 90°.   4   Draw B$\hat{\text{A}}$C equal to 25°.
5   Draw A$\hat{\text{B}}$C equal to 120°. 6   Draw A$\hat{\text{B}}$C equal to 135°.
7   Draw B$\hat{\text{A}}$C equal to 145°. 8   Draw B$\hat{\text{A}}$C equal to 95°.

Example 8

Draw a triangle with AB = 5 cm, $\hat{\text{A}}$ = 50° and $\hat{\text{B}}$ = 70°.
Measure the third angle.

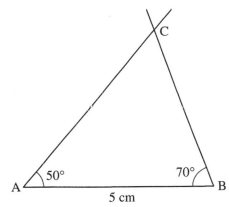

By measurement, $\hat{\text{C}}$ = 60°.

Exercise 19J

For each question, draw the triangle ABC from the details given. Then measure the angle C with a protractor.

1   AB = 5 cm, $\hat{\text{A}}$ = 40°, $\hat{\text{B}}$ = 60°   2   AB = 5 cm, $\hat{\text{A}}$ = 60°, $\hat{\text{B}}$ = 90°
3   AB = 5 cm, $\hat{\text{A}}$ = 60°, $\hat{\text{B}}$ = 60°   4   AB = 6 cm, $\hat{\text{A}}$ = 40°, $\hat{\text{B}}$ = 40°
5   AB = 6 cm, $\hat{\text{A}}$ = 50°, $\hat{\text{B}}$ = 100°   6   AB = 6 cm, $\hat{\text{A}}$ = 20°, $\hat{\text{B}}$ = 110°

20 RECOGNISING AND DRAWING COMMON TWO-DIMENSIONAL AND THREE-DIMENSIONAL SHAPES

20.1 Recognising common two-dimensional shapes and their properties

Any shape made up entirely of straight lines is called a polygon. When a shape has all its edges the same length and all its angles the same size it is called a regular polygon. Some well-known regular polygons are illustrated.

A **triangle** is any shape with 3 edges.
(Tri- is the Latin name for three.)

A **quadrilateral** is any shape with 4 edges.
(Quad- is the Latin name for four.)

Regular triangle
(equilateral triangle)

Regular quadrilateral
(square)

A **pentagon** is any shape with 5 edges. (Pent- is the Latin name for five.)

Regular pentagon

A **hexagon** is any shape with 6 edges. (Hex- is the Latin name for six.)

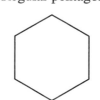

Regular hexagon

A **heptagon** is any shape with 7 edges. (Hept- is the Latin name for seven.)

Regular heptagon

An **octagon** is any shape with 8 edges. (Oct- is the Latin name for eight.)

Regular octagon

Exercise 20A

Use one of the above names to describe each shape drawn below. State also if any shape is regular.

1

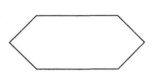

2

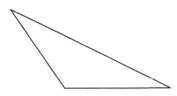

3

4

5

6

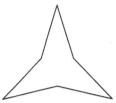

Triangles

Triangles can be classified in three ways by their angles.

i A triangle may be **acute**-angled (if all three angles are less than 90°).

Acute-angled triangle

ii A triangle may be **obtuse**-angled (if one angle is bigger than 90°).

Obtuse-angled triangle

iii A triangle may be **right**-angled (if one angle is equal to 90°).

Right-angled triangle

Triangles can also be classified according to their symmetry (or side lengths).

i A triangle may be scalene, which means that no angles or sides are equal and therefore the triangle has no symmetry.

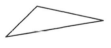

Scalene triangle

ii A triangle may be isosceles, which means that one pair of angles and one pair of sides are equal and therefore the triangle has one line of symmetry.

Line of symmetry

Isosceles triangle

iii A triangle may be equilateral, which means that all three angles and all three sides are equal and therefore the triangle has three lines of symmetry.

Equilateral triangle

There are seven different types of triangle

i   scalene and acute-angled
ii   scalene and obtuse-angled
iii scalene and right-angled
iv isosceles and acute-angled
v   isosceles and obtuse-angled
vi isosceles and right-angled
     (The three angles are 45°, 45° and 90°.)

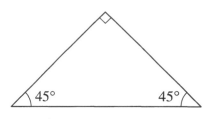

vii equilateral. (The three angles are all equal to 60°.)

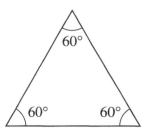

Exercise 20B

(Where asked to classify a triangle use the list given above.)

1 **a** Measure the lengths of AB, BC, AC, AD, BD and CD.
    b Measure the sizes of BÂC, BĈA, AB̂C, AB̂D, AD̂B, BD̂C and DB̂C.
    c Classify the triangles ABC, ABD and BCD, given that AB̂C is a right angle.

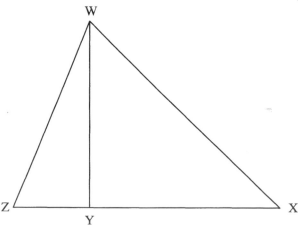

2 **a** Measure the lengths of WX, XY, YW, WZ, XZ and YZ.
    b Classify the triangles WXY, WZY and WXZ, given that WŶX and WŶZ are right angles.

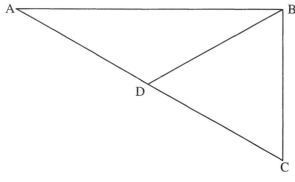

Quadrilaterals

Several kinds of quadrilaterals are illustrated below.

A **square** has 4 right angles and 4 edges the same length

A **rectangle** has 4 right angles.

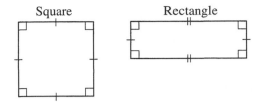

A **rhombus** has 4 edges the same length.

A **parallelogram** has two pairs of opposite edges which are parallel.

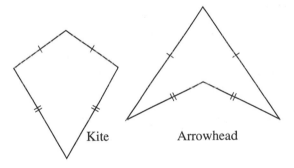

A **kite** has two pairs of adjacent edges (edges which are 'next door' to each other) which are equal in length.

This **arrowhead** has the same properties as a kite, but one of the angles is a reflex angle (an angle bigger than 180°).

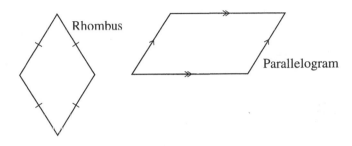

A **trapezium** has one pair of opposite edges which are parallel.

An **isosceles trapezium** is a trapezium whose non-parallel edges are equal in length.

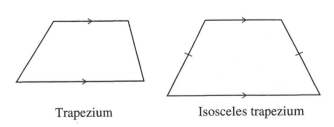

If all 4 angles of a quadrilateral are of different size and all four edges are of different length, the figure is known as an **irregular quadrilateral**.

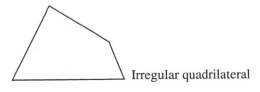

Exercise 20C

(Where asked to classify a quadrilateral use the list given above.)

1

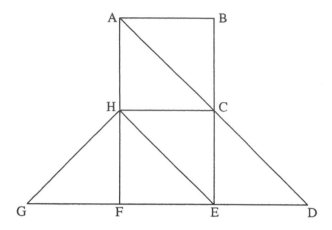

2

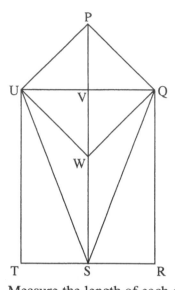

Measure the length of each of the edges and classify the quadrilaterals:

a ABCH	**b** ABEF
c HCDE	**d** ABEH
e HCDG	**f** ADEH

Measure the length of each of the edges and classify the quadrilaterals:

a PQWV	**b** UQRT
c UVST	**d** PQSU
e UWQS	**f** UPST
g UWST	

Symmetry

As we have seen in a simple way with triangles, some shapes are symmetrical. A shape can either have a line (or lines) of symmetry, or it can have rotational symmetry or both types. The shape on the right has one line of symmetry. It can be folded in half so that one half fits exactly on the other half.

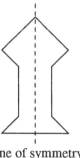
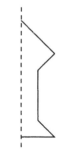

Line of symmetry

The shape on the right has rotational symmetry of order 4.
If it is rotated about its centre it will fit on to itself exactly 4 times in a complete turn.

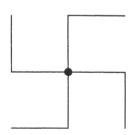

The shape illustrated on the next page has rotational symmetry of order 3. If it is rotated about its centre it will fit on to itself exactly 3 times in a complete turn.

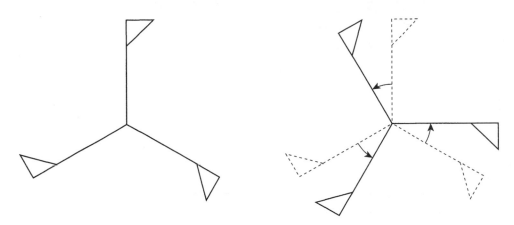

Note   we do not use the term 'rotational symmetry of order 1' for irregular figures.

Example 1

On each diagram mark in any lines of symmetry and state the order of rotational symmetry.

a

b

a Rotational symmetry of order 4.

b Rotational symmetry of order 5.

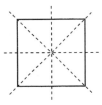   

Exercise 20D

Copy each diagram and mark on any lines of symmetry. State also the order of rotational symmetry.

1

2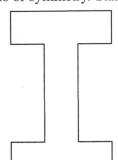

3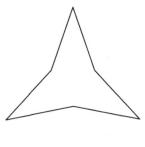

(continued)

4 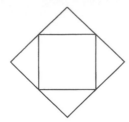   **5** 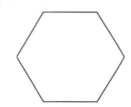   **6**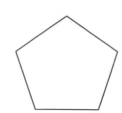

Exercise 20E

Draw a copy of each of the following quadrilaterals and mark on any lines
of symmetry. State also the order of rotational symmetry.

1 Rectangle	**2** Rhombus	**3** Square	**4** Kite
5 Isosceles trapezium	**6** Arrowhead	**7** Parallelogram	

Example 2

How many quadrilateral shapes can you
make from three isosceles, right-angled
triangles?
Illustrate your answers.

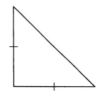

Two quadrilateral shapes can be made from three isosceles, right-angled triangles.

a Trapezium   **b** Isosceles trapezium

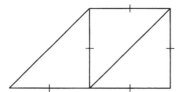 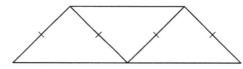

Exercise 20F

What different quadrilateral shapes can you make using each of the following?
Illustrate your answers.

1 Two equilateral triangles	**2** Two isosceles, right-angled triangles
3 Two non-isosceles, right-angled triangles	**4** Three non-isosceles, right-angled triangles
5 Four equilateral triangles	**6** Four isosceles, right-angled triangles

20.2 Drawing two-dimensional shapes

(including the triangle, square, rectangle and circle)

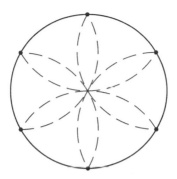
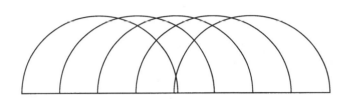

You will need a pair of compasses for this section. Make sure the pencil is sharp and that both parts of the compasses are the same length.

Example 3

Draw a circle of radius 4 cm.

Mark the centre of the circle. Open the compasses so that the distance between the pin end and the pencil is 4 cm.
Place the pin end on the centre of the circle.
Holding the compasses at the top, swing them round so that the pencil traces out the circumference of the circle.

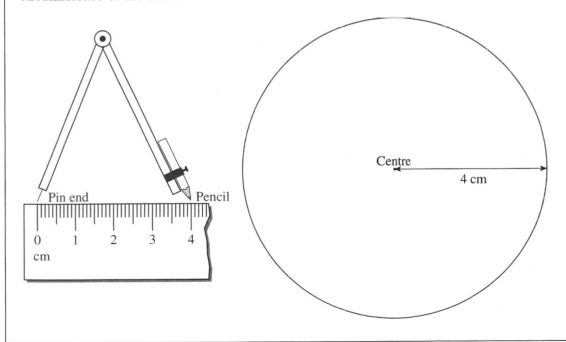

Exercise 20G

1 Draw a set of circles from the same centre with radii of:
   a 3 cm   **b** 5 cm   **c** 6 cm   **d** 8 cm   **e** 9 cm

2 Draw a circle of radius 4 cm. Take any point **i** on its circumference as the centre and draw, with the same radius, a part circle until it meets the original one again. Taking this new point **ii** as the new centre draw another part circle which starts at point **i**, goes through the original centre and finishes at point **iii**. Repeat the above procedure starting at points **iii**, **iv**, **v** and **vi** until you have completed the flower pattern illustrated.

3 Three equal circles touching each other form a triangular arrangement. Find a way of drawing this pattern and find the centre of a larger circle which passes through the centre of each of the three circles.

4 Repeat question 3 for four circles which touch each other and form a square arrangement.

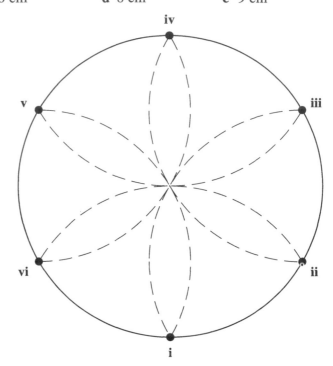

Drawing triangles

Example 4

Use a compass and ruler to draw a triangle with edges of length 5 cm, 4 cm and 3 cm.

First use your ruler to draw a line AB which is 5 cm long.
Open your compasses to 4 cm and with the centre at A draw an arc of a circle as shown in the diagram.

Open your compasses to 3 cm and now with the centre at B draw a second arc of a circle to cut the first arc at the point C. Join AC and BC.

Measure the length of AC and BC to check that they are 4 cm and 3 cm respectively. Triangle ABC is the required triangle.

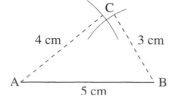

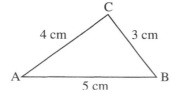

Exercise 20H

Use the method in Example 4 to draw the following triangles.
For each case classify the triangle you have drawn.

1 PQ = 11 cm, PR = 10 cm, QR = 8 cm   **2** XY = 6 cm, XZ = 5 cm, YZ = 5 cm
3 UV = 10 cm, UW = 8 cm, VW = 6 cm   **4** XY = 12 cm, XZ = 7 cm, YZ = 7 cm

Drawing squares and rectangles

If you have centimetre squared paper
drawing squares and rectangles is very easy
because you have right angles already drawn
for you. If you have to draw a rectangle on
plain paper, however, it helps if you have
either of the set squares illustrated.

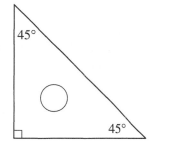

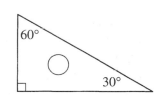

Example 5

Use a set square and a ruler to draw a rectangle
with edge lengths of 5 cm and 3 cm.

First use your ruler to draw a line AB which is 5 cm
long.

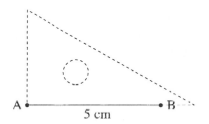

Now place one edge of your set square along the line AB so that the
other edge of the rectangle will start at the point A as shown in the
diagram.

From A draw a line along the edge of the set square.

Mark a point D on this line which is 3 cm from A.

Repeat the above by drawing a line up from B.

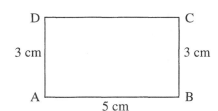

Mark a point C on this second line which is 3 cm from B. Now join DC.

Measure the length of DC as a check. It should be 5 cm.
Rectangle ABCD is the required rectangle.

Exercise 20J

Use the method in Example 5 to draw the following rectangles or squares.

1   6 cm by 4 cm   **2**   5 cm by 5 cm   **3**   9 cm by 4.5 cm   **4**   6 cm by 3.5 cm

20.3   Recognising common three-dimensional shapes and their properties
(including nets of common three-dimensional shapes)

A **cube** has 6 faces each of which is an identical square.

A **cuboid** has 6 faces. Its opposite faces are identical rectangles.

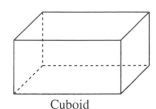

Cube   Cuboid

The **triangular prism** shown has a rectangular base, two identical triangular ends and two rectangular sloping sides.

The **pyramid** shown has a square base and four identical triangular faces.

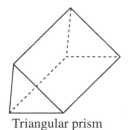

Triangular prism   Pyramid

A **cylinder** has two circular faces with the same radius and one curved face.

A **cone** has one circular face and one curved face.

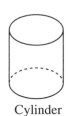

Cylinder   Cone

A **sphere** has a simple curved face.

Sphere

Nets of three-dimensional shapes
Three-dimensional shapes can be made from nets.

The diagram shows the net of a cube.

From the net it can easily be seen that the cube has six faces.

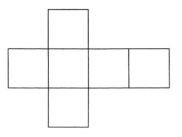

Exercise 20K

Draw to scale each of the following nets. Cut out the net and construct either a cube or a cuboid. (The scale is 1 square equals 1 centimetre and glue tabs are included on the nets.)

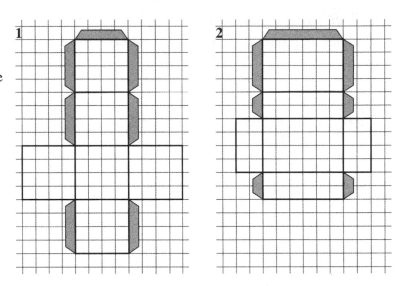

Exercise 20L

Draw to scale each of the following nets. Cut out the net and construct either a triangular prism or a pyramid. (The scale is 1 square = 1 centimetre and glue tabs are included on the nets.) Measure the vertical height of each solid.

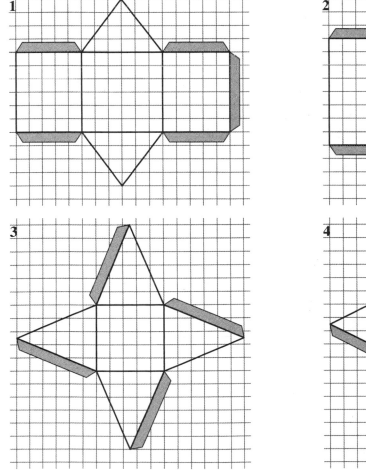

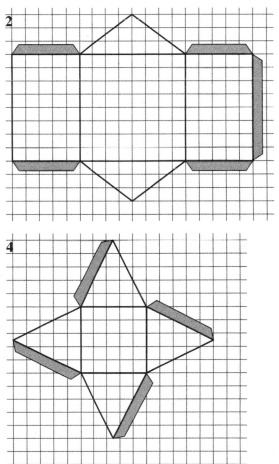

20.4 Drawing three-dimensional shapes

(including cube, cuboid, pyramid, cylinder, sphere and cone)

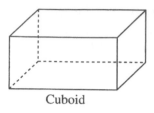

Cuboid

Making two-dimensional drawings of three-dimensional objects can be very useful indeed. Example 6 shows how this is done for a very simple three-dimensional object, namely a cuboid.

Example 6

Make a two-dimensional drawing of a cuboid of length 8 cm, width 2 cm and height 3 cm.

i Draw a parallelogram to represent the base. The side representing the length is drawn to scale, but the side representing the width is conveniently drawn to a length of 2 square diagonals rather than 2 real centimetres.

ii Draw the vertical edges to scale.

iii Draw another parallelogram for the top.

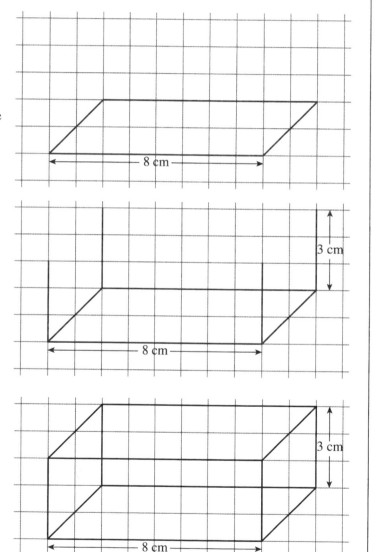

Exercise 20M

Make a two-dimensional drawing of each of the following on squared paper.

1 A cuboid of length 4 cm, width 3cm and height 2 cm
2 A cuboid of length 5 cm, width 3 cm and height 2 cm
3 A cube of side length 3 cm
4 A cube of side length 2 cm

Example 7

Make a two-dimensional drawing of a triangular prism of length 4 cm and with a triangular end as shown.

i Make an accurate copy of the triangular end.

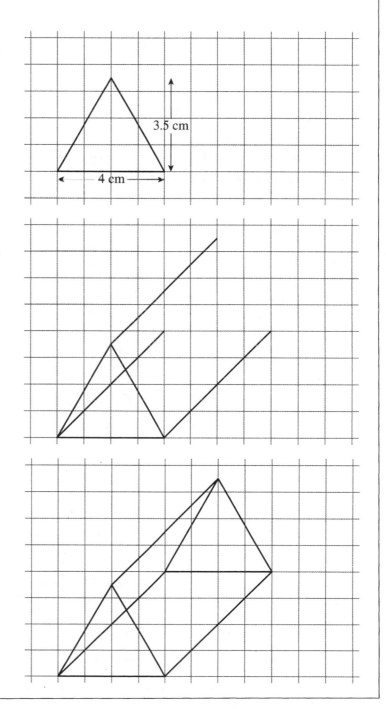

ii Draw the three 'length' edges as 4 square diagonals rather than 4 real centimetres.

iii Draw another trianglar end at the back.

Exercise 20N

Make a two-dimensional drawing of each of the following triangular
prisms on squared paper.

1   Length 3 cm, face as illustrated.
2   Length 2 cm, face as illustrated.
3   Length 3 cm, face as illustrated.

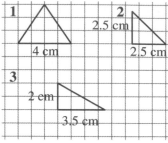

Example 8

Make a two-dimensional drawing of a square-based pyramid which
has a base length 4 cm and a vertical height of 3 cm.

i   Draw a rhombus for the base, by
    by using exactly the same method
    as that for the base in Example 1.

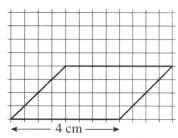

ii Draw in the diagonals to locate
    the centre of the base.

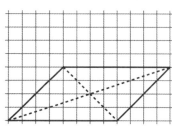

iii Draw in the vertical height.

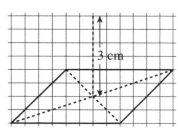

iv Draw in the four slant edges.

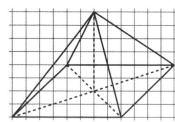

Exercise 20P

Make a two-dimensional drawing of each of the following square pyramids.

1   Base length 4 cm, vertical height 5 cm
2   Base length 2 cm, vertical height 4 cm

Example 9

Make a two-dimensional drawing of a cylinder of radius 2 cm and height 4 cm.

i   Draw an ellipse (or oval) shape for the circular base. Make its 'larger' radius equal to the given radius, but make its smaller radius only half as much.

ii   Draw in two vertical lines of length equal to the height.

iii   Draw in another ellipse for the top.

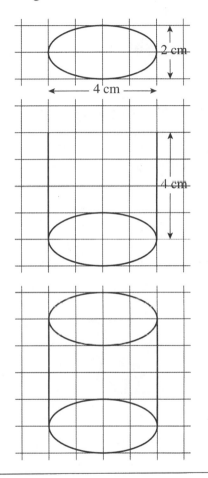

Exercise 20Q

Make a two-dimensional drawing of each of the following cylinders on squared paper.

1   Radius = 2 cm, height = 3 cm
2   Radius = 4 cm, height = 5 cm

Many three-dimensional objects can conveniently be drawn two-dimensionally on isometric paper.

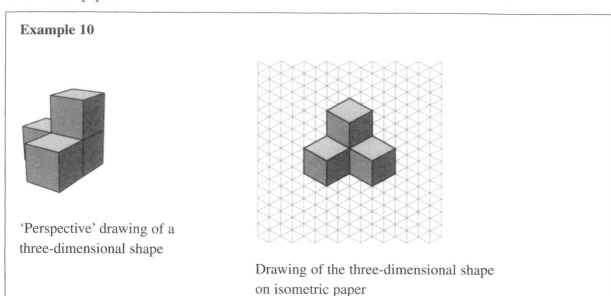

Example 10

'Perspective' drawing of a three-dimensional shape

Drawing of the three-dimensional shape on isometric paper

Exercise 20R

Make a drawing of each of the following three-dimensional shapes on isometric paper.

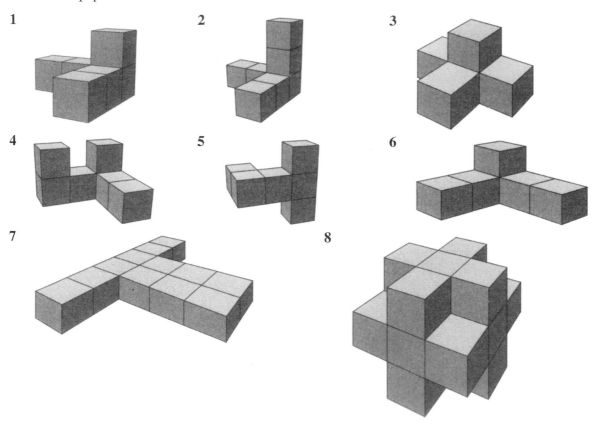

1

2

3

4

5

6

7

8

20.5 Using the theorem of Pythagoras to find lengths in right-angled triangles and rectangles

Over 2000 years ago a Greek mathematician found a way of finding the length of the third side of a right-angled triangle when the lengths of the other two sides were known.

Pythagoras discovered that the areas of squares drawn on the two shorter edges of a right-angled triangle, when added together, were the same as the area of the square drawn on the longest side.

In the first diagram (i) the area of each of the two smaller shaded squares is 4 cm².

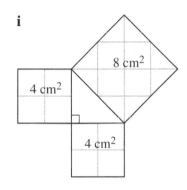

The area of the larger square is made up of 4 small squares and 8 half squares or 8 cm².

In the second diagram (ii) the areas of the two smaller squares are 4 cm² and 9 cm². The area of the larger square is made up of 1 small square plus four triangles identical to the original triangle.

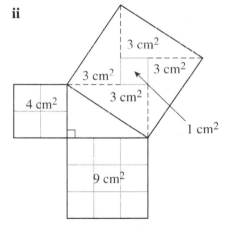

Each of these four triangles is half of a rectangle which is 3 cm by 2 cm, so each has an area of $\frac{1}{2} \times 3 \times 2$ cm² = 3 cm².

The area of the larger square is thus $(1 + 4 \times 3)$ cm² or 13 cm².

The area of the two smaller squares added together is $(4 + 9)$ cm² = 13 cm².

The result that Pythagoras discovered can be summarised as follows:

Area of square on edge c cm = Area of square on edge a cm
                                    + Area of square on edge b cm

or:

$c \times c = a \times a + b \times b$
which can also be written as $c^2 = a^2 + b^2$

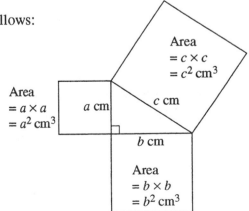

Example 11

Use the theorem of Pythagoras to find the length of the longest edge in a right-angled triangle if the lengths of the shorter edges are 3 cm and 4 cm.

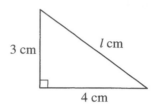

Area of the square on the long edge is $(l \times l)$ cm^2

Areas of the squares on the other two edges are (3×3) cm^2 and (4×4) cm^2.

So, using the theorem of Pythagoras: $\quad l \times l = 3 \times 3 + 4 \times 4$

$$\text{so} \quad l^2 = 9 + 16 = 25$$

$$\text{If} \quad l^2 = 25 \text{ then } l = \sqrt{25} = 5$$

The length of the longer edge is therefore 5 cm.

Exercise 20S

For questions 1–4 find the length of AC, the longest side in a right-angled triangle.

1 AB = 8 cm, BC = 15 cm

2 AB = 20 cm, BC = 21 cm

3 AB = 9 cm, BC = 40 cm

4 AB = 24 cm, BC = 70 cm

5 Find the length of **a** the diagonal of the rectangle and **b** the side length of the rhombus.

a

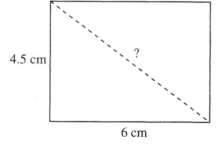

b

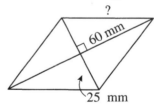

6 Find the side lengths of the kite.

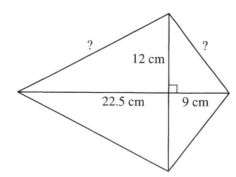

Example 12

The longest edge of a right-angled triangle is 13 cm in length. If one of the shorter edges is 5 cm long, use the theorem of Pythagoras to find the length of the third edge.

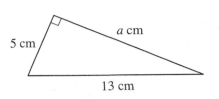

Area of square on the longest edge is (13×13) cm^2 = 169 cm^2

Area of square on one of the shorter edges is (5×5) cm^2 = 25 cm^2

Area of square on the third edge is $(a \times a)$ cm^2 = a^2 cm^2

So, by using the theorem of Pythagoras $169 = 25 + a^2$

so $169 - 25 = a^2$

so $a^2 = 144$

therefore $a = \sqrt{144} = 12$

The length of the third edge is therefore 12 cm.

Exercise 20T

For questions 1–4 find the length of QR.

1   PR = 20 cm, PQ = 16 cm
2   PR = 34 cm, PQ = 16 cm
3   PR = 53 cm, PQ = 28 cm
4   PR = 12.5 m, PQ = 7.5 m

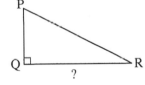

For questions 5–8 find the length of LM.

5   LN = 26.9 cm, MN = 6.9 cm
6   LN = 55.4 mm, MN = 50.4 mm
7   LN = 22.1 mm, MN = 2.1 mm
8   LN = 6.5 m, MN = 5.6 m

9   The diagram shows a 'roll a coin' chute at a fete. Find its vertical height.

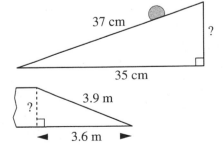

10   The ramp at the end of a railway station platform is 3.9 m in length. If its horizontal length is 3.6 m, what is the height of the platform?

21 CLASSIFYING AND GROUPING DATA

21.1 Using lists and tables

We live in a world where we are surrounded by information (or data). This information is presented in many different ways, in supermarkets, in newspapers, on television, in opinion polls, as well as in offices and factories. It may be in the form of a list, a table, or some type of diagram or graph. The data is used to convey a message and it is important for us to understand how this information is collected and how to interpret correctly whether the message conveyed is accurate or not.

Discrete data

Information collected in a survey may be in the form of individual items of data, for example, the colours, or the number of doors, of different cars. This type of information is called **discrete** data. However, information such as a set of lengths, or a set of times, where the measurements are made on a continuous scale, is called **continuous** data.

Example 1

Traffic surveys are often carried out at junctions and roundabouts to collect data so that the design can be improved to minimise delays. Car manufacturers also use information on make of car, body shape (saloon, hatchback or estate), colour, two- or four-door model, and number of occupants. Melissa carried out a traffic survey. Here is her observation sheet.

	Make of car	Body shape (S, H or E)	Colour	Doors	Number of occupants
1	Rover	S	red	4	1
2	Cavalier	H	red	4	1
3	Ford	E	blue	4	5
4	Volvo	E	blue	4	1
5	Rover	H	green	4	1
6	Rover	H	blue	4	1
7	Cavalier	S	red	4	4
8	Rover	S	green	2	1
9	Cavalier	S	white	2	1
10	Ford	H	white	2	2

(**Note** she made 10 entries in her table.)

a Use the details from Melissa's survey to complete each of the following frequency tables.
  (Frequency means how often the event has occurred.)

b Only three cars had more than one occupant. Suggest a reason for each of the three cars.

Frequency tables for Melissa's survey

Make	Cavalier	Ford	Rover	Volvo
Frequency				

Body shape	saloon	hatchback	estate
Frequency			

Colour	blue	green	red	white
Frequency				

Number of doors	2	4
Frequency		

Number of occupants	1	2	3	4	5
Frequency					

When completed, the frequency tables for Melissa's survey appear as follows:

a

Make	Cavalier	Ford	Rover	Volvo
Frequency	3	2	4	1

Body shape	saloon	hatchback	estate
Frequency	4	4	2

Colour	blue	green	red	white
Frequency	3	2	3	2

Number of doors	2	4
Frequency	3	7

Number of occupants	1	2	3	4	5
Frequency	7	1	0	1	1

b Car 3 has five occupants. It is probably a family.
  Car 7 has four occupants. It could be a family, or four business
  people or two couples.
  Car 10 has two occupants. It could be two friends or two
  work colleagues.

Exercise 21A

1 The form captain of class 11B has made out an observation sheet about the 24 boys in his class.

Pupil	Colour of hair	Sports option	How he travels to school
Julian	Dark	Rugby	By bus
Ronnie	Blond	Football	Walks
Wayne	Dark	Football	Cycles
Martyn	Ginger	Cross-country	Walks
Ayo	Blond	Football	By bus
Jisanne	Dark	Rugby	Walks
Josiah	Blond	Rugby	Walks
Marlon	Ginger	Cross-country	By train
Jordan	Blond	Football	By bus
Marcus	Dark	Rugby	Cycles
George	Dark	Cross-country	Walks
Bernard	Ginger	Football	Walks
Tony	Ginger	Cross-country	Cycles
Bobbie	Blond	Rugby	By train
Sunil	Dark	Football	Walks
Sanjay	Blond	Rugby	By bus
Nishil	Ginger	Cross-country	Walks
Asif	Blond	Football	Cycles
Arthur	Dark	Cross-country	Walks
William	Dark	Football	By bus
Thomas	Ginger	Rugby	Walks
Derek	Dark	Cross-country	Cycles
John	Blond	Football	Walks
Geoffrey	Dark	Rugby	By bus

Copy and complete the following frequency tables.

Colour of hair	Dark	Blond	Ginger
Frequency			

Sports option	Football	Rugby	Cross-country
Frequency			

Transport to school	Walks	Cycles	By bus	By train
Frequency				

2 The form captain of class 10C has made out an observation sheet about the 20 girls in her class.

Pupil	Colour of eyes	Sports option	How she travels to school
Jean	Dark	Netball	Walks
Barbara	Blue	Hockey	Cycles
Rita	Green	Netball	By bus
Suzanne	Dark	Lacrosse	By train
Candace	Blue	Netball	By bus
Shani	Green	Lacrosse	Cycles
Tnisha	Blue	Netball	Walks
Anne	Dark	Hockey	By train
Margaret	Blue	Netball	By bus
Nicola	Green	Lacrosse	Cycles
Diane	Dark	Hockey	Walks
Laura	Blue	Netball	Walks
Patricia	Green	Hockey	By bus
Gillian	Dark	Netball	Cycles
Jane	Dark	Lacrosse	Walks
Kanika	Blue	Hockey	Cycles
Afiya	Green	Netball	Walks
Eshe	Blue	Lacrosse	By train
Natalie	Blue	Hockey	Walks
Joanna	Dark	Netball	Walks

Copy and complete the following frequency tables.

Colour of eyes	Dark	Blue	Green
Frequency			

Sports option	Netball	Hockey	Lacrosse
Frequency			

Transport to school	Walks	Cycles	By bus	By train
Frequency				

3 Fifteen children on an excursion each bought a sandwich, a packet of crisps and a drink from a set of vending machines. Their supervisor made out the observation sheet which is shown below.

Name	Filling (sandwich)	Flavour (crisps)	Drink
Sally	Cheese	Plain	Coffee
Kate	Ham	Cheese and onion	Lemonade
Janet	Egg	Bovril	Orange squash
Jodie	Cheese	Cheese and onion	Coffee
Elaine	Egg	Cheese and onion	Lemonade
Sharon	Tomato	Plain	Orange squash
Samantha	Ham	Cheese and onion	Tea
Mumbi	Cheese	Plain	Lemonade
Peter	Egg	Cheese and onion	Lemonade
Matthew	Ham	Cheese and onion	Coffee
Bradley	Egg	Bovril	Orange squash
Adam	Tomato	Plain	Coffee
Richard	Egg	Salt and vinegar	Coffee
Sanjay	Cheese	Plain	Lemonade
Sunil	Egg	Cheese and onion	Coffee

Copy and complete the following frequency tables.

Sandwich filling	Cheese	Ham	Egg	Tomato
Frequency				

Flavour (crisps)	Plain	Bovril	Salt and vinegar	Cheese and onion
Frequency				

Drink	Tea	Coffee	Lemonade	Orange squash
Frequency				

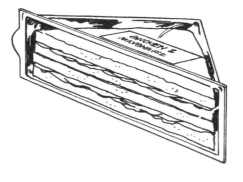

Grouped data

When we are dealing with large quantities of information, such as the heights (or weights) of a large number of children, it is often helpful to group this information into class intervals covering a range of heights (or weights). In these cases the frequency will be the number of heights (or weights) that occurs in a particular class interval. Usually it is a good idea first to rewrite the data in ascending order.

The heights (correct to the nearest cm) and weights (correct to the nearest kg) of 20 children in a class were collected.

Child	Height (cm)	Weight (kg)
1	146	42
2	152	46
3	137	39
4	142	41
5	159	51
6	143	47
7	154	43
8	155	48
9	161	53
10	129	35

Child	Height (cm)	Weight (kg)
11	138	37
12	142	46
13	149	42
14	153	45
15	158	51
16	142	47
17	147	43
18	135	38
19	146	45
20	158	53

Example 2

Write: **a** the heights **b** the weights as lists in ascending order.

a 129, 135, 137, 138, 142, 142, 142, 143, 146, 146, 147, 149, 152, 153, 154, 155, 158, 158, 159 and 161 cm.

b 35, 37, 38, 39, 41, 42, 42, 43, 43, 45, 45, 46, 46, 47, 47, 48, 51, 51, 53 and 53 kg.

Example 3

Using a class interval of: **a** 10 cm for the heights **b** 10 kg for the weights, show the information in Example 2 on frequency tables.

a

Height	120–129 cm	130–139 cm	140–149 cm	150–159 cm	160–169 cm
Frequency	1	3	8	7	1

b

Weight	30–39 kg	40–49 kg	50–59 kg
Frequency	4	12	4

Example 4

Using a class interval of: **a** 5 cm for the heights   **b** 5 kg for the weights,
show the above information on frequency tables.

a

Height	125–129 cm	130–134 cm	135–139 cm	140–144 cm	145–149 cm	150–154 cm	155–159 cm	160–164 cm
Frequency	1	0	3	4	4	3	4	1

b

Weight	35–39 kg	40–44 kg	45–49 kg	50–54 kg
Frequency	4	5	7	4

Exercise 21B

1 Eighteen children took part in an archery contest where they shot
three arrows each. Their scores were as follows.

Derek	11	Leslie	13	Judith	14
Carl	6	Brian	25	Lorraine	23
Sunil	1	William	8	Candace	15
Sanjay	19	Shani	18	Laura	13
Raymond	12	Joanna	11	Mumbi	3
Nishil	21	Elaine	16	Wambui	9

a Write down the above scores in ascending order.
b Copy and complete the frequency table below.

Score	0–4	5–9	10–14	15–19	20–24	25–29
Frequency						

2 The league points obtained by a football team over 12 seasons were as follows.

1985:52   1986:38   1987:47   1988:44   1989:42   1990:65
1991:55   1992:48   1993:39   1994:45   1995:56   1996:63

a Write down the above numbers in ascending order.
b Copy and complete the frequency table below.

Number of points	30–39	40–49	50–59	60–69
Frequency				

3 A rugby club's record over twelve matches was as follows.

Win 15–6   Win 24–12   Win 36–20   Lose 5–22   Win 32–20   Win 35–15
Lose 27–41   Lose 21–27   Win 42–26   Lose 8–25   Win 18–16   Lose 28–35

a Write down the points scored by the club in ascending order.
b Copy and complete the frequency table below.

Points scored	0–9	10–19	20–29	30–39	40–49
Frequency					

c Write down the points scored against the club in ascending order.

d Copy and complete the frequency table below.

Points scored	0–9	10–19	20–29	30–39	40–49
Frequency					

21.2 Using tally charts

When you need to collect a lot of information it can be helpful for one person to read the item and another person to record that item on a tally chart.

Each time the item is called a tally mark is made like this: |

To make counting easier every fifth tally mark is drawn across the previous four, so the sequence up to 5 is |, ||, |||, ||||, ⅢⅠ.

A count of 6 begins with a new 'bundle' (ⅢⅠ|), and so on.

The total number of items is called the frequency.

Discrete data

Example 5

Fifteen children were asked their favourite drink from: tea, coffee, chocolate, Horlicks, hot milk, Bournvita.

Their answers were:

Anne: tea	George: tea	Azil: hot milk
Adam: Horlicks	Miranda: coffee	Melissa: Bournvita
David: coffee	Razi: chocolate	Paul: coffee
Emma: coffee	Salik: hot milk	Satwinder: chocolate
Fran: hot milk	Zorba: coffee	Yusuf: coffee

Draw a tally chart to show this information.

Drink	Tally	Total
Bournvita	|	1
chocolate	||	2
coffee	ⅢⅠ|	6
Horlicks	|	1
hot milk	|||	3
tea	||	2
Total tally		15

Note ⅢⅠ means 5.

Exercise 21C

For each question below show the information on a tally chart.

1 All fifteen children in Class 9A bought a sandwich during one morning break. The sandwiches they bought were as follows.

Name	Sandwich
Ronnie	Tomato
Josiah	Beef
Ayo	Cheese
Jordan	Ham
Charmaine	Egg

Name	Sandwich
Marcus	Tomato
Jisanne	Egg
Marlon	Ham
Afiya	Cheese
Tnisha	Tomato

Name	Sandwich
Shani	Beef
Candace	Cheese
Zoey	Ham
Eshe	Egg
Kanika	Cheese

2 All twenty-five children in Class 10B were asked to choose an afternoon activity. Their choices were as follows.

Name	Subject
Bernard	Metalwork
Tony	Woodwork
Julian	Drama
Martyn	Needlework
Anish	Woodwork
Sanjay	Electronics
Sunil	Dance
Matthew	Woodwork
Rahul	Electronics

Name	Subject
George	Metalwork
Bobbie	Needlework
Wayne	Woodwork
Ronnie	Metalwork
Joanna	Needlwork
Anne	Metalwork
Margaret	Drama
Laura	Dance

Name	Subject
Jean	Electronics
Rita	Woodwork
Barbara	Needlework
Jodie	Dance
Suzanne	Woodwork
Nicola	Dance
Diane	Metalwork
Elaine	Needlework

3 The children at High Lane School had an excursion day and there were five excursions to choose from. The children in Class 8B chose as follows.

Name	Place
Mary	London Zoo
Jane	Brighton
Vepula	Portsmouth
Mumbi	Thorpe Park
Gillian	Portsmouth
Sunil	North Downs
Nishil	Thorpe Park

Name	Place
Derek	Brighton
Geoffrey	Portsmouth
Matthew	Brighton
Janet	Thorpe Park
Melissa	North Downs
Natalie	Portsmouth
Rosie	Brighton

Name	Place
Naomi	Thorpe Park
Sanjay	London Zoo
Asif	Brighton
John	Thorpe Park
Chris	North Downs
Peter	Thorpe Park

Example 6

The fifteen children in Example 5, who were all born in 1980, were asked their month and date of birth. Their answers were:

Name	Date	Name	Date	Name	Date	Name	Date
Anne	12 July	George	12 January	Azil	15 November	Adam	15 May
Miranda	15 October	Melissa	4 July	David	7 January	Razi	17 December
Paul	12 December	Emma	9 June	Salik	9 April	Satwinder	1 February
Fran	14 July	Zorba	12 March	Yusuf	14 January		

a Write their names in order of age, starting with the eldest.

b Draw a tally chart to show how many were born in each month.

c Draw a tally chart to show how many were born on a particular date in the month.

a David, George, Yusuf, Satwinder, Zorba, Salik, Adam, Emma, Melissa, Anne, Fran, Miranda, Azil, Paul, Razi.

b

Month	Tally	Totals
January	|||	3
February			1
March			1
April			1
May			1
June			1
July	|||	3
August		0
September		0
October			1
November			1
December	||	2
Total tally		15

c

Date of month	Tally	Totals
1			1
4			1
7			1
9				2
12						4
14				2
15					3
17			1
Total tally		15

Exercise 21D

1   A cafe employs fifteen people. The table below shows certain details.

Employee	Working capacity	Rest day	Employee	Working capacity	Rest day
Vepula	Waitress	Monday	Sheila	Dish washer	Tuesday
Wambui	Cook	Thursday	Lesley	Waitress	Saturday
Patricia	Waitress	Thursday	Jimmy	Cook	Tuesday
Julie	Cleaner	Monday	Peter	Cashier	Monday
Jane	Waitress	Friday	Tom	Dish washer	Wednesday
Dawn	Cook	Sunday	Anish	Cleaner	Tuesday
Valerie	Cleaner	Wednesday	Andrew	Dish washer	Monday
Barbara	Cashier	Tuesday			

a Make out a tally chart which shown how many workers are employed in each of the five capacities.

b Make out a tally chart which shows how many workers are off work on each of the days of the week.

2   One summer Saturday sixteen coaches left a coach station in London for four different resorts between 0800 and 1000.

Departure time	Destination	Seating capacity of coach	Departure time	Destination	Seating capacity of coach
0800	Hastings	50	0900	Hastings	50
0805	Brighton	45	0905	Southend	60
0810	Southend	55	0910	Bournemouth	50
0815	Bournemouth	50	0920	Brighton	55
0825	Bournemouth	60	0930	Hastings	45
0830	Brighton	50	0935	Bournemouth	60
0840	Southend	45	0945	Brighton	50
0845	Brighton	55	1000	Southend	55

a Make out a tally chart which shows how many coaches went to each of the four destinations.

b Make out a tally chart which shows how many coaches had each of the four different seating capacities.

Grouped data

Example 7

The heights of the children in Example 5 are:

Anne: 127 cm	Fran: 142 cm	Salik: 148 cm	Paul: 145 cm
Adam: 136 cm	George: 111 cm	Zorba: 151 cm	Satwinder: 128 cm
David: 158 cm	Miranda: 125 cm	Azil: 119 cm	Yusuf: 149 cm
Emma: 147 cm	Razi: 116 cm	Melissa: 120 cm	

a Write their names in order of height, starting with the shortest.

b Draw a tally chart to show how many are in each of these height groups:

110–119 cm   120–129 cm   130–139 cm   140–149 cm   150–159 cm

a George, Razi, Azil, Melissa, Miranda, Anne, Satwinder, Adam, Fran, Paul, Emma, Salik, Yusuf, Zorba, David.

b

Height	Tally	Frequency
110–119 cm	|||	3
120–129 cm	||||	4
130–139 cm			1
140–149 cm	ЖН	5
150–159 cm	||	2
Total tally		15

Exercise 21E

1 The table below shows the weight of each pupil in Class 10C.

Name	Weight	Name	Weight	Name	Weight
Lynn	42 kg	Shani	46 kg	David	43 kg
Sheila	28 kg	Rita	47 kg	Michael	41 kg
Margaret	32 kg	Mary	34 kg	Geoffrey	56 kg
Dawn	48 kg	Frances	55 kg	Tom	54 kg
Susan	45 kg	Peter	39 kg	Daniel	52 kg
Lisa	27 kg	Andrew	38 kg	Ian	63 kg
Natalie	33 kg	Paul	57 kg	Robert	58 kg
Candace	44 kg	John	51 kg		
Tnisha	35 kg	Sunil	53 kg		

(continued)

Copy and complete the table below.

Weight	Tally	Frequency
20–29 kg		
30–39 kg		
40–49 kg		
50–59 kg		
60–69 kg		

2   All of the pupils in Class 10C took a general knowledge test.
Their marks out of one hundred are shown below.

Name	Mark
Lynn	41
Sheila	56
Margaret	35
Dawn	63
Susan	24
Lisa	15
Natalie	57
Candace	48
Tnisha	54

Name	Mark
Shani	61
Rita	78
Mary	67
Frances	85
Peter	51
Andrew	32
Paul	53
John	75
Sunil	68

Name	Mark
David	36
Michael	65
Geoffrey	28
Tom	71
Daniel	45
Ian	58
Robert	46

Copy and complete the tally chart below.

Mark	Tally	Frequency
10–19		
20–29		
30–39		
40–49		
50–59		
60–69		
70–79		
80–89		

22 UNDERSTANDING DIAGRAMS AND GRAPHS AND REPRESENTING DATA

22.1 Reading and drawing pictograms, bar charts and block graphs

Pictograms and bar charts

a

b

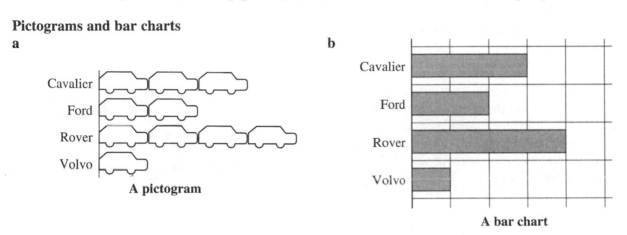

A pictogram

A bar chart

Melissa decided to show the information in Example 1 on page 238 by using **a** a pictogram and **b** a bar chart. In the pictogram a separate picture is used to represent each car, whereas in the bar chart the length of each bar is used to show the number of each type of car. There are 3 Cavaliers, 2 Fords, 4 Rovers and 1 Volvo.

Example 1

Show the information about the children's favourite drink in Example 5 on page 245 using
a a pictogram **b** a bar chart.

a

b

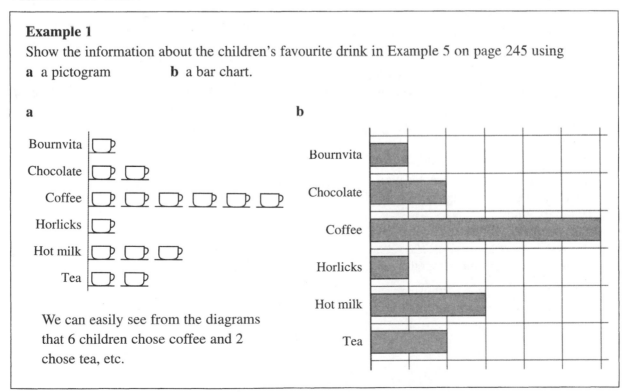

We can easily see from the diagrams that 6 children chose coffee and 2 chose tea, etc.

Exercise 22A

1   The pictogram shows how many fizzy drinks
    of five different flavours were dispensed by a
    vending machine on a certain day. If the symbol
    stands for 10 drinks, find:
    a the number of drinks of each flavour
        dispensed
    b the total number of drinks dispensed
        altogether.

    If the cost of each drink is 60p, find:
    c the total amount of money collected.

2   The pictogram shows how many packets of
    crisps of five different flavours were dispensed
    by a vending machine on a certain day. If the
    symbol stands for 5 packets of crisps, find:
    a the number of packets of each
        flavour dispensed
    b the total number of packets dispensed
        altogether.

    If each packet costs 40p, find:
    c the total amount of money collected.

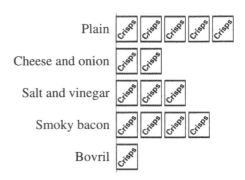

3   The pictogram shows how many cornets an ice
    cream seller sold over an Easter holiday period.
    If the symbol stands for 50 cornets, find:
    a the number he sold on each of the days
    b the number he sold altogether.

    If he sells the cornets for 75p each, find:
    c the total amount of money he collected
    d the number of wholesale boxes of cornets he
        used if each box contains 450.

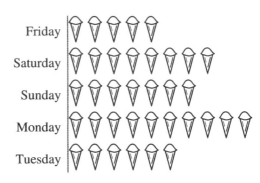

4   The bar chart shows how many
    letters a firm sent out on each day of
    a certain week. If the scale is 1 cm to
    10 letters, find:
    a the number sent out on each of the
        days
    b the number sent out altogether.

    If each letter requires a 20p stamp,
    find: **c** the total amount that the
    firm spent on postage.

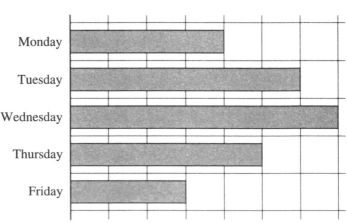

5 The bar chart shows how many barges passed through a set of lock gates on a canal on each day of a certain week. If the scale is 1 cm to 5 barges, find:

a the number that passed through the lock on each of the days

b the number that passed through altogether.

If the lock takes 4 minutes to fill, find the total time that the lock was operating in:

c minutes   **d** hours.

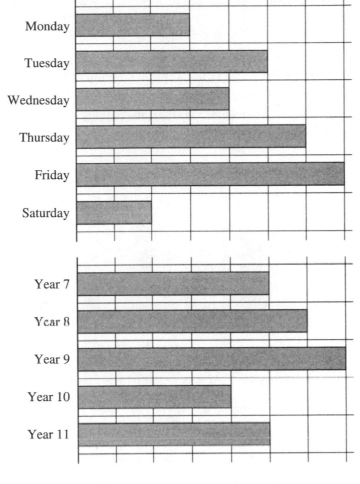

6 The bar chart shows how many pupils there are in each of the five years in a secondary school.

If the scale is 1 cm to 20 pupils find:

a the number of pupils in each year

b the total number of pupils in the school.

One day the whole school went on an excursion to the coast. If the coach fare was £7.50 each, find:

c the total amount paid in fares.

If they hired 60-seater coaches, find:

d the number of coaches required.

7 Display the details for each of questions 1–3 on a bar chart.

8 Display the details for each of questions 4–6 on a pictogram.

Block graphs for discrete data

Both the pictogram and the bar chart show the frequency of each event occurring. This information can also be shown on a block graph where the height of each block represents the frequency. In the example which follows this is how often the drink was chosen. This type of block graph is called a **frequency diagram**.

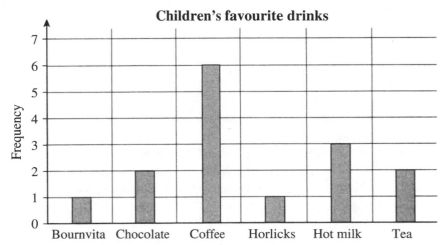

It is important to remember to label clearly what information is being represented on each axis of the graph and also to give the graph a title.

Example 2

a Show the information about the number of cars of each type given in Example 1 on page 238 as a frequency diagram.

b Show the information about the heights of the children given in Example 7 on page 249 as a frequency diagram.

a

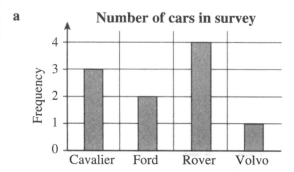

b

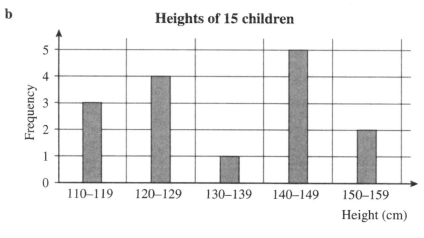

Exercise 22B

1 Look at the information in Example **2a** above.
   a Which type of car occurred most often?
      How often was this?
   b Which type of car occurred least often?
      How often was this?

2 Look at the information in Example **2b** above.
   a In which range of heights did most children occur?
      How many children were there in this class interval?
   b In which range of heights did least children occur?
      How many children were there in this class interval?

3 In a certain town there is a bus service that leaves the town centre and then stops at only four places. Frequency diagram **i** shows how many passengers on one such service travelled to each of the four stops and frequency diagram **ii** shows how they gained access to the bus.

a To which stop did the largest number of passengers travel?
How many was this?

b To which stop did the smallest number of passengers travel?
How many was this?

i

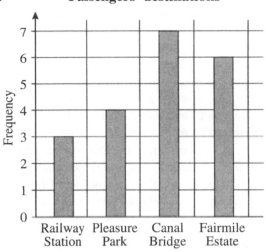

Passengers' destinations

c By which means did the largest number of passengers gain access to the bus?
How many was this?

d By which means did the smallest number of passengers gain access to the bus?
How many was this?

e If all of the school pupils travelled to the same stop and none of the other passengers did, near which stop was their school?

f How many passengers boarded the bus at the town centre altogether?

ii

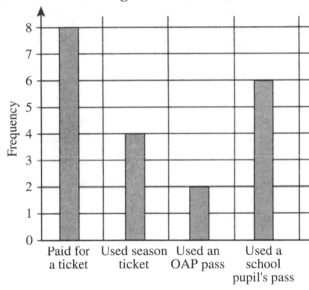

Passengers' access to the bus

4 One morning Kanika went to the railway station and recorded how many passengers there were on each of the trains. Then she drew the following frequency diagrams.

i First-class passengers per train

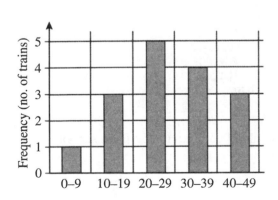

ii Second-class passengers per train

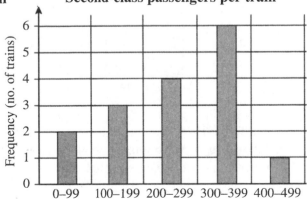

(continued)

a For first-class passengers which number range was the most common?
How many trains carried a number of passengers in this range?

b For first-class passengers which number range was the least common?
How many trains carried a number of passengers in this range?

c For second-class passengers which number range was the most common?
How many trains carried a number of passengers in this range?

d For second-class passengers which number range was the least common?
How many trains carried a number of passengers in this range?

e How many trains departed during the morning altogether?

f The trains contain one first-class seat for every five second-class seats.
Some people say that this is too many first-class seats. Would you agree?

5 Display all the details for question 1 in Exercise 21B on page 244 on a frequency diagram.

6 Display all the details for question 2 in Exercise 21B on page 244 on a frequency diagram.

Example 3

The tally chart shows the number of cars passing my window between each of the given times.

Time	9–10 a.m.	10–11 a.m.	11 a.m.–12 noon	12 noon–1 p.m.	1–2 p.m.	2–3 p.m.	3–4 p.m.
No. of cars	200	100	50	100	50	150	250

a Draw a frequency diagram to show this information.

b During which time interval does the greatest number of cars pass?

c Suggest reasons why a large number pass between 9 and 10 a.m. and between 3 and 4 p.m.

d Suggest reasons why the number of cars passing increases between 12 noon and 1 p.m.

a

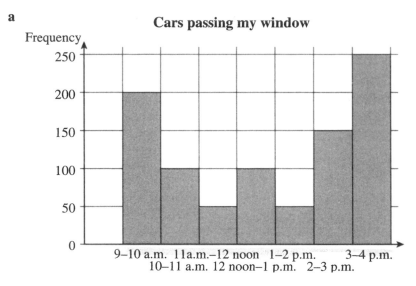

b 3–4 p.m. (250 cars)

c People going to or coming from work and people taking children to and from school.

d People going out or home for lunch.

Exercise 22C

1 A cinema is open from 12 noon to 10 p.m. The film sequence is shown three times over and the starting times are 1 p.m., 4 p.m. and 7 p.m. The table below shows the number of tickets sold during each of the hourly intervals on a certain day.

Time	Tickets
12 noon – 1 p.m.	200
1–2 p.m.	150
2–3 p.m.	50
3–4 p.m.	150
4–5 p.m.	100

Time	Tickets
5–6 p.m.	50
6–7 p.m.	200
7–8 p.m.	150
8–9 p.m.	50
9–10 p.m.	Office closed

   a Draw a frequency diagram to show this information.
   b During which intervals were the largest numbers of tickets sold?
   c Explain why few tickets were sold between 2 p.m. and 3 p.m., 5 p.m and 6 p.m., and 8 p.m and 9 p.m.
   d How many tickets were sold altogether?
   e Find the total amount of money collected if the entrance charge is £2.50 until 6 p.m., but £3 after that.

2 Mr and Mrs Patel drove their car from London to Glasgow. The table below shows how many kilometres they covered during each hourly interval.

Time	Distance
9–10 a.m.	30 km
10–11 a.m.	90 km
11 a.m.–12 noon	80 km
12 noon–1 p.m.	20 km
1–2 p.m.	100 km
2–3 p.m.	80 km

Time	Distance
3–4 p.m.	40 km
4–5 p.m.	70 km
5–6 p.m.	10 km
6–7 p.m.	90 km
7–8 p.m.	50 km

   a Draw a block graph to show this information.
   b During which hourly interval did they travel the longest distance?
   c Explain (or suggest) why they covered only a short distance between each of the following times:
      i 9 a.m. to 10 a.m.   ii 7 p.m. to 8 p.m.   iii 12 noon to 1 p.m.   iv 5 p.m. to 6 p.m.
      v 3 p.m. to 4 p.m.
   d How many kilometres did they travel altogether?
   e By dividing the total distance that they travelled by the total time taken, find their average speed.

Frequency diagrams for continuous data

In the block graphs and frequency diagrams for discrete data that we have looked at so far, each of the blocks could have been drawn separated from the next block.

With continuous data, such as a set of measurements, there is no such gap between the blocks, so we need to know whether an item on a boundary between two blocks belongs to the block on the left or on the right of the boundary.

With class intervals such as 120–125 and 125–130 it would be normal to assume that the item 120 was in the class interval 120–125 and that the item 125 was in the class interval 125–130.

Example 4

Look at the frequency diagram below.

a Write down the class intervals and state the frequency for each.

b Find the total number of children.

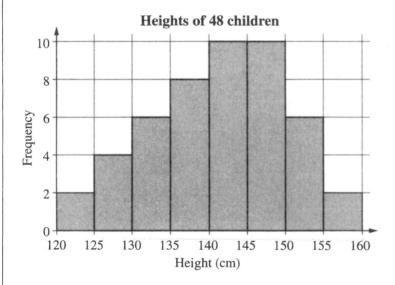

Heights of 48 children

a

Class interval	Frequency
120 to 125	2
125 to 130	4
130 to 135	6
135 to 140	8

Class interval	Frequency
140 to 145	10
145 to 150	10
150 to 155	6
155 to 160	2

(**Note**   120 to 125 means that the height can be anything from 120 cm to 125 cm except 125 cm itself, which is in the next interval.)

b The total number of children = 2 + 4 + 6 + 8 + 10 + 10 + 6 + 2 = 48

Exercise 22D

1 The frequency diagram below shows the hours of sunshine on each day during a certain month.
 a Write down the class intervals and state the frequency for each.
 b How many days did this month have?   **c** What month was this one likely to have been?

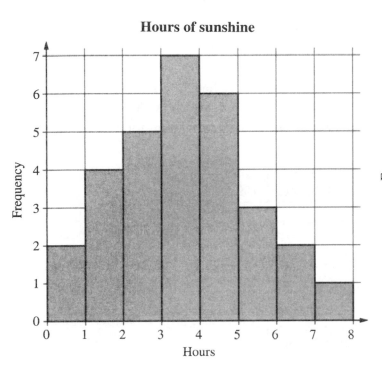

Hours of sunshine

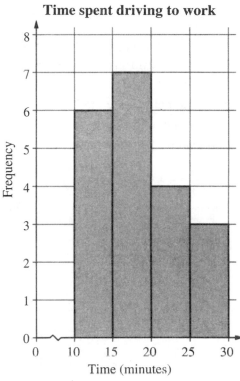

Time spent driving to work

2 The frequency diagram above shows the time that Ayo had to spend in driving to work on each of the days of a certain month.
 a Write down the class intervals and state the frequency for each.
 b On how many days did he go to work during this particular month?
 c If he works Monday to Friday and the month included five Saturdays and Sundays, list the possible months that this one could have been.

3 The frequency diagram shows the weights of the children in Class 8B.
 a Write down the class intervals and state the frequency for each.
 b How many children are there in the class altogether?
 c The diagram has a symmetry axis which is marked with a dashed line. Find the average weight for the children by reading the weight where this line crosses the kilogram axis.

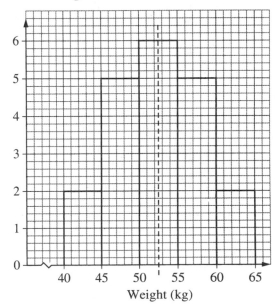

Weights of children in Class 8B

Example 5

The heights of 20 children measured to the nearest centimetre are:

127 cm, 128 cm, 128 cm, 129 cm, 130 cm, 134 cm, 135 cm, 137 cm, 139 cm, 140 cm,
140 cm, 142 cm, 144 cm, 145 cm, 148 cm, 149 cm, 150 cm, 154 cm, 155 cm, 157 cm

a Construct a frequency table using suitable class intervals of: **i** 10 cm   **ii** 5 cm.
b Show the information on frequency diagrams.

a As the heights are measured to the nearest whole centimetre, a height of 129.49 cm would be recorded as 129 cm, whereas a height of 129.50 cm would be recorded as 130 cm. The boundary between these two class intervals is strictly 129.5 cm rather than 130 cm.

i

Class interval	119.5–129.5 cm	129.5–139.5 cm	139.5–149.5 cm	149.5–159.5 cm
Frequency	4	5	7	4

ii

Class interval	124.5–129.5 cm	129.5–134.5 cm	134.5–139.5 cm	139.5–144.5 cm	144.5–149.5 cm	149.5–154.5 cm	154.5–159.5 cm
Frequency	4	2	3	4	3	2	2

b i

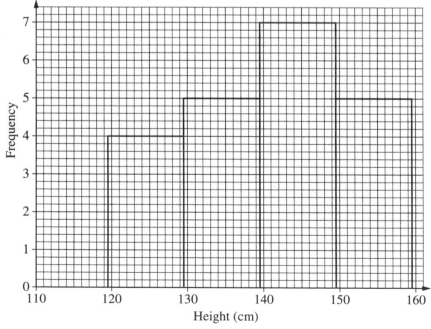

Heights of 20 children

ii

Heights of 20 children

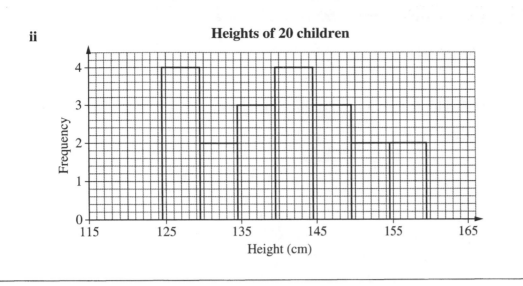

Exercise 22E

1 The weight of each of the children in Class 10C was recorded to the nearest kilogram. The weights were as follows:
     33, 36, 38, 41, 42, 43, 44, 46, 47, 47, 48, 49, 49, 51, 52, 52, 53, 54, 54, 56, 57, 59, 61, 64 and 66 kg.
   a Construct a frequency table using suitable class intervals of:
      i 10 kg   **ii** 5 kg.
   b Show the information on frequency diagrams.

2 The temperature on each of the days of a certain month was recorded to the nearest degree and the results were as follows:
     1, 2, 3, 3, 4, 6, 6, 7, 8, 8, 9, 11, 11, 12, 12, 12, 13, 13, 14, 16, 17, 17, 18, 18, 19, 19, 21, 23, 24 and 26 °C.
   a Construct a frequency table using suitable class intervals of:
      i 10 degrees   **ii** 5 degrees.
   b Show the information on frequency diagrams.
   c What month was this one likely to have been?

3 A travelling salesman recorded his daily travelling distances over a twenty-four-day working period.
   The distances were as follows:
     92, 97, 98, 102, 103, 104, 104, 106, 107, 108, 109, 109, 112, 113, 113, 114, 114, 117, 118, 118, 119, 122, 124 and 127 kilometres.
   a Construct a frequency table using suitable class intervals of:
      i 10 km   **ii** 5 km.
   b Show the information on frequency diagrams.
   c Comment on the shape of your frequency diagrams.

22.2   Reading and drawing line graphs and $x - y$ graphs

Bar line graphs and line graphs

Example 6

A patient in hospital had his temperature taken at hourly intervals from 6 a.m. to 12 noon. The readings were:

Time	6 a.m.	7 a.m.	8 a.m.	9 a.m.	10 a.m.	11 a.m.	12 noon
Temperature	35.7°C	35.3°C	35.4°C	36.0°C	36.4°C	37.0°C	36.4°C

a Draw a bar line graph for this information.   **b** Draw a line graph for this information.
c At what time was the temperature highest?   **d** At what time was the temperature lowest?
e Estimate the patient's temperature at: **i** 6.30 a.m.   **ii** 9.30 a.m.   **iii** 10.30 a.m.

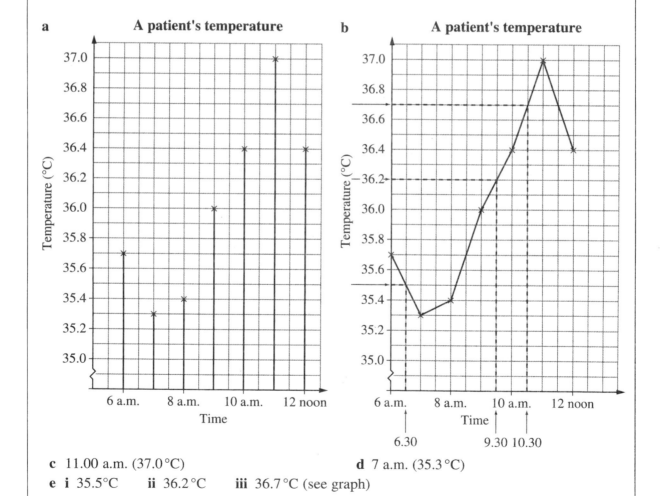

c 11.00 a.m. (37.0°C)   **d** 7 a.m. (35.3°C)
e i 35.5°C   **ii** 36.2°C   **iii** 36.7°C (see graph)

Exercise 22F

1 a Mary was born in 1984. The bar line graph shows her weight at two-year intervals.
Use the bar line graph to complete your own copy of the table.

Year	1984	1986	1988	1990	1992	1994	1996
Weight (kg)							

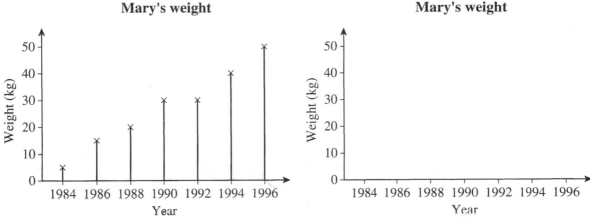

b Use your table in part **a** to draw a line graph on your own copy of the grid illustrated.
c Use your graph to find Mary's weight in: **i** 1985 **ii** 1989 **iii** 1993 **iv** 1995.

2 An immersion heater is turned on at 8 a.m. and turned off at 3 p.m. The bar line graph shows the temperature of the water at hourly intervals.

a Use the bar line graph to complete your own copy of the table.

Time	8 a.m.	9 a.m.	10 a.m.	11 a.m.	12 noon
Temperature					

Time	1 p.m.	2 p.m.	3 p.m.	4 p.m.	5 p.m.
Temperature					

b Use your table to draw a line graph on your own copy of the grid illustrated on the next page.
c Find from your graph the temperature of the water at:
i 8.30 a.m. **ii** 9.30 a.m.
iii 10.30 a.m. **iv** 3.30 p.m.
v 4.30 p.m.
d Explain why the temperature oscillates between 11 a.m. and 3 p.m.

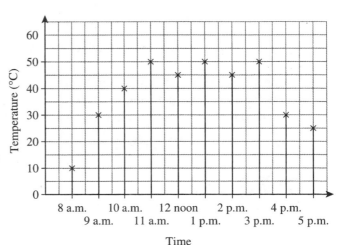

(continued)

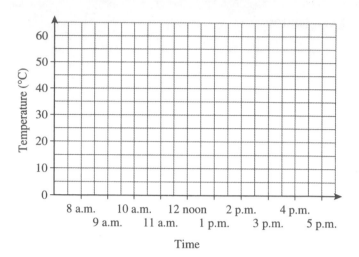

3 a The table below shows the depth of a river at various distances from the left-hand bank.

Distance from bank (m)	0	20	40	60	80	100	120	140	160
Depth (cm)	0	40	100	180	180	180	160	80	0

Draw a line graph of the details on your own copy of the grid illustrated.

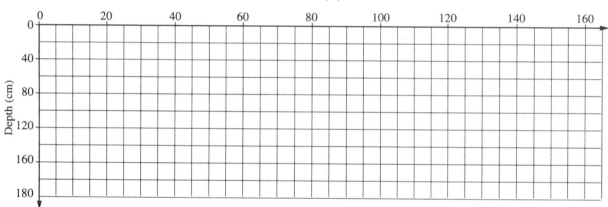

b Find the depth of the water at each of the following distances from the bank:
   i 10 m   **ii** 50 m   **iii** 130 m   **iv** 150 m.
c John swims across the river from the left-hand bank, but he is out of his depth at 120 cm. Find how far he is from the bank when he:
   i goes out of his depth   **ii** comes back into his depth again.

Coordinates and $x - y$ graphs

We can use a pair of numbers called coordinates to represent a particular point on a grid.

The point P, for example, is represented by (3, 6).

The first coordinate, 3, tells us how far to go to the right and the second coordinate, 6, tells us how far to go up.

The point (0, 0) is called the origin.

This is zero in both directions.

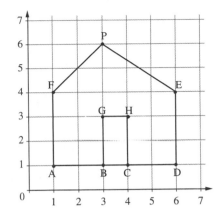

Example 7

Use the grid above to write down the coordinates of the points A, B, C, D, E, F, G and H.

A is 1 across and 1 up, therefore A is (1, 1)   E is 6 across and 4 up, therefore E is (6, 4)
B is 3 across and 1 up, therefore B is (3, 1)   F is 1 across and 4 up, therefore F is (1, 4)
C is 4 across and 1 up, therefore C is (4, 1)   G is 3 across and 3 up, therefore G is (3, 3)
D is 6 across and 1 up, therefore D is (6, 1)   H is 4 across and 3 up, therefore H is (4, 3)

Note   (4, 1) and (1, 4) represent different points, so the order of the numbers is important.

Exercise 22G

1   State the coordinates of each of the points A to Z on the grid illustrated.

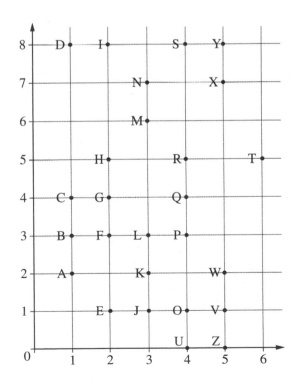

(continued)

2   State the coordinates
    of the four corners of
    a the square ABCD
    b the square PQRS
    c the rectangle LMNP
    d the rectangle UVWX.

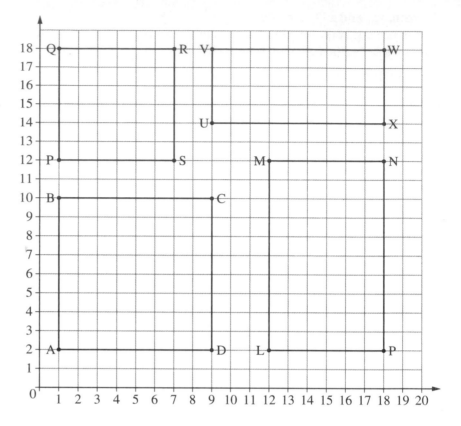

3   State the coordinates of
    the four corners of:
    a the square ABCD
    b the square KLMN
    c the square UVWX
    d the square PQRS.

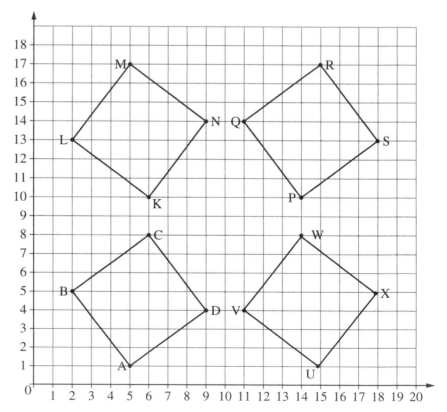

4 State the coordinates of each of the eight corners, A, B, C, D, E, F, G and H, of the figure illustrated.

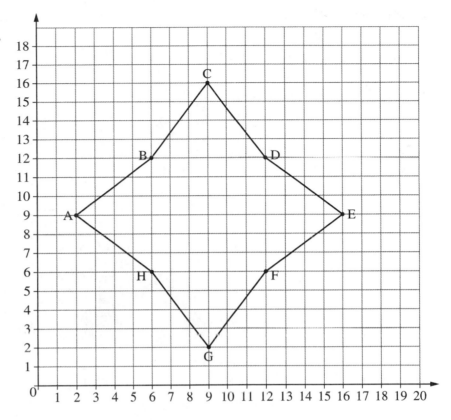

Example 8

Plot the following points on a copy of the grid illustrated:
A (1, 3), B (5, 1), C (3, 3) and D (5, 5).

Join A to B, B to C, C to D and D to A. Name the shape that you have made.

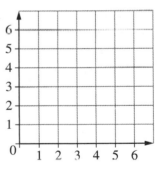

The points A, B, C and D are shown on the right.
The shape made by joining the points is an arrowhead.

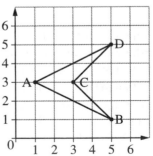

Exercise 22H

1   Copy the grid illustrated
    and mark each of the following points on it.

    A (1, 5),   B (1, 6),   C (1, 7),   D (1, 9),
    E (1, 1),   F (1, 0),   G (2, 1),   H (2, 2),
    J (2, 6),   K (2, 10),   L (2, 0),   M (3, 4),
    N (3, 5),   P (3, 8),   Q (3, 9),   R (3, 0),
    S (4, 1),   T (4, 2),   U (4, 7),   V (4, 10),
    W (5, 3),   X (5, 4),   Y (5, 9),   Z (5, 10)

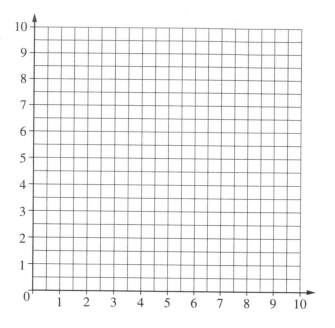

Make four copies of the grid illustrated,
one for each of the remaining questions.

2   For each of the following, plot the four points
    on your grid, join the points in alphabetical
    order and name the shape that you have
    made.
    a A (2, 2),   B (2, 6),   C (6, 6),   D (6, 2)
    b K (2, 10),   L (2, 17),   M (9, 17),
        N (9, 10)
    c U (14, 10),   V (14, 17),   W (18, 17),
        X (18, 10)
    d E (8, 2),   F (8, 6),   G (18, 6),   H (18, 2)

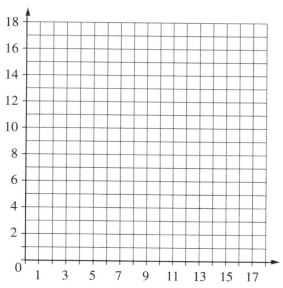

3   Plot each of the following points on a grid, join them in alphabetical
    order and comment on the shape you have made.
    A (6, 16),   B (14, 16),   C (18, 9),   D (14, 2),   E (6, 2),   F (2, 9)
4   Plot each of the following points on a grid, join them in alphabetical
    order and comment on the shape you have made.
    A (1, 6),   B (1, 13),   C (6, 18),   D (13, 18),   E (18, 13),   F (18, 6),
    G (13, 1),   H (6, 1)
5   Plot each of the following points on a grid and join them in alphabetical order.
    A (1, 1),   B (3, 7),   C (1, 13),   D (7, 11),   E (13, 13),   F (11, 7),
    G (13, 1),   H (7, 3)

Example 9

a Copy the grid below and use the table to complete it.

Draw a line through your grid points.

Number of pencils bought	0	1	2	5
Cost	0p	5p	10p	25p

b Find from your line the cost of: **i** 3 pencils **ii** 4 pencils.

a **Cost of buying pencils**

b i Cost of 3 pencils = 15p

ii Cost of 4 pencils = 20

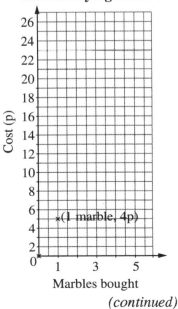

Exercise 22J

1 Copy the grid illustrated and use the table below to complete it.

Draw a line through your grid points.

Cost of buying marbles

Number of marbles bought	0	1	2	3	4	5	6
Cost		0p	4p	8p	12p	16p	20p	24p

(continued)

2 **a** Copy the grid illustrated and use the table below to complete it.
Draw a line through your graph points.

Number of fuses bought	0	1	2	3	4	6	8	10
Cost	0p	2p	4p	6p	8p	12p	16p	20p

b Find from your line the cost of:
i 5 fuses
ii 7 fuses
iii 9 fuses.

Cost of buying fuses

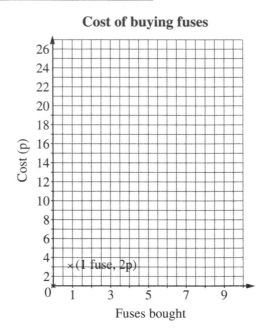

3 **a** Copy the grid illustrated and use the table below to complete it.
Draw a line through your grid points.

Number of litres of turpentine bought	0	1	2	5	7	9	10
Cost	£0	£2	£4	£10	£14	£18	£20

b Find from your line the cost of
i 3 litres
ii 4 litres
iii 6 litres
iv 8 litres.

Cost of buying turpentine

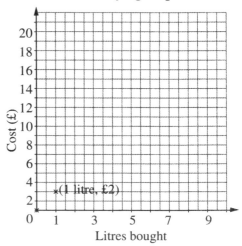

4 A soap bubble measured 3 cm across when it was first blown, but its size increased in accordance with the details below until it burst.

Time after bubble was blown	0 seconds	1 second	2 seconds	5 seconds	7 seconds
Size of bubble	3 cm	4 cm	5 cm	8 cm	10 cm

a Copy the grid illustrated and use the table to complete it. Draw a line through your grid points.

b Use your line to find the size of the bubble after:
  i 3 seconds
  ii 4 seconds
  iii 6 seconds.

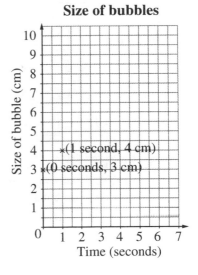

Size of bubbles

5 Julie weighed 4 kilograms when she was born and her weight increased as shown in the table below.

Julie's age	0 months	1 month	2 months	3 months	5 months	7 months	9 months
Julie's weight	4 kilograms	5 kilograms	6 kilograms	7 kilograms	9 kilograms	11 kilograms	13 kilograms

a Copy the grid illustrated and use the table to complete it. Draw a line through your grid points.

b Use your line to find Julie's weight after:
  i 4 months
  ii 6 months
  iii 8 months.

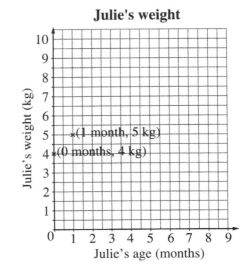

Julie's weight

Example 10

The table below shows how far a cyclist has travelled after various times. Show this information on a graph.

Time (minutes)	0	10	20	30	40	50	60
Distance travelled (miles)	0	4	8	12	16	20	24

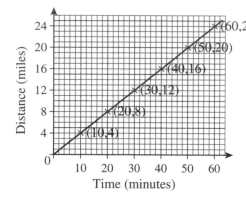

Note all the points lie on a straight line.

Exercise 22K

For each of the following show the given information on a graph. Copy the grid illustrated in order to draw your graph.

1   The table below shows the distance covered by a boy running in a 400 metre race after various times.

Time (seconds)	0	15	30	45	60
Distance covered (m)	0	100	200	300	400

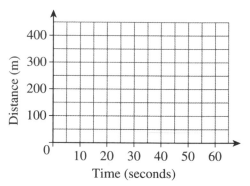

2   The table below shows the distance covered by a girl swimming the length of a pool after various times.

Time (seconds)	0	5	10	15	20	25	30
Distance covered (m)	0	10	20	30	40	50	60

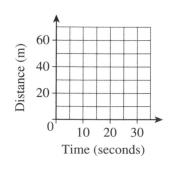

3 The table below shows the distance travelled by a ferry boat after various times.

Time (minutes)	0	1	2	3	4	5
Distance covered (m)	0	50	100	150	200	250

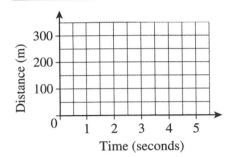

4 The table below shows the altitude reached by a balloon after various times.

Time (minutes)	0	2	4	6	8	10
Altitude (m)	0	10	20	30	40	50

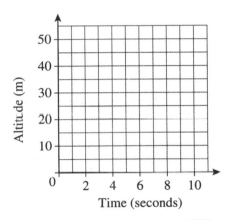

Example 11

Complete a table for the mapping $x \rightarrow x + 4$ using values of x from 0 to 5 and draw this mapping on a graph.

$x \rightarrow x + 4$ $3 \rightarrow 7$
$0 \rightarrow 4$ $4 \rightarrow 8$
$1 \rightarrow 5$ $5 \rightarrow 9$
$2 \rightarrow 6$

On an (x, y) graph the above mapping can be shown as the coordinates (0, 4), (1, 5), (2, 6), (3, 7), (4, 8) and (5, 9).

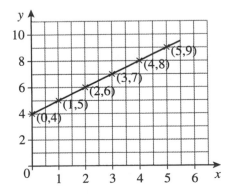

Note the six pairs of coordinates all lie on the same straight line.
The line can be represented by $y = x + 4$.

Exercise 22L

For this exercise eight copies of the grid illustrated are required.

For each question complete a table for the mapping using values of x from 0 to 5 and draw the mapping on a graph.

1	$x \rightarrow x + 3$	**2**	$x \rightarrow x + 5$
3	$x \rightarrow x + 2$	**4**	$x \rightarrow x + 4$
5	$x \rightarrow x - 1$	**6**	$x \rightarrow x - 2$
7	$x \rightarrow x - 4$	**8**	$x \rightarrow x - 3$

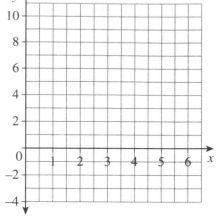

22.3 Reading and drawing pie charts

Example 12

Look at the first frequency table in Example 1a on page 239.
Construct a pie chart to show the details.
As there are 10 cars altogether and 360° in a circle,
36° can be used to represent each car.

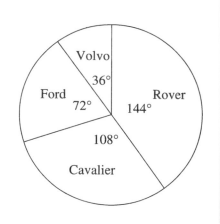

Make	Frequency	Angle in pie chart
Cavalier	3	$3 \times 36° = 108°$
Ford	2	$2 \times 36° = 72°$
Rover	4	$4 \times 36° = 144°$
Volvo	1	$1 \times 36° = 36°$
Check	10	360°

From the pie chart it is easy to see that Rover cars were the most common and Volvos were the least common.

Exercise 22M

1 Refer to question 1 in Exercise 21A on page 240. Construct a pie chart for each of the three frequency tables.

2 Refer to question 2 in Exercise 21A on page 241. Construct a pie chart for each of the three frequency tables.

3 Refer to question 3 in Exercise 21A on page 242. Construct a pie chart for each of the three frequency tables.

Example 13

Look at the first frequency table in Example 3a on page 243.

Construct a pie chart to show the details.

As there are 20 pupils altogether and 360° in a circle, 18° can be used to represent each pupil.

Height	Frequency	Angle in pie chart
120–129 cm	1	$1 \times 18° = 18°$
130–139 cm	3	$3 \times 18° = 54°$
140–149 cm	8	$8 \times 18° = 144°$
150–159 cm	7	$7 \times 18° = 126°$
160–169 cm	1	$1 \times 18° = 18°$
Check	20	360°

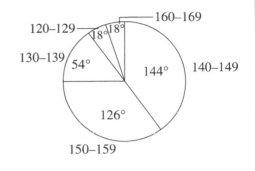

From the pie chart it is easily seen that most children were in the interval 140–149 cm.

Exercise 22N

1–2 Refer to question 1–2 in Exercise 21E on page 249. Draw a pie chart for each frequency table.

3 Look at the frequency table in Example 7 on page 249.
Draw a pie chart for this frequency table.

4 For Example 7 on page 249, regroup the data using class intervals of 100–119 cm, 120–139 cm, 140–159 cm, and then redraw the pie chart for the new frequency table.

Example 14

The pie chart shows how the 20 pupils in class 3B travel to school. Find from the chart:

a the number who travel by each method   **b** the percentage who travel by each method.

a The number who walk $= \dfrac{162°}{360°} \times 20 = 9$

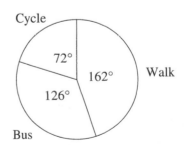

The number who travel by bus $= \dfrac{126°}{360°} \times 20 = 7$

The number who cycle $= \dfrac{72°}{360°} \times 20 = 4$

b The percentage who walk $= \dfrac{162°}{360°} \times 100\% = 45\%$

The percentage who travel by bus $= \dfrac{126°}{360°} \times 100\% = 35\%$

The percentage who cycle $= \dfrac{72°}{360°} \times 100\% = 20\%$

Exercise 22P

1 The pie chart shows how all 180 boys in Year 5 chose
   their sport option.
   Find from the chart the number who chose each of the
   five sports.

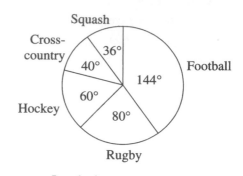

2 The pie chart shows how all 240 girls in Year 5 chose
   their sport option.
   Find from the chart the number who chose each of the
   five sports.

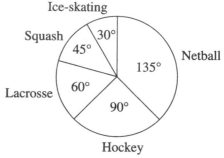

3 One day 150 packets of crisps are dispensed by
   a vending machine and the pie chart shows how many of
   each flavour.
   Find from the chart the number for each flavour.
   Find also the percentage of the total for each flavour.

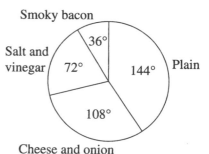

4 One day 200 hot drinks are dispensed by a vending
   machine and the pie chart shows how many of each kind.
   Find from the chart the number for each kind.
   Find also the percentage of the total for each kind of drink.

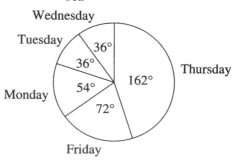

5 One week a car dealer sold 80 cars and the pie chart
   shows how many on each day.
   Find from the chart the number sold on each day.
   Find also the percentage of the total for each day.

Example 15

The crowd at a football match consisted of 45% men, 25% boys, 20% women and 10% girls. Display these details on a pie chart.

The sector angles are as follows:

Men	45% of 360° = 162°
Boys	25% of 360° = 90°
Women	20% of 360° = 72°
Girls	10% of 360° = 36°

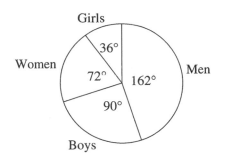

The pie chart can therefore be drawn as shown.
Note   the sector angles must total 360°.

Exercise 22Q

1   On an island the population is distributed as follows:
40% live in North Region
25% live in South Region
20% live in East Region
15% live in West Region.
Display these details on a pie chart.

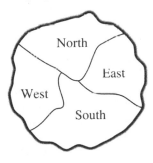

2   One Saturday a large number of people travelled from London to Glasgow for an international football match:
35% went by train
25% went by car
30% went by coach
10% went by aeroplane.
Display these details on a pie chart.

3   One year a census was taken to find out how many people went to Europe by the four different modes:
40% went through the Chunnel
35% went by boat
15% went by air
10% went by hovercraft.
Display these details on a pie chart.

4   A railway company made a census on its revenue collection:
30% came from long-distance passengers
35% came from short-distance passengers
20% came from freight
15% came from mail haulage,
10% came from car carrying.
Display these details on a pie chart.

5   A certain car is available in five different colours. One year the sales were as follows:
40% were black   10% were green
25% were white   10% were blue
15% were red.
Display these details on a pie chart.

Example 16

480 people who are able to vote live in a Scottish village. At one election they voted as follows:

120 voted Labour   160 voted Liberal Democrat

120 voted Conservative   80 voted Scottish Nationalist.

Display these details on a pie chart.

Sector angle for Labour and Conservative $= \dfrac{120}{480} \times 360° = 90°$

Sector angle for Liberal $= \dfrac{160}{480} \times 360° = 120°$

Sector angle for Scottish Nationalist $= \dfrac{80}{480} \times 360° = 60°$

The pie chart can therefore be drawn as shown.
Note   the sector angles must total 360°.

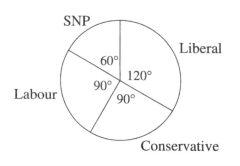

Exercise 22R

For all questions display the details on a pie chart.

1   120 girls choose from four summer sport options:
    40 choose tennis   30 choose swimming
    30 choose rounders   20 choose athletics.

2   180 boys choose from five summer sport options:
    60 choose cricket   30 choose tennis
    45 choose athletics   15 choose golf
    30 choose swimming.

3   720 men from six different cities attend a business meeting:
    120 from Manchester
    80 from Leeds
    120 from Liverpool
    80 from Newcastle
    80 from Birmingham
    240 from London.

4   A small country town spends its revenue from local taxes as follows:
    $\frac{1}{5}$ General public services
    $\frac{1}{8}$ Public transport
    $\frac{1}{5}$ Education
    $\frac{1}{10}$ Landscape improvements
    $\frac{1}{6}$ Police
    $\frac{1}{12}$ Investments
    $\frac{1}{8}$ Road maintenance.

5   The Wonderful Western Coach Company operates coaches from London to Bristol, Exeter, Plymoth, Newport, Cardiff and Swansea. One year bookings were as follows:
    $\frac{7}{20}$ to Bristol $\frac{1}{8}$ to Newport
    $\frac{1}{5}$ to Cardiff $\frac{1}{8}$ to Plymouth
    $\frac{3}{20}$ to Swansea $\frac{1}{20}$ to Exeter.

23 EXTRACTING INFORMATION FROM DATA AND GRAPHS

23.1 Understanding and using averages and the idea of the range for a set of data

Often in newspapers you will read phrases such as:

"The average house price is £62 000."   "The average annual earnings are £12 000."
"The average family has 1.7 children."
Unfortunately most of us do not fit into these descriptions. Our house is
either worth more or less than £62 000, our annual earnings are either more
or less than £12 000 – and no one has exactly 1.7 children!
The word 'average' is used to describe a typical item in a set of data, but
unfortunately there are three different ways of calculating the average and
we need to know which method is being used to make any real sense of
statements such as those above.

In a small firm the two bosses pay themselves £22 000 each per year. They
pay their two senior employees £12 000 each and their three junior
employees £10 000 each. They want to know what is the 'average' annual
salary.

The set of seven salaries in this firm is:
£10 000, £10 000, £10 000, £12 000, £12 000, £22 000 and £22 000

Range
The salaries range from £10 000 up to £22 000.
We say that the **range** of these salaries is the difference between the most
and the least, i.e. £22 000 – £10 000 or £12 000.

Mode
The junior employees say that most people in the firm are paid £10 000 so
this is the typical salary.
The *most frequent* member of the set of salaries is called the **mode** of the set.
For this example the mode is £10 000 and we say that the average (modal)
salary is £10 000.

Median
The senior employees say that a typical salary is the one in the middle,
which in this case is £12 000.
The *middle* item in a set when arranged in ascending order is called the
median of the set.
For this example the average (median) salary is £12 000.

Mean

The bosses say that a typical salary is the total salary bill divided by the number of people working for the firm (which is 7 for this case).

The total of all the items added together, divided by the number of items is called the **mean**.

The total salary bill is:

£10 000 + £10 000 + £10 000 + £12 000 + £12 000 + £22 000 + £22 000 = £98 000

For this example the average (mean) salary is £98 000 ÷ 7 = £14 000.

Note that none of the employees actually earn this mean salary of £14 000.

When we use the word 'average' for a set of data we need to know whether it is the mode, median or mean average. It is also helpful to know the range for the data because this tells us whether the data has a large or small spread (or **variation**).

Example 1

Find the range for each set of data.

a shoe sizes: $6\frac{1}{2}$, 7, 7, 7, 7, 7, 7, $7\frac{1}{2}$

b number of eggs laid per week: 4, 5, 5, 6, 6, 6, 6, 6, 6, 7

c house prices: £40 000, £55 000, £57 000, £60 000, £75 000

a 7.5 − 6.5 = 1   **b** 7 − 4 = 3   **c** £75 000 − £40 000 = £35 000

Exercise 23A

Find the range for each of the following sets of data.

1 The heights of six people are 158 cm, 159 cm, 161 cm, 162 cm, 163 cm and 166 cm.

2 A ferry makes six daily sailings. The numbers of cars on one day were: 12, 17, 19, 11, 8 and 13.

3 There are five supermarkets near to where Nicola lives. One day their prices for a loaf of bread were: 54p, 58p, 62p, 60p and 56p.

4 A small junior school has five classes. There are 17 pupils in Class One, 20 pupils in Class Two, 19 pupils in Class Three, 18 pupils in Class Four and 22 pupils in Class Five.

5 The weights of six people are 65 kg, 76 kg, 93 kg, 52 kg, 47 kg and 88 kg.

6 James ran for his school in the 100 m race on seven occasions. His times were: 13.5, 13.4, 13.8, 13.7, 14.0, 13.9 and 13.2 seconds.

7 Mrs Gates wishes to buy a certain model of car. She visits eight garages and finds that the prices are: £7500, £7250, £7750, £7150, £7650, £7350, £7800 and £7450.

8 A ferry sails six times daily across a tidal estuary. The crossing times on Saturday are: 15 min, 13 min, 16 min, 15 min, 16 min and 12 min. The crossing times on Sunday are 9 min, 12 min, 11 min, 14 min, 17 min and 10 min.

Example 2

Say whether you think the word 'average' is being used to describe the mode, median or mean for each set of data from Example 1.

a The average shoe size of all my shoes is 7.

b The average number of eggs that the chicken laid is 5.7.

c The average of the house prices is £57 000.

a The most common shoe size is the mode.

b No chicken can lay 5.7 eggs, so this must be the mean.

c This could be any, but it is the middle value or median for the data in Example 1.

Exercise 23B

For each of the following three average figures are given. State which one is likely to be **a** the mode, **b** the median, **c** the mean.

1 One day there was a long traffic queue in the High Street. Most of the cars had only one occupant, but others had up to five and a few were illegally carrying as many as eight people. The average figures were 1, 2 and 4.

2 One week the postman called at Jane's house on each day from Monday to Friday. He only delivered one letter on the first two days, but he brought several on Thursday and Friday because it was Jane's birthday on Thursday. The average figures were 1, 5 and 3.

3 One month the early morning train to London was very often on time, but sometimes only a few minutes late and once very late because of a breakdown. The average figures were 2, 9 and 0.

4 A shoe shop carried out a survey on shoes bought (whole sizes only). The average figures for shoe size were 6, 6.5 and 6.7.

5 A batsman had six innings in three cricket matches. He was out without scoring twice but did achieve a century once. His average figures were 10, 0 and 22.

6 A short bus service which operates between two points only runs seven times a day. Only two of the journeys carried the same number of passengers and they both ran during the quiet part of the day. For two peak-hour journeys the bus was nearly full. The average figures were 11, 5 and 8.

7 One day a taxi driver answered several calls. For most of them he carried his maximum number of five passengers. His average figures were 3, 5 and 2.5.

8 An estate agent carried out a survey of house prices on the houses he sold during 1997. The figures given for the average house price were £68 000, £125 000 and £137 463.

23.2 Finding the mode, median and mean for given data and from a graph

---

Example 3

Find the mode of each set of data.

a The numbers 0, 2, 3, 3, 3, 2, 1

b The heights 145 cm, 150 cm, 150 cm, 155 cm, 155 cm, 155 cm and 161 cm.

c The house prices £48 000, £45 000, £47 000, £40 000, £50 000 and £40 000.

a 3 occurs most frequently, so 3 is the mode.

b 155 cm occurs most frequently, so 155 cm is the modal height.

c £40 000 occurs most frequently, so £40 000 is the modal house price.

Exercise 23C

1 A primary school has ten classes. The number in each of the classes is as follows:
   16, 18, 20, 16, 18, 19, 18, 17, 18 and 20.
   Find the mode of these numbers.

2 Laura travels to school by bus. Over a two-week period her journey times were:
   33, 32, 34, 33, 31, 32, 33, 34, 34 and 33 minutes.
   Find the mode of these times.

3 Twelve taxis departed from a rank and the passenger numbers were:
   4, 3, 1, 5, 2, 4, 5, 4, 2, 5, 1 and 5.
   Find the mode of these numbers.

4 Clare travels to work by train on Mondays to Saturdays.
   She recorded how late her train was over a two-week period:
   2, 3, 0, 1, 4, 0, 1, 3, 2, 1, 0 and 1 minutes.
   Find the mode of these times.

5 John is a train spotter. One day he noticed that nine trains departed from a station in the evening peak hour. He also noticed that the trains had the following numbers of coaches:
   6, 8, 4, 12, 4, 6, 4, 12 and 8.
   Find the modal number of coaches.

6 Fifteen children went strawberry picking. The amounts they each picked were as follows.

Name	Weight	Name	Weight	Name	Weight
Mary	17 kg	Gaynor	17 kg	John	18 kg
Sheila	18 kg	Julie	15 kg	James	19 kg
Joanna	15 kg	Linda	18 kg	Alan	17 kg
Christine	16 kg	Paul	17 kg	David	18 kg
Rosemary	18 kg	Geoffrey	19 kg	Raymond	16 kg

Find the modal weight picked.

7 There are fifteen trees along a short avenue. The details for both sides of the avenue are given below.
North Side: Beech, Ash, Poplar, Beech, Beech, Poplar, Poplar, Ash
South Side: Poplar, Beech, Ash, Poplar, Ash, Poplar, Ash
Which kind of tree is the modal one?

8 All fifteen children in Class 9B bought a sandwich during one morning break. The sandwiches they bought were as follows.

Name	Sandwich
John	Tomato
Andrew	Paste
Julian	Cheese
Patrick	Ham
Paul	Egg

Name	Sandwich
Mark	Tomato
Gordon	Egg
Roger	Ham
Dawn	Cheese
Laura	Tomato

Name	Sandwich
Julie	Paste
Judith	Cheese
Gaynor	Ham
Joanna	Egg
Andrew	Cheese

Which kind of sandwich was the modal one?

Example 4

Find the median of each set of data in Example 3 on page 282.

First it is necessary to arrange the items in ascending order.

0, 1, 2, 2, 3, 3:

2 is the middle number, so 2 is the median.

145 cm, 150 cm, 150 cm, 155 cm, 155 cm, 155 cm, 161 cm:

155 cm is the middle number, so 155 cm is the median height.

£40 000, £40 000, £45 000, £47 000, £48 000, £50 000:

there are two middle numbers, £45 000 and £47 000, so we take the middle of these two, i.e. £46 000, as the median.

Exercise 23D

Find the median for each of the following. (Remember to arrange the data in order first.)

1 Mary counted the number of sweets in each of five similar packets. The numbers were:
24, 26, 23, 27 and 22.

2 One week the attendance figures for Class 10A were:
21, 18, 17, 20 and 19.

3 Mrs Brown has five children. Their weights are:
Tina 51 kg,   John 39 kg,   Jane 48 kg,   Bill 53 kg,   Anne 42 kg.

(continued)

4 There are fifteen children in Class 9B. Their heights are given below.

Name	Height	Name	Height	Name	Height
Anne	127 cm	George	111 cm	Azil	119 cm
Adam	136 cm	Miranda	125 cm	Melissa	120 cm
David	158 cm	Razi	116 cm	Paul	145 cm
Emma	147 cm	Salik	148 cm	Tina	128 cm
Fran	142 cm	Zorba	151 cm	Yusuf	149 cm

5 There are fifteen houses in Oak Tree Walk. One day the postman delivered the following numbers of letters to them:
3, 1, 0, 3, 0, 4, 2, 0, 1, 5, 4, 6, 3, 5 and 0.

6 The distances between successive locks along a canal are:
500, 300, 1000, 900, 650, 600, 400, 1100, 750, 450, 950, 800 metres.

7 The prices of fish and chips in ten different shops were:
£1.90, £1.60, £1.50, £1.80, £1.65, £1.95, £1.70, £1.95, £1.85, £1.65.

8 Sunil ran for his school in the 200 m race on ten occasions. His times were:
27.1, 26.4, 26.2, 26.5, 27.2, 26.3, 27.4, 27.2, 26.9, 26.3 seconds.

9 One week the thermometer in Janet's garden shows the temperatures at midday:
Sunday 8 °C, Monday 11 °C, Tuesday 13 °C, Wednesday 9 °C, Thursday 10 °C, Friday 12 °C, Saturday, 14 °C.

10 One week a cafe sold these numbers of lunches:
Sunday 7, Monday 5, Tuesday 4, Wednesday 8, Thursday 13, Friday 6, Saturday 19.

11 At Susan's school there is a small class with only ten children. Their heights are:
120, 116, 117, 113, 122, 114, 121, 124, 112 and 117 cm.

12 The weights of the children in question 11 are:
37, 35, 32, 33, 31, 38, 39, 40, 29 and 36 kg.

Example 5

Find the mean of each set of data in Example 3 on page 282.

a $\dfrac{0 + 1 + 2 + 2 + 3 + 3 + 3}{7} = \dfrac{14}{7} = 2$, therefore the mean is 2.

b $\dfrac{145 + 150 + 150 + 155 + 155 + 155 + 161}{7} = \dfrac{1071}{7} = 153$,

so 153 cm is the mean height.

c $\dfrac{40\,000 + 40\,000 + 45\,000 + 47\,000 + 48\,000 + 50\,000}{6} = \dfrac{270\,000}{6} = 45\,000$,

so £45 000 is the mean price paid.

Exercise 23E

For questions 1–8 find the mean.

1 Wendy's mother took her to school by car one week and the journey times were as follows: 14, 18, 21, 13, 19 minutes.

2 Five children picked some blackberries. The weights they picked were: 320, 300, 290, 370, 350 grams.

3 A football team survived four rounds of a cup contest. The crowds at each match were: 18 530, 19 640, 21 325, 24 265.

4 A packet contains four fruit pies. Their weights are: 51.3, 50.9, 51.8, 51.6 grams.

5 One week, when a harvest was being gathered, a farmer had to work on all seven days. The hours he worked were as follows:

Monday	10
Tuesday	9
Wednesday	11
Thursday	8
Friday	7
Saturday	8
Sunday	10

6 Last week Jean was not very well and on each day she recorded her temperature:

Monday	39.0 °C
Tuesday	38.5 °C
Wednesday	38.5 °C
Thursday	37.5 °C
Friday	38.0 °C
Saturday	37.5 °C
Sunday	37.0 °C

7 James performed for his school athletics team on ten occasions. His times for the 400 m race were:
58 s, 59 s, 57 s, 1 min 5 s (or 65 s), 1 min 3 s, 1 min 1 s, 1 min 4 s, 56 s, 58 s, and 59 s.

8 Nicola worked out the acceleration due to gravity in a physics experiment. She made ten measurements in order to get a good average:
9.8, 9.6, 9.9, 10.1, 10.2, 9.7, 9.8, 9.6, 10.2 and 10.1 metres per second squared.

9 Kate recorded the temperature at midday on every day in February. Her temperatures are given in degrees Celsius:

Day	Temperature			
Sunday	1	10	5	4
Monday	8	1	10	4
Tuesday	5	0	6	5
Wednesday	6	1	3	3
Thursday	5	3	1	3
Friday	2	5	1	4
Saturday	1	8	2	5

Find the mean and range for each of the four weeks and comment on any differences that you notice.

(continued)

10 Peter recorded the number of wet days in each month over a three-year period.

Month	1993	1994	1995
January	10	14	9
February	12	18	7
March	11	19	6
April	11	15	8
May	10	17	8
June	13	12	7
July	14	8	10
August	9	6	15
September	9	5	14
October	10	6	16
November	11	5	15
December	12	7	17

Find the mean and range for each of the three years and comment on any differences that you notice.

Example 6

The block graph shows the frequency that each of the numbers 1 to 6 occurred in 30 throws of a dice. Use this graph to find the mode, median and mean for this set of results. Explain your answers.

Using the graph we can list all 30 results as follows:

1, 1, 2, 2, 2, 2, 2, 3, 3, 3, 3, 3, 3, 4, 4, 4, 4, 5, 5, 5, 5, 5, 5, 5, 6, 6, 6, 6, 6 and 6.

The *mode* is 5. It occurred eight times.
The *median* is 4. The two middle numbers (i.e. the 15th and 16th numbers) are both 4.

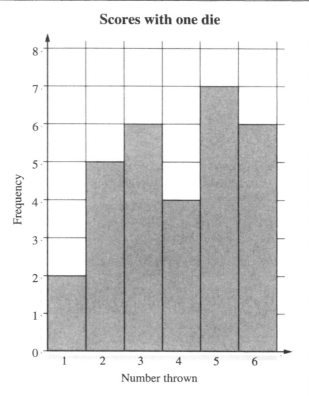

Scores with one die

The *mean* is 3.9. $\dfrac{2\times1 + 5\times2 + 6\times3 + 4\times4 + 7\times5 + 6\times6}{30} = \dfrac{117}{30} = 3.9$

Exercise 23F

For each of the following use the block graph to find the mode, median and mean.

1 Two dice were thrown twenty-five times over.

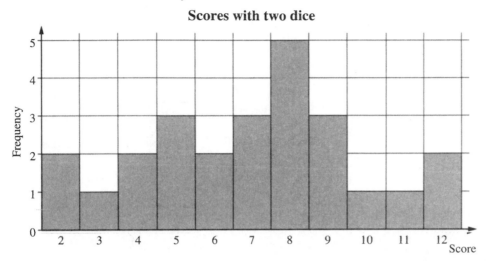

Scores with two dice

2 The temperature was recorded at midday on each day in January.

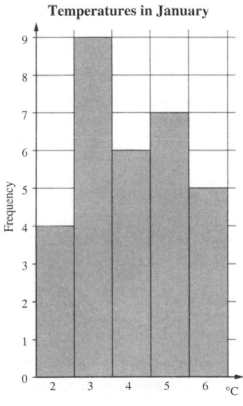

Temperatures in January

3 Mrs Patel recorded how many phone calls she received per day over a two-week period.

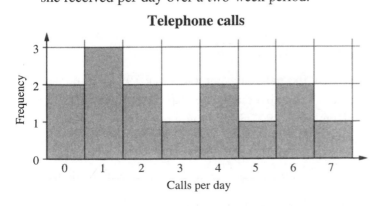

Telephone calls

(continued)

4 Three coins were tossed sixteen times. The number of heads was recorded for each case.

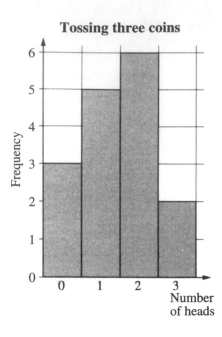

Tossing three coins

23.3 Identifying trends from graphs

Example 7

Jenny makes and sells hand-painted egg cups at her local craft fairs. The line graph below shows her sales for each year from 1989 to 1996. Estimate her likely sales for 1997 to the nearest 10.

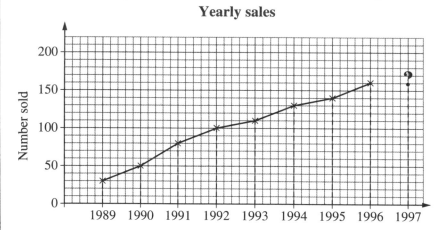

Yearly sales

Each year Jenny has managed to sell more than in the previous year, but since 1993 the increase has been only 10 or 20 more than in the previous year. Given that she sold an extra 20 in 1996 a realistic guess might be that she would sell 10 more in 1997, i.e. 170 egg cups in all. However, she might be able to sell 180 or maybe she has reached her limit and 160 would be a more conservative estimate.

Example 8

David has entered for the London Marathon for each of the past 7 years (1990–1996).

His improving times are shown on the line graph.

Assuming he continues to improve, estimate his time for 1997.

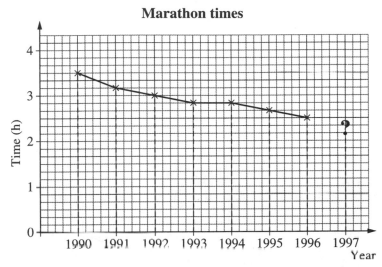

Marathon times

Each year David's time has either remained the same or improved by about ten minutes, so a time between 2 h 20 min and 2 h 30 min would seem a reasonable guess.

Exercise 23G

1 The line graph shows how a tree has grown since it was planted in 1980.
   Estimate its height in the year 2000.

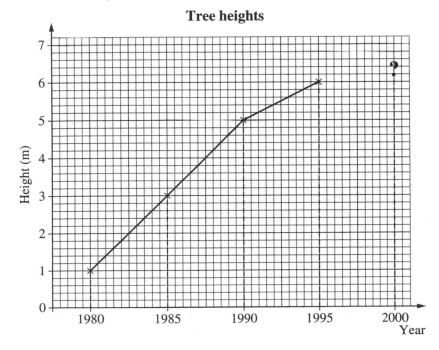

Tree heights

(continued)

2   The block graph shows the crowd that a football
    team attracted for the first four rounds of a cup
    contest. Predict the crowd for their fifth round
    match.

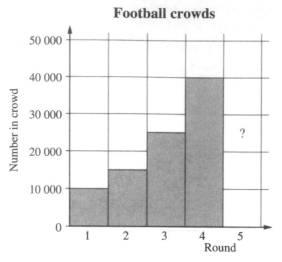

Football crowds

3   The line graph shows how
    far the water's edge is from
    a lighthouse as the tide is
    going out. Predict the
    distance at 2 p.m. if the
    tide is still going out.

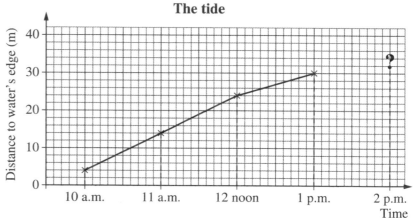

The tide

4   The line graph shows how
    the temperature drops one
    November afternoon.
    Predict the temperature
    at 9 p.m.

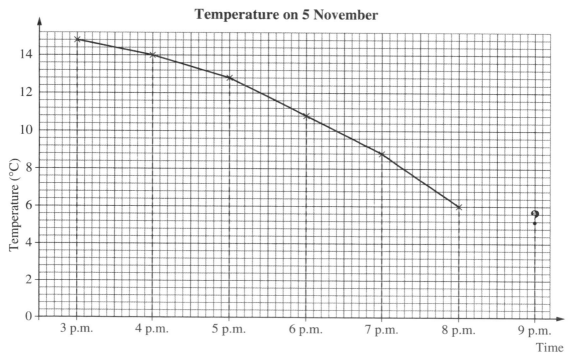

Temperature on 5 November

24 SPEED

24.1   Understanding the idea of speed and average speed

Speed

We use the word 'speed' to describe how fast something is travelling.

In a built-up area a car may not travel faster than 30 mph, i.e. 30 miles per hour. On a normal road we may not drive at more than 60 mph, i.e. 60 miles per hour. On a continental motorway the maximum allowed speed is often 120 kilometres per hour.

Each of these three speeds tells us how far we can travel in 1 hour.

Clearly when driving a car, at one moment the speedometer is registering say 60 mph, but having braked it may then register say 40 mph. The speedometer in the car tells us how fast we are going at that instant.

60 mph means that if we were to drive for one hour at this speed we could travel 60 miles, or since there are 60 minutes in one hour, if we were to drive for one minute at the same speed, we could travel $\frac{1}{60}$th of 60 miles, which is 1 mile, or in one second we could travel $\frac{1}{60}$th of a mile (or 88 feet).

In the same way a speed of 120 kph means we could travel 120 km in one hour at this speed or 2 km in one minute or $\frac{1}{30}$th of a kilometre in one second.

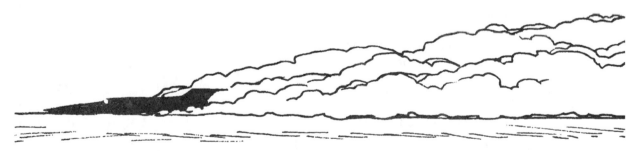

Average speed

In a one hour's car journey we start from rest, accelerate to say 60 mph, slow down, and finally come to rest. If we do not exceed 60 mph we certainly do not 'average' as much as 60 mph.

We use the term 'average speed' to describe the constant speed we would have to travel at to cover the whole journey in the same time.

24.2 Finding average speeds for simple journeys

Example 1

A man drives from London to Birmingham, a distance of 120 miles, in
2 hours but because of heavy traffic his return journey takes 3 hours.
What is his average speed: **a** on the way there   **b** on the way back
c for the whole return journey?

a 120 miles in 2 hours is $\dfrac{120}{2}$ or 60 miles per hour (or 60 mph).

So his average speed on the way there is 60 mph.

b 120 miles in 3 hours is $\dfrac{120}{3}$ or 40 miles per hour (or 40 mph).

So his average speed on the way back is 40 mph.

c The total journey distance is 120 + 120 or 240 miles. The total time
taken is 2 + 3 or 5 hours.

So his average speed for the whole journey is given by:

240 miles in 5 hours = $\dfrac{240}{5}$ = 48 miles per hour (or 48 mph).

Therefore his overall average speed is 48 mph.

Always remember that:

$$\text{Average speed} = \frac{\text{Total distance for the journey}}{\text{Total time for the journey}}$$

Example 2

Find the average speed for each of these journeys:

a 200 miles in 4 hours
b 24 miles in $\frac{1}{2}$ hour
c 100 kilometres in $2\frac{1}{2}$ hours
d 220 kilometres in 4 hours 24 minutes

a Average speed = 200 ÷ 4 mph = 50 mph
b Average speed = 24 ÷ $\frac{1}{2}$ mph (i.e. 24 ÷ 0.5) = 48 mph
c Average speed = 100 ÷ $2\frac{1}{2}$ kph (i.e. 100 ÷ 2.5) = 40 kph
d 24 minutes = $\frac{24}{60}$ hours = 0.4 hours, so 4 hours 24 minutes = 4.4 hours
Average speed = 200 ÷ 4.4 kph = 50 kph

Exercise 24A

1 Find the average speed for these air flights:
  a Birmingham to Gibraltar, 1185 miles in 3 hours
  b London to Istanbul, 1710 miles in 6 hours
  c London to Moscow, 1720 miles in 4 hours
  d London to San Francisco, 5160 miles in 12 hours
  e Manchester to Chicago, 4235 miles in 11 hours.

2 Find the average speed for these train journeys:
  a London to Glasgow, 405 miles in $4\frac{1}{2}$ hours
  b Penzance to Manchester, 375 miles in $7\frac{1}{2}$ hours
  c London to Plymouth, 224 miles in $3\frac{1}{2}$ hours
  d London to Sheffield, 162 miles in $2\frac{1}{4}$ hours
  e London to Bristol, 119 miles in $1\frac{3}{4}$ hours.

3 Find the average speed for these car journeys:
  a London to Liverpool, 192 miles in 5 hours 20 minutes (or $5\frac{20}{60}$ hours)
  b London to Leicester, 98 miles in 2 hours 48 minutes
  c London to Wolverhampton, 121 miles in 3 hours 40 minutes
  d Nottingham to Edinburgh, 286 miles in 7 hours 20 minutes
  e Newcastle to Glasgow, 144 miles in 3 hours 36 minutes.

4 Josiah drives his car from London to Birmingham, 120 miles, in 3 hours
  and then from Birmingham to Preston, a further 100 miles, in 2 hours.
  Find each of the following:
  a his average speed from London to Birmingham
  b his average speed from Birmingham to Preston
  c his overall average speed from London to Preston.

5 A train travels from London to Plymouth, 360 kilometres, in 4 hours and
  then from Plymouth to Penzance, a further 126 kilometres in 2 hours.
  Find each of the following:
  a the average speed from London to Plymouth
  b the average speed from Plymouth to Penzance
  c the overall average speed from London to Penzance.

Example 3

A car is travelling at an average speed of 40 miles per hour. Find each of the following.
a how far it goes in: **i** 3 hours   **ii** $\frac{1}{2}$ an hour
b how long it takes to cover: **i** 80 miles   **ii** 10 miles.

a i 40 miles in 1 hour means (3×40) miles in 3 hours, i.e. 120 miles
  ii 40 miles in 1 hour means $(\frac{1}{2} \times 40)$ miles in $\frac{1}{2}$ an hour, i.e. 20 miles
b i 40 miles in 1 hour means 80 miles in (2×1) hours, i.e. 2 hours
  ii 40 miles in 1 hour means 10 miles in $(\frac{1}{4} \times 1)$ hours, i.e. 15 minutes.

Exercise 24B

1   Copy and complete this table

	Mode of transport	Average speed	Time of journey	Distance covered
a	Train	80 mph	3 hours	
b	Car	45 mph	7 hours	
c	Car	34 mph	5 hours	
d	Train	80 mph	$2\frac{1}{2}$ hours	
e	Motor cycle	32 mph	$1\frac{3}{4}$ hours	
f	Bicycle	16 mph	$2\frac{3}{4}$ hours	
g	Train	72 mph	2 h 15 min	
h	Car	48 mph	1 h 40 min	

2   A train travelling at 128 kph takes 1 h 30 min to travel from London (Paddington) to Bristol. Find the distance between the two stations.

3   A car travelling at an average speed of 66 kph takes 3 h 30 min to travel from Newcastle to Glasgow. Find the distance between the two cities.

4   A car travelling at an average speed of 64 kph takes 1 h 15 min to travel from Leeds to Hull. Find the distance between the two cities.

5   A ship sailing at an average speed of 27 kph takes 1 h 20 min to cross the English Channel from Dover to Calais. Find the distance between the two ports.

6   Copy and complete the table.

	Mode of transport	Distance covered	Average speed	Time taken
a	Train	320 miles	80 mph	
b	Car	240 miles	30 mph	
c	Moped	175 miles	25 mph	
d	Train	90 miles	60 mph	
e	Car	60 miles	48 mph	
f	Motor cycle	63 miles	36 mph	

7   Find the time taken by a train which travels a distance of 405 km from London to Holyhead at an average speed of 90 kph.

8   Find the time taken by a train which travels a distance of 275 km from London to Exeter at an average speed of 110 kph.

9   Find the time taken by a bus which travels a distance of 56 km from Liverpool to Manchester at an average speed of 32 kph.

10 Find the time taken by a motorway coach which travels a distance of 161 km from London to Leicester at an average speed of 92 kph.

24.3   Finding distances and average speeds from simple travel graphs

Example 4

The table below shows how far a cyclist has travelled after various times.

Show this information on a graph, and find her average speed from the graph.

Time (minutes)	0	10	20	30	40	50	60
Distance travelled (miles)	0	4	8	12	16	20	24

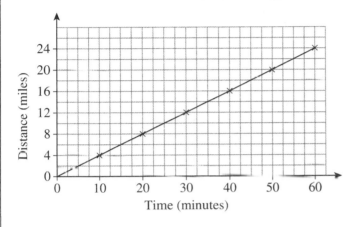

Note   all the points lie on a straight line.

Average speed = 24 miles ÷ 1 hour = 24 mph

Example 5

The table shows the distance covered by a boy running in a 400-metre race after various times.

Show the information on a graph. Find his average speed from the graph.

Time (seconds)	0	20	40	60	80
Distance covered (m)	0	100	200	300	400

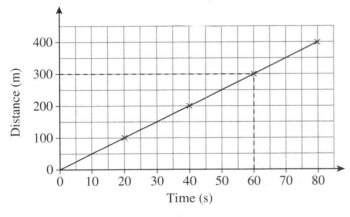

Average speed = 300 ÷ 60 metres per second

        = 5 metres per second

        = 5 × 60 × 60 metres per hour

        = 18 000 metres per hour

        = 18 000 ÷ 1000 kilometres per hour

        = 18 kilometres per hour (kph)

Exercise 24C

1 Brad is cycling across a bridge and the table shows the time he takes
to reach each of the five given points after starting from the west end
of the bridge.

Position	Distance from west end of bridge (metres)	Time taken from west end of bridge (seconds)
West end of bridge	0	0
Support A	10	2
Support B	30	6
Support C		16
Support D		20
East end of bridge		24

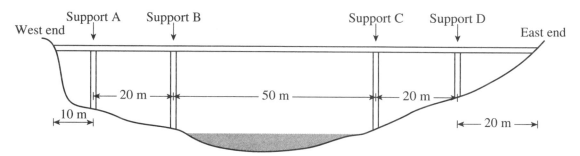

Copy and complete the table and draw a graph of distance against
time. (Use a vertical scale of 1 cm = 10 m and a horizontal scale of
1 cm = 1 second.)
Find from your graph:
a Brad's speed (in both m/s and km/h)
b the distance Brad has covered after cycling for:
   i 4 seconds   **ii** 10 seconds   **iii** 14 seconds
   iv 18 seconds from the west end of the bridge.
c how long it takes him to reach points at each of the following
   distances from the west end of the bridge:
   i 40 m   **ii** 60 m   **iii** 110 m

2 Lee runs in an 800 metre race on the track illustrated.
The race starts at A and consists of two laps of the track and
then a run off from A to the finishing point shown.
The table below shows details of his running times.

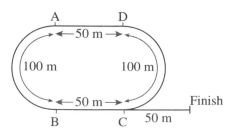

Position	Distance from start (metres)	Time taken from start (seconds)
A (Start)	0	0
B (1st time)	100	20
C (1st time)	150	30
D (1st time)		50
A (2nd time)		60
B (2nd time)		80
C (2nd time)		90
D (2nd time)		110
A (3rd time)		120
B (3rd time)		140
C (3rd time)		150
Finish		160

Copy and complete the table and draw a graph of distance against time.
(Use a vertical scale of 1 cm = 50 m and a horizontal scale of 1 cm = 10 seconds.)

Find from your graph:
a Lee's speed (in both m/s and km/h)
b the distance he has covered after each of the following times:
   i 40 seconds   **ii** 100 seconds   **iii** 70 seconds   **iv** 150 seconds
c the time he takes to cover each of the following distances from the start:
   i 300 m   **ii** 650 m   **iii** 50 m

(For questions 3 and 4 remember that 60 minutes = 1 hour.)

3 The table below shows details of a car journey by motorway from Birmingham to Bristol. The times after which the car passes the service areas are given. Complete the table and then draw a graph of distance against time. Find the speed of the car from the slope of the graph.

Distance	Location	Time	Time (h)
0 km	Birmingham	0 min	0
20 km	Frankley	12 min	0.2
80 km	Strensham	48 min	
130 km	Michaelwood	1 h 18 min	1.3
160 km	Bristol	1 h 36 min	

(Use a horizontal scale of 1 cm to 0.1 h and a vertical scale of 1 cm to 10 km.)

(continued)

4 The table below shows details of an aeroplane flight from London to Moscow. The times after which the aeroplane passes over places on the way are given. Complete the table and then draw a graph of distance against time. Find the speed of the aeroplane from the slope of the graph.

Distance	Location	Time	Time (h)
0 km	London	0 min	
300 km	Amsterdam	30 min	
900 km	Berlin	1 h 30 min	
2100 km	Minsk	3 h 30 min	
2700 km	Moscow	4 h 30 min	

(Use a horizontal scale of 1 cm to 0.2 h and a vertical scale of 1 cm to 200 km.)

Example 6

A man takes 30 minutes to travel from home to work which is 20 miles away and then 2 more hours to travel to a business appointment which is 60 miles from his work. Show this information on a travel graph and find the average speed for each part of the journey and the whole journey.

First show the point representing 30 minutes and 20 miles on the graph. Then show the point representing 2 hours 30 minutes and 80 miles on the graph. (These times and distances are measured from home.)

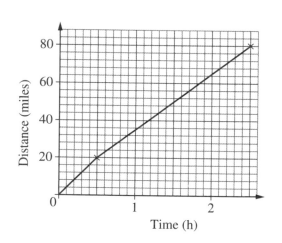

Average speed to work = 20 miles in 30 minutes or 40 miles per hour.
Average speed to the appointment = 60 miles in 2 hours or 30 miles per hour.
Average speed for whole journey = 80 miles in 2 hours 30 minutes or 32 miles per hour.

Exercise 24D

In questions 1–3 a two-stage journey is illustrated on the graph. Find the average speed for both parts of the journey, and also for the whole journey

1 Marcus drives his car to his uncle's house. For the first ten miles he uses a motorway, but he has to use an ordinary road for the remaining fifteen miles.

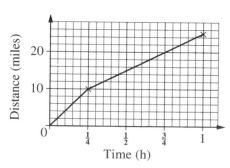

2 Tnisha travels to her sister's house by train.
She has to change trains, but the connection is immediate.

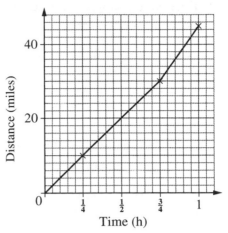

3 Candace drives her car from
Manchester to Hull, but as far as
Barnsley her progress is rather
slow due to bad weather.

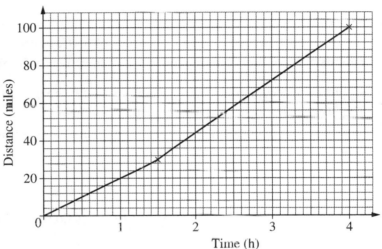

4 A group of hikers walk over Cloudy Pike Mountain and their times at
each of the five marked points are as follows:
  a West Side Foot 10.00 a.m.   **b** Waterfall 12.30 p.m.   **c** Summit 3.00 p.m.
  d Cloudy Edge 4.00 p.m.   **e** East Side Foot 6.00 p.m.

Plot these details on a
travel graph. (Use a
horizontal scale of
2 cm to 1 hour and a
vertical scale of 1 cm
to 1 mile.)
Find each of the
following:
 i their average speed
   on ascending
 ii their average speed
   on descending
iii their overall average
   speed.

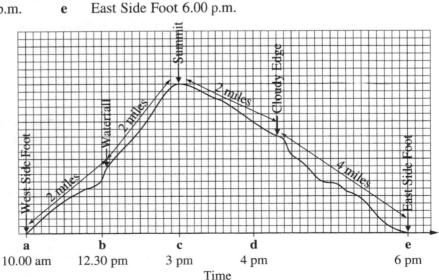

24.4   Finding average fuel consumption for simple journeys

Just as we use mph (miles per hour) and kph (kilometres per hour) to
describe average speed, we can also use mpg (miles per gallon) and
kpl (kilometres per litre) to describe average fuel consumption.

Example 7
A car uses 5 gallons of petrol for a journey of 200 miles.
Find its average fuel consumption in mpg (miles per gallon).

5 gallons are needed for 200 miles, so 1 gallon is needed for $\frac{1}{5}$ of 200 or 40 miles.
The average fuel consumption is therefore 40 mpg.

Example 8
A van uses 40 litres of diesel for a journey of 360 kilometres.
Find its average fuel consumption in kpl (kilometres per litre).

40 litres are needed for 360 kilometres, so 4 litres are needed for 36 kilometres.
Therefore 1 litre is needed for $\frac{1}{4}$ of 36 or 9 kilometres.
The average fuel consumption is therefore 9 kilometres per litre.

Exercise 24E

1   Copy and complete the table below. (Take 1 gallon = 4.5 litres.)

	Mode of transport	Fuel	Distance covered	Fuel consumed	Consumption rate (mpg)	Consumption rate (mpl)
a	Car	Petrol	180 miles	4 gallons		
b	Van	Petrol	72 miles	2 gallons		
c	Bus	Diesel	135 miles	6 gallons		

2   Copy and complete the table below. (Take 1 mile = 1.6 kilometres.)

	Mode of transport	Fuel	Distance covered	Fuel consumed	Consumption rate (kpl)	Consumption rate (mpl)
a	Railway locomotive	Diesel	80 km	200 litres		
b	Taxi	Diesel	23 km	2.5 litres		
c	Pick-up truck	Diesel	108 km	15 litres		

Example 9

A car averages 35 miles per gallon on a long journey.

a Find how far it can travel on: **i** 3 gallons   **ii** 8 gallons.

b Find how many gallons it will consume for a journey of:

  i 70 miles   **ii** 385 miles.

a **i** 35 mpg is (3×35) miles per 3 gallons, i.e. 105 miles.

  ii 35 mpg is (8×35) miles per 8 gallons, i.e. 280 miles.

b **i** 35 mpg is 70 miles per 2 gallons, so 2 gallons are required.

  ii 35 mpg is 385 (or 35×11) per 11 gallons, so 11 gallons are required.

Exercise 24F

1 A car can travel 36 miles on one gallon of petrol.
Find how far it can travel on:
a 4 gallons   **b** 9 gallons
c 1.5 gallons.

2 A bus can travel 20 miles on one gallon of diesel.
Find how far it can travel on:
a 5 gallons   **b** 8 gallons
c 2.5 gallons.

3 A motorcycle can travel 12 kilometres on one litre of petrol.
Find how far it can travel on:
a 8 litres   **b** 12.5 litres
c 4.5 litres.

4 A railway locomotive can travel 0.36 kilometres on one litre of diesel.
Find how far it can travel on:
a 100 litres   **b** 250 litres
c 450 litres.

5 For the car in question 1 find the number of gallons of petrol required for a journey of:
a 180 miles   **b** 252 miles
c 162 miles.

6 For the bus in question 2 find the number of gallons of diesel required for travelling:
a 120 miles   **b** 70 miles
c 250 miles.

7 For the motorcycle in question 3 find the number of litres of petrol required for a journey of:
a 84 km   **b** 36 km
c 30 km.

8 For the railway locomotive in question 4 find the number of litres of diesel required for travelling:
a 540 km   **b** 405 km
c 135 km.

25 SHOPPING

25.1 Shopping at the supermarket (including best buys)

Example 1

Mrs Fitness eats a lot of fruit, which she buys at the Somerway supermarket.
If she buys the following how much change will she get from a £10 note?

 2 lb of bananas at 39p per lb   3 lb of apples at 65p per lb
 4 grapefruits at 27p each   1 lb of pears at 49p per lb
 10 oranges at £1.39 for a net of 5

Her total = £(2 × 0.39 + 4 × 0.27 + 2 × 1.39 + 3 × 0.65 + 1 × 0.49) = £7.08.
Her change out of a £10 note will be £10 − 7.08 = £2.92.

Exercise 25A

Find the change from a £20 note in questions 1 and 2.

1   Rosalia   4 lemons at 29p each
                     4 tins of beans at 26p per tin
                     3 fruit pies at 40p each
                     6 bread buns at 20p each
                     6 bars of soap at 50p each

2   Isabella   4 lb of tomatoes at 60p per lb
                     4 tins of soup at 30p each
                     2 cartons of yoghurt at £1.30 each
                     3 meat pies at 90p each
                     3 packets of beefburgers at £1.20 per packet

Find the change from a £50 note in questions 3–6.

3   Tnisha   4 lb of raisins at 80p per lb
                     4 hot cross buns at 20p each
                     6 packets of crisps at 35p per packet
                     3 tins of peas at 40p per tin
                     3 cream cakes at 90p each

4   Marcus   4 doughnuts at 30p each
                     4 kilograms of strawberries at £1.30 per kilogram
                     2 tins of shoe polish at £1.05 per tin
                     6 cartons of apple juice at 80p per carton
                     6 crumpets at 20p each

5   Marlon   2 cherry cakes at 40p each
3 lb of sultanas at £1.20 per lb
3 cans of orangeade at 35p per can
4 tins of tomatoes at 50p per tin
4 packets of soup at 45p per packet

6   Jordan   3 lb of cooking apples at 55p per lb
3 tins of carrots at 50p per tin
5 lb of potatoes at 30p per lb
5 kiwi fruits at 25p each
2 lb of plums at £1.30 per lb

Example 2

Mr Drowsy is trying to decide which jar of coffee offers the best buy.

The 100 g jar costs £1.35, the 200 g jar costs £2.30, the 300 g jar costs £3.78 and the 500 g tin costs £6.00. There is also a special offer of two 300 g jars for £6.96.

100 g costs £1.35
200 g costs £2.30 which is £1.15 for 100 g   (2.30 ÷ 2 = 1.15)
300 g costs £3.78 which is £1.26 for 100 g   (3.78 ÷ 3 = 1.26)
500 g costs £6.00 which is £1.20 for 100 g   (6.00 ÷ 5 = 1.20)
600 g costs £6.96 which is £1.16 for 100 g   (6.96 ÷ 6 = 1.16)

The 200 g jar represents the best buy.

Exercise 25B

For questions 1–5 find the price per lb for each item in order to decide which is the best buy.

1   3 lb of apples costing £1.35,
4 lb of apples costing £1.92
or 5 lb of apples costing £2.35

2   3 lb of pears costing £1.26,
6 lb of pears costing £2.68
or 5 lb of pears costing £2.05

3   4 lb of tomatoes costing £2.52,
5 lb of tomatoes costing £3.20
or 6 lb of tomatoes costing £3.72

4   a 4 lb bunch of bananas costing £1.48,
a 2½ lb bunch costing 95p
or a 1½ lb bunch costing 54p

5   a 2½ lb bunch of grapes costing £3.50,
a 3½ lb bunch of grapes costing £5.04
or a 1½ lb bunch of grapes costing £2.13

For questions 6–10 find which is the best buy by any convenient method.

6   a 400 g packet of sugar costing 50p,
a 450 g packet costing 60p
or a 680 g packet costing 80p

7   a 120 g jar of coffee costing 48p,
a 108 g jar costing 45p
or a 135 g jar costing 60p

8   a 405 g bag of flour costing 30p,
a 420 g bag costing 35p
or a 500 g bag costing 40p

9   a 1750 ml bottle of orange squash costing £1.25, a 1620 ml bottle costing £1.20
or a 1650 ml bottle costing £1.10

10   a box containing 90 tea bags costing 75p, one containing 100 bags costing 80p
or one containing 135 bags costing £1.20

25.2 Shopping from home (mail order catalogues)

Example 3

Mrs Jones belongs to the Giant Shop Order Catalogue Club. She wants to buy a jumper listed at £17.95 together with a pair of shoes listed at £34.25. She is allowed 10% off the cost of the above order for being a member of the club, but after that has to pay an additional charge of £2.95 to cover the cost of packing, postage and insurance.

How much does she actually pay for this order?

Jumper	£17.95	
Shoes	£34.25	
Subtotal	£52.20	
Less 10% discount	£ 5.22	(10% of £52.20 = $\frac{1}{10}$th of £52.20 = £5.22)
	£46.98	
Postage etc.	£ 2.95	
Total cost	£49.93	Therefore the cost to Mrs Jones is £49.93.

Exercise 25C

Find the total cost for each of the following orders.

	Name	Mail order details	Items ordered	Discount and reason	Cost of postage or delivery, packing and insurance	Total cost
1	Jean	Examination publications by post	Examination paper £1.90 and syllabus £4.30	20% for being a regular customer	£1.95	
2	Rita	Drugs mail order club	Tablets £5.70 and medicine £3.90	20% for being a member of the club	£1.95	
3	Bobbie	Film developing by postal arrangement	Standard prints £2.40 and large prints £3.20	20% during a special offer trial period	£1.95	
4	Janet	Toys by post	Dolls' house kit £18.50 and toy sewing machine £50.10	10% during the January Sales period	£2.95	
5	Deena	Hardware by post club	Kitchen scales £10.40 and kettle £35.20	10% for being a member of the club	£3.95	

Example 4

Mr Greenfingers always buys his bulbs and plants through the Tulip Home Garden Club Catalogue. He wants to order 5 packets of ten mixed tulips at £2.49 per packet, 4 individual hyacinth bulbs at 60p each, 3 border roses at £4.95 each and 1 set of three climbing roses which costs £9.99. He is allowed a 10% discount if the total order is more than £10 or a 20% discount if the total order is more than £25. After that there is a standard charge of £5 for postage and packing, etc. if the total before discount is less than £40.

How much does Mr Greenfingers actually have to pay?

5 packets of tulips at £2.49 each	= £12.45	
4 hyacinths at 60p each	= £ 2.40	
3 border roses at £4.95 each	= £14.85	
1 set of climbing roses	= £ 9.99	
Subtotal	£39.69	
Less 20% discount on order of more than £20	= £ 7.94	(20% of £39.69 = £7.94)
	£31.75	
Postage etc. (order is less than £40)	£ 5.00	
Total cost	£36.75	

So Mr Greenfingers pays £36.75.

Exercise 25D

A mail order company sells electrical goods and offers a 10% discount to its club members. After that a delivery charge of £2.50 is payable if the cost of the order is less than £60 before the discount. Find the amount payable by each of the following members.

1 Martyn   4 switches at £1.50 each   2 reels of wire at £9.50 each
              4 sixty-watt bulbs at 35p each   6 light fittings at £2.20 each

2 Wayne   3 timer switches at £5.20 each   4 low-wattage bulbs at 80p each
              4 wire connectors at £2.10 each   1 soldering iron at £15.40.

A builders' merchant, for a trial period, decides to offer a 20% discount to all of its customers. A delivery charge of £5 is payable if the cost of the order is less than £100 before the discount. Find the amount payable by each of the following.

3 Marcus   2 cans of bitumen at £9.20 each   4 tins of paint at £10.50 each
              4 packets of polyfilla at £2.40 each   2 tins of aquaseal at £11.25 each

4 Josiah   4 bags of shingle at £6.70 each   4 packets of grouting cement at £1.60 each
             8 paving stones at £4.50 each   3 bags of sand at £5.40 each..

25.3 Postage

Posting letters

The cost of posting letters of different weights in 1997 is shown in the table below.

Weight	Less than 60 g	60 to 100 g	100 to 150 g	150 to 200 g
First class	26p	39p	48p	58p
Second class	20p	30p	37p	44p

Example 5

Mr Penman has to post four letters weighing 20 g, 30 g, 80 g and 120 g. Find the cost of posting each using:

a first class post   **b** second class post.

Find also the total cost of posting the four letters by both classes.

a The cost of 20 g is 26p; 30 g is 26p; 80 g is 39p; 120 g is 48p; so the total is £1.39.

b The cost of 20 g is 20p; 30 g is 20p; 80 g is 30p; 120 g is 37p; so the total is £1.07.

Exercise 25E

Find the total postage cost for all cases.

1   One week Anne had to post several letters in order to advertise the opening of her new hairdressing salon and the details are given below.

a First class

Number of letters	Weight
6	30 g
5	80 g
3	120 g
2	170 g

b Second class

Number of letters	Weight
4	30 g
4	80 g
2	120 g
1	170 g

2   One week Nicola had to post a large number of letters in order to advertise the opening of her new boutique and the details are shown below.

a First class

Number of letters	Weight
10	40 g
5	70 g
2	110 g
2	160 g

b Second class

Number of letters	Weight
6	40 g
3	70 g
1	110 g
1	160 g

Posting parcels

The list below shows the cost of posting parcels of different weights

Up to and including 1 kg	£2.70	More than 6 kg and including 8 kg	£6.30
More than 1 kg and including 2 kg	£3.35	More than 8 kg and including 10 kg	£7.30
More than 2 kg and including 4 kg	£4.90	More than 10 kg and including 30 kg	£8.55
More than 4 kg and including 6 kg	£5.50		

Example 6

Mrs Advent is trying to decide whether it is cheaper to send presents to her grandchildren separately or whether to pack all of them into a single parcel.

The weights of the individual presents are 1 kg, 2 kg and 6 kg.

Use the above list to find the cost of posting:

a each present separately

b all the presents in a single parcel.

a The costs for each separate present are £2.70, £3.35 and £5.50.
   Therefore the total cost is £2.70 + £3.35 + £5.50 = £11.55.

b The total weight is 9 kg, so the cost for a single parcel is £7.30.

Exercise 25F

1 Ronnie's aunt has four children, two boys and two girls. Ronnie has Christmas presents for his four cousins as follows:
Julian's present weighs 2.5 kg
Charmaine's present weighs 1.5 kg
Wayne's present weighs 5 kg
Zoey's present weighs 7 kg.
Find the total postage cost if he sends them:
a all separately
b all together in one parcel
c the boys' presents in one parcel and the girls' presents in another.

2 Laura has two nephews and one niece who are triplets. Laura has birthday presents for them as follows:
Matthew's present weighs 1.5 kg
Suzanne's present weighs 5 kg
Peter's present weighs 3 kg.
Find the total postage cost if she sends them:
a all separately
b all together in one parcel
c the boys' presents in one parcel and Suzanne's present in another.

3 Deena has two presents to send to her grandsons for Christmas and both weigh 1.5 kg. It is cheaper to send them together but she can put them separately into a letter box, whereas the return bus fare to the nearest post office is £1.90.
Which is the cheaper option for her and by how much?

4 Boutheina has two Christmas presents for her cousins, one of weight 3.5 kg and the other of weight 5 kg. It is cheaper to send them together but she has no wrapping paper for a bigger parcel.
If the only wrapping paper she would like to use can only be bought in bundles costing £3.15 each, which is the cheaper option for her and by how much?

5 Find the total cost of posting 40 parcels whose weights are as follows:
10 parcels – 2.5 kg   4 parcels – 7 kg
12 parcels – 3.5 kg   5 parcels – 8.5 kg
 7 parcels – 5 kg   2 parcels – 12 kg

25.4 Value-added tax (VAT)

Most things we purchase have a sales tax (or VAT) added to the cost of the article to help to produce revenue for the government. VAT is expressed as a percentage of the cost of the article. At present, where it applies, the rate is $17\frac{1}{2}\%$, though in some cases (such as gas and electricity) the rate is only 8%. Certain things, such as food or children's clothes are zero-rated. With these no tax is added to the cost of the article.

Example 7

In each case below find the VAT added and the total cost of the article.

	Article	Basic cost	VAT rate
a	Armchair	£200	$17\frac{1}{2}\%$
b	Electric plug	£1.50	$17\frac{1}{2}\%$
c	Gas bill	£60	8%
d	Turkey	£8.70	0%

a VAT is $17\frac{1}{2}\%$ of £200 = 0.175 × £200 = £35 so the total cost is £235.

b VAT is $17\frac{1}{2}\%$ of £1.50 = 0.175 × £1.50 = 26p to the nearest penny, so the total cost is £1.76.

c VAT is 8% of £60 = 0.08 × £60 = £4.80 so the total cost is £64.80.

d VAT is zero, so the total cost is £8.70.

Exercise 25G

For questions 1–8 find the VAT (charged at $17\frac{1}{2}\%$) and the total cost.

1 Ayo buys a video of exclusive price £348.

2 Jisanne buys a bicycle of exclusive price £180.

3 Kanika buys a word processor of exclusive price £244.

4 Josiah buys a calculator of exclusive price £25.60.

5 The exclusive charge for Afiya's television repair bill is £63.20.

6 The exclusive charge for Eshe's car repair bill is £125.20.

7 The exclusive charge for Marlon's solicitor's bill is £162.80.

8 Last year the exclusive charges for Jordan's four telephone bills were: £93.20, £86.40, £77.60 and £94.80.

For questions 9 and 10 find the VAT (charged at 8%) and the total cost.

9 Last year the exclusive charges for Shani's four gas bills were: £68.50, £26.25, £21.50 and £53.75.

10 Last year the exclusive charges for Candace's electricity bills were: £51.25, £38.50, £25.75 and £42.25.

COMPUTER SALE
5% DISCOUNT

Example 8

a A restaurant offers both a cafeteria and a waitress service, but there is a 10% surcharge for the waitress service. VAT at $17\frac{1}{2}$% is added to the cost of the meal. Find the total cost of a meal of basic price £20 if the waitress service is used.

The service charge = 10% of £20 = £2 so the exclusive cost = £20 + £2 = £22.
VAT = 17.5% of £22 = £3.85 so the inclusive cost = £22 + £3.85 = £25.85.

b In a sale a computer of exclusive price £800 is discounted by 5%. Find the inclusive cost of the computer.

The discount – 5% of £800 – £40 so the charged exclusive price = £800 – £40 = £760.
VAT = 17.5% of £760 = £133 so the inclusive price is £760 + £133 or £893.

Exercise 25H

Find the total cost for each case if the VAT rate is $17\frac{1}{2}$%.

1 Bobbie buys a new set of car tyres but he has to pay a surcharge of 3% on the basic price of £120 because he uses a credit card.

2 George goes to the theatre but he has to pay a surcharge of 20% on the basic price of £10 because he wants a seat on the balcony.

3 Barbara has her central heating boiler repaired, but she has to pay a surcharge of 15% on the basic cost of £160 because of late payment.

4 Rita has to pay a surcharge of 8% on the basic cost of £200 for a car repair because she had to call the mechanic out.

5 Jean has to pay a surcharge of 6% on the basic cost of £40 for a television repair because she had to call the engineer out.

6 Marlon buys a coat in a sale which is offered for 5% less than its normal price of £80.

7 Jordan buys a video and he is given a discount of 10% off the usual price of £260 because he pays promptly.

8 Josiah buys a cabinet but it is discounted at 20% of the normal price of £140 because it is scratched.

9 Deena has a new exhaust fitted to her car but she is given 15% off the usual price of £120 because she forfeits the guarantee.

10 Eva buys a carpet but it is discounted at 8% off the usual price of £300 because it is shop-soiled.

26 HOUSEHOLD EXPENSES AND BILLS

26.1 Council tax

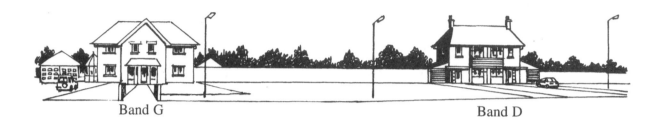

Band G   Band D

In Littletown the full council tax payable in each house price band is as follows.

Band	House price	Council tax
Band A	Up to £40 000	£426
Band B	£40 001 to £52 000	£497
Band C	£52 001 to £68 000	£568
Band D	£68 001 to £88 000	£639

Band	House price	Council tax
Band E	£88 001 to £120 000	£781
Band F	£120 001 to £160 000	£923
Band G	£160 001 to £320 000	£1065
Band H	More than £320 000	£1278

If only one person lives in the property, the above figures are reduced by 25%. If the property is empty or is a second home, the above figures are reduced by 50%.

Example 1

Mr and Mrs Smith are moving from their three-bedroom house which is rated in Band D to a two-bedroom flat which is rated in Band B.

a How much council tax are they presently paying and how much will they pay when they move? How much will they save in a year?

b They can pay their council tax in ten instalments, nine of these are an exact number of pounds with the tenth including the extra to make up the total tax due. How much are these instalments for the two different houses?

a Band D has a council tax of £639. Band B has a council tax of £497. So Mr and Mrs Smith will save £142 each year when they move.

b Band D £639 ÷ 10 = £63.90, so 9 instalments of £63 and 1 of £72. Band B £497 ÷ 10 = £49.70, so 9 instalments of £49 and 1 of £56.

Exercise 26A

All the people in questions 1–5 pay their council tax by the instalment method described above. For each person find the instalments payable.

1 Mr and Mrs Jones, who are a newly married couple and live in a one-bedroom flat which is rated in Band A

2 Mr and Mrs Patel, who live in a two-bedroom house which is rated in Band C

3 Mr and Mrs Brown, who live in a bungalow which is rated in Band E

4 Mr and Mrs Thompson who live in a four-bedroom house which is rated in Band F

5 Mr and Mrs Nouihed who live in a large chalet which has a big garden and is rated in Band G

For questions 6 and 7 find the extra tax that the people will have to pay when they move:

6 Mr and Mrs Jones in question 1, who move from their flat to a house rated in Band D when Mr Jones gets a promotion

7 Mr and Mrs Roberts, who move from a house rated in Band B to one rated in Band E when their first baby is born

For questions 8 and 9 find how much tax the people will save when they move:

8 Mr and Mrs Green, who move from a house rated in Band E to one rated in Band A when Mr Green is made redundant

9 Mr and Mrs Ahmed, who move from a house rated in Band F to one rated in Band C when Mr Ahmed retires

---

Example 2

Mrs Merrywidow has unfortunately lost her husband. She lives in a house which is valued at £100 000. As she now lives alone she is entitled to a 25% reduction on her council tax bill. What amount of council tax does she now pay?

Mr Merrywidow also owned a holiday cottage rated in Band A. As this cottage is now empty, what amount of council tax has to be paid for it?

Her house is rated in Band E, therefore the council tax is 75% of £781 or £585.75. The council tax on the cottage is 50% of £426 or £213.

Exercise 26B

Find the council tax paid by the following single people:

1 Simone, who lives in a flat which is valued at £35 000
2 Julian, who lives in a flat which is valued at £50 000
3 Helen, who lives in a house which is valued at £75 000.

Find the council tax paid by the following people who live elsewhere but have second homes for their holidays in Littletown:

4 Mr and Mrs James, whose holiday chalet is valued at £60 000
5 Mr and Mrs Bailey, whose holiday cottage is valued at £100 000
6 Mr and Mrs Udoma, whose holiday home is valued at £140 000.

26.2 Gas and electricity bills

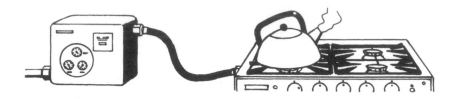

Example 3

Mr Cook pays his gas bill quarterly. It includes a £9 per quarter standing charge, and the gas he uses is charged at 15p per cubic metre. The bill is subject to VAT at 8%. His current gas meter reading is 8510 cubic metres, whereas it read 8170 cubic metres at the end of the previous quarter. Find each of the following:

a the number of cubic metres consumed during this quarter
b the charge for the gas consumed
c his gas bill excluding VAT
d his gas bill including VAT.

a The number of cubic metres consumed = 8510 − 8170 = 340
b The cost of the gas = 340 × 15p = 5100p = £51
c Exclusive charge = £51 + £9 = £60
d Inclusive charge = £60 × 1.08 = £64.80

Exercise 26C

Copy and complete the table below which shows the gas meter readings for eight houses. (The charge is 15p per cubic metre.)

	Initial reading	Final reading	Cubic metres consumed	Consumption charge	Standing charge	Exclusive cost	Inclusive cost
1	6250	6640			£9		
2	9160	9580			£9		
3	4520	4970			£9		
4	2730	3340			£9		
5	3490	4070			£9		
6	5670	6220			£9		
7	8080	8810			£9		
8	1440	2250			£9		

Example 4

Mrs Savit is on the Economy Seven Tariff with her electricity supplies. This means that any electricity used between 12 midnight and 7 a.m. is cheaper than that used during the rest of the day. As a result Mrs Savit tries to do her washing overnight to save money.

Normal units of electricity used are charged at 9p. If Economy Seven units are used, they are charged at 7p. There is a standing charge of £12.50 per quarter and VAT is charged at 8%. Her readings for units used in the last two quarters were 31 762 and 31 983 for the normal units and 4516 and 4962 for the Economy Seven units. Find the total electricity bill for the last quarter.

i Normal units are 31 983 − 31 762 = 221 units. Therefore the cost at 9p each is £19.89.
ii Economy Seven units are 4962 − 4516 = 446 units. Therefore the cost at 7p each is £31.22.
iii Bill including standing charge = £12.50 + £19.89 + £31.22 = £63.61.
iv VAT due on the bill is 8% of £63.61 = £5.09 to the nearest penny.
v So the total bill payable is £63.61 + £5.09 = £68.70.

Exercise 26D

1 If normal units are charged at 9p and Economy Seven units at 7p find the exclusive and inclusive bill for each of the following cases:
   a 50 normal units and 100 Economy Seven units
   b 100 normal units and 100 Economy Seven units
   c 50 normal units and 50 Economy Seven units
   d 100 normal units and 50 Economy Seven units
   e 100 normal units and zero Economy Seven units.

Copy and complete the table below that shows the meter details for seven houses. (Unit prices are as shown in Example 4.)

	Normal units			Economy Seven units			Exclusive bill	Inclusive bill
	Initial no.	Final no.	Units used	Initial no.	Final no.	Units used		
2	3452	3702		1124	1174			
3	2137	3087		2356	2481			
4	4326	4851		4253	4503			
5	1902	2577		6102	6177			
6	5310	5760		3754	4079			
7	7024	7749		5206	5381			
8	9007	9382		2450	2600			

26.3 Telephone bills

Example 5

Mr Ringer's telephone bill showed that he had spent 50 minutes making local calls, 200 minutes making long-distance calls and 10 minutes making international calls.

If the local call rate is 3p per minute, the long-distance call rate is 9p per minute and the international call rate is 22p per minute, find the cost of his bill if the quarterly rental and equipment charge is £28.30.

If VAT is then added at $17\frac{1}{2}\%$, find the total amount that he has to pay.

50 minutes of local calls at 3p per minute is £1.50.
200 minutes of long-distance calls at 9p per minute is £18.00.
10 minutes of international calls at 22p per minute is £2.20.

Total bill including rental charge is £1.50 + £18.00 + £2.20 + £28.30 = £50.00.

The VAT at $17\frac{1}{2}\%$ on this total is $17\frac{1}{2}\%$ of £50.00 = £8.75.

So the total Mr Ringer has to pay is £58.75.

Exercise 26E

Find the total payable for each of the following cases. (The charges are as given in Example 5.)

	Time for local calls	Time for long-distance calls	Time for international calls
1	60 minutes	100 minutes	15 mintes
2	80 minutes	50 minutes	20 minutes
3	100 minutes	30 minutes	40 minutes
4	120 minutes	60 minutes	5 minutes
5	150 minutes	90 minutes	25 minutes
6	200 minutes	70 minutes	30 minutes
7	250 minutes	80 minutes	10 minutes
8	40 minutes	30 minutes	10 minutes
9	50 minutes	40 minutes	30 minutes
10	60 minutes	50 minutes	10 minutes

Example 6

Dr Gossip has her telephone from a company who charge for local calls at a rate of 4p per call for calls of less than 3 minutes but charge at a rate of 3.2p per minute for calls which are longer than that. Find the cost of a call which lasts for each of the following times:

a 2 minutes   **b** 5 minutes   **c** 7 minutes
d 11 minutes   **e** 4.5 minutes.

a 4p   **b** 16p   **c** 22.4p   **d** 35.2p   **e** 14.4p.

Exercise 26F

For questions 1–3 find the cost of the call for each given time.

1   Rosalia's telephone, for which the local charge is 5p for any time less than 5 minutes but 3.5p per minute for calls of more than 5 minutes:
   a 8 minutes   **b** 10 minutes   **c** 7 minutes   **d** 5 minutes
   e 3 minutes   **f** 4 minutes   **g** 1 minute.

2   Isabella's telephone for which the local charge is 6p for any time less than 5 minutes but 2.5p per minute for calls of more than 5 minutes:
   a 6 minutes   **b** 8 minutes   **c** 15 minutes   **d** 9 minutes
   e 5 minutes   **f** 2 minutes   **g** 1 minute.

3   Maria's telephone, for which the medium-distance charge is 10p for any time less than 6 minutes but 4p per minute for calls of more than 6 minutes:
   a 8 minutes   **b** 12 minutes   **c** 15 minutes   **d** 6 minutes
   e 4 minutes   **f** 3 minutes   **g** 1 minute.

4   The graph shows the cost of local calls from Peter's telephone. Find the cost of a call which lasts each of the following times:
   a 2 minutes   **b** 4 minutes
   c 7 minutes   **d** 9 minutes.

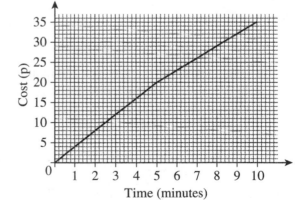

For each of the following find the total cost of the calls.

5   Rosalia, in question 1, made the following calls during the first quarter of last year:
   15 which lasted 4 minutes
   10 which lasted 3 minutes
   5 which lasted 8 minutes
   25 which lasted 10 minutes.

6   Maria, in question 3, made the following calls during the second quarter of last year:
   15 which lasted 3 minutes
   25 which lasted 5 minutes
   20 which lasted 8 minutes
   5 which lasted 10 minutes.

26.4   Water rates

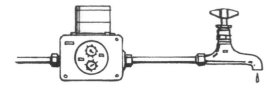

Example 7

Mrs Drought received her annual water rate demand for £489.20.
She was given three options for payment:

a a lump sum payment with a 5% reduction

b two equal instalments, one on 1 April and the other on 1 October

c eight instalments, seven equal ones corrected to the nearest £1
below, and an eighth for the balance.

Find the payment details for each option.

a 5% of £489.20 = £24.46 so Mrs Drought would pay £464.74.

b $\frac{1}{2}$ of £489.20 = £244.60. This amount is payable on both dates.

c £489.20 ÷ 8 = £61.15, so seven instalments of £61 and one of
£62.20.

Exercise 26G

For all questions below find the payment details for each of the three options.

For questions 1–5 the options are as follows:

  a a lump sum payment with a 5% reduction
  b two equal instalments, one on 1 April and the other on 1 October
  c eight instalments, seven equal ones corrected to the nearest £1
    below, and an eighth one for the balance.

1   £423.60   **2**   £396.40   **3**   £452.80   **4**   £546.80   **5**   £507.60

For questions 6–10 the options are as follows:

  a a lump sum payment with a $7\frac{1}{2}$% reduction
  b four equal instalments, one on 1 January, one on 1 April, one on
    1 July and one on 1 October
  c ten instalments, nine equal ones corrected to the nearest £1 below
    and a tenth one for the balance.

6   £516.40   **7**   £432.80   **8**   £539.20   **9**   £493.60   **10**   £582.40

Example 8

Mr Thrift's house has a water meter. He pays a standing charge of £14 for using water and one of £18 for using sewage. He pays 74p for each cubic metre of water used and an additional charge of 80p per cubic metre for 95% of the water he uses as a sewage charge.

If he uses 60 cubic metres of water, what is his total bill?

60 cubic metres of water at 74p per cubic metre is £44.40.
95% of 60 cubic metres (i.e. 57 cubic metres) of water at 80p per cubic metre for sewage is £45.60.

Standing charges for water and sewage are £14 + £18 = £32.
The total bill is therefore £44.40 + £45.60 + £32 = £122.

Exercise 26H

Copy and complete the table below. All details are worked out by the method shown in Example 8.

	Standing charge (water)	Volume used (m³)	Cost per m³	Water cost	Standing charge (sewage)	95% of volume of water used	Cost per m³	Sewage cost	Total cost
1	£14	80	74p		£18		80p		
2	£14	65	74p		£18		80p		
3	£14	95	74p		£18		80p		
4	£14	70	74p		£18		80p		
5	£16	90	68p		£20		70p		
6	£16	60	68p		£20		70p		
7	£16	80	68p		£20		70p		
8	£20	100	60p		£15		75p		
9	£20	120	60p		£15		75p		
10	£20	80	60p		£15		75p		

27 LEISURE AND HOLIDAYS

27.1 Entertainment

Example 1

Mr and Mrs Viewit like to take their three children and their 65-year-old mother to the cinema. The tickets cost £3.50 for each adult, half price for the children and there is a senior citizen's concession of £2.50. Find the total cost to Mr Viewit and what he will have left from a £20 note if he also buys some chocolates which cost £3.99.

Adults: 2 × £3.50 = £7.00 Children: 3 × £1.75 = £5.25 Senior citizen: 1 × £2.50 = £2.50
Chocolates = £3.99. Therefore the total = £7.00 + £5.25 + £2.50 + £3.99 = £18.74.
The change from a £20 note is £20 − £18.74 = £1.26.

Exercise 27A

1 Mr and Mrs Rathod go with their three children to the ice rink. The cost is £5.60 for adults and half that price for children. If they all have lunch at the ice rink cafe at £2.58 each, find:
   a the total that Mr Rathod pays
   b what he will have left from a £50 note.

2 Mr and Mrs Johnson and their two children all go on a boat trip to an island. The fare is £4.80 for adults and half that price for children.
   If they all have a cup of tea at a jetty food bar at 50p each, find:
   a the total that Mr Johnson pays
   b what he will have left from a £20 note.

3 Mr and Mrs Patel and their four children all go to the swimming pool. The cost is £3.20 for adults and half that price for children.
   If they all have a sandwich (55p) and a cup of coffee (45p) at the pool snack bar, find:
   a the total that Mr Patel pays
   b what he will have left from a £20 note.

4 Professor Brown takes her three children to the theatre. The tickets cost £8.40 for adults and half that price for children. If they each have an ice cream (65p) and a cold drink (45p) at the theatre kiosk, find:
   a the total that Professor Brown pays
   b what she will have left from a £50 note.

5 Mrs Newby takes her two children and their two grandparents to the zoo. The cost is £6.50 and half that price for children and senior citizens. If they all have a hot dog (60p) at the zoo cafeteria, find:
   a the total that Mrs Newby pays
   b what she will have left from a £50 note.

6 Dr and Mrs Schultz take their two children and the children's two grandparents to a castle which is open to the public. The cost is £8.50 for adults and half that price for children and senior citizens.
   If they each have a cake (50p) and a cup of tea (40p) at the castle snack bar, find:
   a the total amount that Dr Schultz pays
   b the amount that he has left from a £50 note.

Example 2

Mr and Mrs Church like Chinese food. The prices in their local restaurant do not include the $17\frac{1}{2}\%$ VAT. In addition there is a 15% surcharge if the waitress service is used. They usually choose Wanton soup (£1.95) as a starter and then chicken chop suey (£3.25), sweet and sour prawns (£3.75), black bean beef (£3.50) and have lychees for sweet (£2.25). Find the cost of the food, the VAT element, the service charge and the total bill.

Soup (2 × £1.95)	£3.80	VAT is $17\frac{1}{2}\%$ of £18.80 = £3.29
Chicken	£3.25	
Prawns	£3.75	Food plus VAT = £22.09
Beef	£3.50	Service charge = 15% of £22.09 = £3.31
Lychees (2 × £2.25)	£4.50	
Subtotal	£18.80	

Therefore the total bill is £22.09 + £3.31 = £25.40

Exercise 27B

Calculate the total bill for each of the following cases. (VAT is charged at $17\frac{1}{2}\%$.)

All the people in questions 1–4 go to the Eatupp Restaurant where the waitress service carries a surcharge of 10%.

1 Joanna and Jodie each have:
   Tomato juice 70p   Baked potato with cheese £1.60   Fruit jelly and cream £1.10   Coffee 60p
2 Deena and Julian each have:
   Pea soup £1.70   Toad in the hole £2.40   Rice pudding £1.20   Hot chocolate 70p
3 Peter and Matthew each have:
   Mushroom soup £2.40   Irish stew £4.00   Ice cream sundae £2.70   Horlicks 90p
4 Rita and Bob each have:
   Tomato soup £2.05   Fish and chips £2.80   Ice cream gateau £2.40   Creamy coffee 75p

All the people in questions 5 and 6 go to the Diggin Restaurant where the waitress service carries a surcharge of 15%.

5 Marcus and Josiah each have:
   Lentil soup £2.10   Curried eggs £3.50   Jam tart and custard £1.90   Tea 50p
6 Boutheina, Najwa and Heba each have:
   Vegetable soup £1.90   Pie and chips with vegetables £3.20   Treacle sponge £2.10   Coffee 80p

All the people in questions 7 and 8 go to the Lotsofgrub Tuckhouse where the waitress service carries a surcharge of 5%.

7 Rosalia, Isabella and Maria each have:
   Minestrone soup £2.40   Spanish omelette £3.50   Sago pudding £1.50   Tea 60p
8 Jisanne and Ayo each have:
   Onion soup £2.20   Mushroom omelette £3.00   Fresh fruit salad £2.10   Orange squash 70p

27.2 Weather

Example 3

Mr and Mrs Shady are planning a day out. They look at the weather reports in the newspaper.

Location	Sunshine (hours)	Rainfall (inches)	Maximum temperature		Weather (daytime)
			°F	°C	
London	7.2	0.01	45	7	Sunny but cold
Folkestone	5.9	0.14	49	9	Sunny (a.m.)
Margate	1.4	0.02	46	8	Bright (a.m.)
Brighton	9.7	0.00	55	13	Warm and sunny
Guildford	2.3	1.30	50	10	Showery

a Which place had: **i** the most rain **ii** the least rain?
b Which place had: **i** the highest temperature in °C **ii** the lowest temperature in °C?
c Which places had the greatest difference of: **i** hours of sunshine **ii** temperature in °C?
d What was the average (mean) of: **i** hours of sunshine **ii** temperature in °F?

a **i** Guildford 1.3 in   **ii** Brighton 0.0 in   b **i** Brighton 13 °C   **ii** London 7 °C
c **i** Brighton and Margate 9.7 − 1.4 = 8.3 hours   **ii** Brighton and London 13 − 7 = 6 °C.
d **i** (7.2 + 5.9 + 1.4 + 9.7 + 2.3) ÷ 5 = 26.5 ÷ 5 = 5.3 hours
   ii (45 + 49 + 46 + 55 + 50) ÷ 5 = 245 ÷ 5 = 49 °F

Exercise 27C

For each of the towns find the following:

a the place which had: **i** the most rain   **ii** the least rain
b the place which had: **i** the highest temperature   **ii** the lowest temperature
c the places which had the greatest difference of: **i** hours of sunshine   **ii** temperature in °C.

1

Location	Sunshine (hours)	Rainfall (inches)	Maximum temperature		Weather (daytime)
			°F	°C	
Torquay	6.9	0.01	52	11	Sunny
Penzance	6.4	0.02	54	12	Sunny
Exmouth	7.0	0.02	50	10	Sunny
Minehead	4.6	0.04	48	9	Bright
Newquay	3.4	0.06	52	11	Cloudy

Find also the mean temperature in both °C and °F.

2

Location	Sunshine (hours)	Rainfall (inches)	Maximum temperature		Weather (daytime)
			°F	°C	
Scarborough	3.9	0.08	46	8	Bright
Whitley Bay	1.5	0.03	45	7	Dull
Redcar	3.3	0.06	43	6	Bright
Seaburn	3.8	0.01	46	8	Bright
Bamburgh	1.9	0.02	48	9	Cloudy

Find also the mean number of hours of sunshine.
Give the answer in both hours and hours and minutes.

Exercise 27D

The charts show the average (mean) temperature and rainfall for each month of the year in Madrid.
Find each of the following:

1 the month with the hottest temperature.   **2** the month with the coldest temperature
3 the month with the most rainfall   **4** the month with the least rainfall
5 the average summer temperature (April to September inclusive)
6 the average winter temperature (October to March inclusive)
7 the average summer rainfall   **8** the average winter rainfall

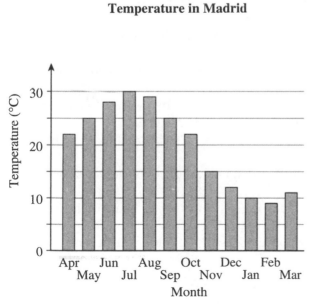

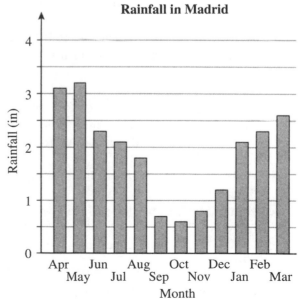

27.3 Booking holidays

Exercise 27E

1 Mr and Mrs Kirk are planning a holiday in Palma, Majorca. The brochure shows the following prices per person. (They intend to fly from Gatwick.)

Arrival date	Cost per person at Maria's Chalets		Cost per person at Yolanda's Bay View Hotel	
	7 days	**14 days**	**7 days**	**14 days**
17.5 to 31.5	£200	£280	£350	£480
1.6 to 16.6	£240	£320	£380	£520
17.6 to 30.6	£270	£350	£420	£570
1.7 to 16.7	£300	£400	£450	£600
17.7 to 31.7	£280	£380	£435	£570
1.8 to 16.8	£260	£300	£400	£510

Notes i Airport surcharges per person: Gatwick – £0, Birmingham – £8.
      ii Accompanied children: 75% of adult rate.

a Find the cost per person if they stay two weeks in Maria's Chalets and the arrival date is:
   i 17 May   **ii** 1 July   **iii** 17 July
b Find the cost per person if the Kirks stay one week in Yolanda's Bay View Hotel and the arrival date is: **i** 1 June   **ii** 17 June   **iii** 1 August.
c Find the difference in cost per person between the two accommodations for two weeks if the arrival date is: **i** 1 June   **ii** 17 July   **iii** 1 August.
d For the third case in part **c** find how much they would each be able to spend on food per day if they stayed in Maria's Chalets before the total cost is more than paying for two weeks in Yolanda's Bay View Hotel.
e Between which arrival dates is the difference between the two accommodation costs for two weeks the greatest and how much is this difference?
f Between which arrival dates is the difference between the two accommodation costs for one week the greatest and by how much?

2 If insurance costs £25 per person for one week and £30 per person for two weeks find the total cost of the holiday for each family below. Each family flies from Birmingham.
   a Mr and Mrs Kirk and their one child decide to spend one week in Yolanda's Bay View Hotel and arrive on 17 May.
   b Mr and Mrs Mortimer and their one child decide to spend one week in Yolanda's Bay View Hotel and arrive on 1 July.
   c Mr and Mrs Underwood and their one child decide to spend one week in Maria's Chalets and arrive on 17 May.
   d Mr and Mrs Jehta and their one child decide to spend one week in Maria's Chalets and arrive on 1 July.

27.4 Foreign currency

Example 4

Mr and Mrs Hague are going to France for their holiday. They decide to change £200 in cash into French Francs and to buy £500 worth of traveller's cheques in French Francs. Their travel agent has a Bureau de Change with a notice which gives the buying and selling price of French Francs per £1.

Buy	Cash	Cheques
FF	8.2	8.1

Sell	Cash	Cheques
FF	7.8	7.9

a How many French Francs will they receive for their £200 and what will the value of their traveller's cheques be in French Francs?

b On their return they have FF410 left in cash. How many pounds will they receive when they change this back into British money?

a The bureau are selling their French Francs so Mr and Mrs Hague will receive 200 × FF7.8 or FF1560 in cash and 500 × FF7.9 or FF3950 in traveller's cheques. They therefore have a total of FF5510.

b 410 ÷ 8.2 = 50 so FF410 will buy back £50.

Exercise 27F

1 Copy and complete the table.

Name	Where going	British money (cash)	Exchange rate	British money for travellers' cheques	Exchange rate	Foreign money bought
Shani	France	£300	£1 = FF8.1	£400	£1 = FF8.2	
Zoey	Germany	£350	£1 = DM2.3	£200	£1 = DM2.4	
Janet	Belgium	£240	£1 = BF49	£300	£1 = BF50	
Afiya	Holland	£500	£1 = G2.6	£250	£1 = G2.7	
Rita	USA	£350	£1 = $1.5	£560	£1 = $1.6	

2 All of the holiday makers in question 1 have to pay a commission fee to the Bureau de Change. The commission is a percentage of the total value of foreign currency bought.
If the first three people go to a bureau that charges 2% and the last two go to one that charges $2\frac{1}{2}$%, find for each person:
a the commission charged **b** the net amount of foreign currency that they receive.

28 PERSONAL FINANCE

28.1 Budgeting

Example 1

Most people have regular bills coming in for Gas, Electricity, Council Tax, Water Rates, Telephone, Housekeeping, Insurances and Rent or Mortgage Payments. Some of these are paid once a year, some twice a year, some quarterly and some every month. It helps to work out the total for the year and how much this would be each month if they were evenly spread. The table below shows Miss Prudence's bills for the year.

Period	Bills	Amount
Yearly	Council Tax	£420
	Insurances	£260
Monthly	Housekeeping	£200
	Rent	£360

Period	Bills	Amount
Half-yearly	Water Rates	£120
Quarterly	Gas	£90
	Electricity	£60
	Telephone	£40

a Work out Miss Prudence's total outgoings for the year and what her average monthly cost is.

b If Miss Prudence's net monthly pay is £830, how much on average does she have left over at the end of each month for other expenses?

a Her total annual bill is:

£420 + £260 + 2 × £120 + 4 × £90 + 4 × £60 + 4 × £40 + 12 × £200 + 12 × £360 = £8400

Therefore her average monthly bill is £8400 ÷ 12 or £700

b Miss Prudence will have £830 − £700 = £130 left over each month.

Exercise 28A

For Anne, whose net monthly pay is £850, find:

1 the total yearly outgoings   **2** the average outgoings per month

3 the average amount left per month to spend.

Period	Bills	Amount
Yearly	Council Tax	£450
	Insurances	£270
Monthly	Housekeeping	£250
	Rent	£300

Period	Bills	Amount
Half-yearly	Water Rates	£120
Quarterly	Gas	£50
	Electricity	£70
	Telephone	£60

Example 2

Most bills can now be paid by Direct Debit, at no extra cost, and are spread out over 12, 10 or 8 months starting in April. Often Council Tax bills are spread over 10 months and Water Rates over 8 months, but all other bills are usually spread over 12 months. Using the figures in Example 1, find Miss Prudence's actual outgoings for each of the twelve months starting from April and hence how much she has left to spend each month.

April to November	Water Rates	£240 ÷ 8 = £30
April to January	Council Tax	£420 ÷ 10 = £42
April to March	Insurances	£260 ÷ 12 = £21.67
	Gas	£90 ÷ 3 = £30
	Electricity	£60 ÷ 3 = £20
	Telephone	£40 ÷ 3 = £13.33
	Housekeeping	£200
	Rent	£360

Totals: April to November £727, therefore leaving £103

December and January £697, therefore leaving £133 (no water rates)

February and March £655, therefore leaving £175 (no water rates or council tax)

Exercise 28B

For each of the following individuals find, using the information in Example 2 above:

a how much is payable in outgoings each month from April to March
b how much is left to spend at the end of each of these same months.

1 Rosalia (net monthly pay £850)

Period	Bills	Amount
Yearly	Council Tax	£450
	Insurances	£204
	Water Rates	£248
Monthly	Housekeeping	£180
	Rent	£320

Period	Bills	Amount
Quarterly	Gas	£105
	Electricity	£93
	Telephone	£126

2 Julian (net monthly pay £950)

Period	Bills	Amount
Yearly	Council Tax	£430
	Insurances	£168
	Water Rates	£216
Monthly	Housekeeping	£210
	Rent	£370

Period	Bills	Amount
Quarterly	Gas	£75
	Electricity	£81
	Telephone	£105

28.2 Hire purchase, mortgages and tax

Example 3

John Splashout wants to buy a new TV/video system which costs £650. His local superstore is offering to spread the payments over three years by charging interest at a rate of 12% of the cost price per annum.

Find each of the following:

a the total interest he will have to pay

b the total cost of the system including the interest

c the monthly payments over the three-year period.

a Total interest = 3 × 12% of £650 = 3 × £78 = £234

b Total cost = £650 + £234 = £884

c Cost of each monthly payment = £884 ÷ 36 = £24.56

Note as the interest is worked out from the cost price and not from the outstanding balance, the real interest figure is much higher than 12% (in fact it is approximately 20%). The true interest is usually called the APR figure which stands for the 'annualised percentage rate'.

Exercise 28C

For all questions find each of the following:

a the yearly interest   **b** the total interest

c the total cost of the item   **d** the cost of each monthly instalment.

	Item	Cost price	Interest rate	Time to pay
1	Television	£360	12%	3 years
2	Cooker	£396	15%	3 years
3	Microwave oven	£252	15%	2 years
4	Photocopier	£480	10.5%	2 years

For many hire-purchase arrangements a deposit is paid. The yearly interest paid is then the given percentage of the amount outstanding.

	Item	Cost price	Deposit	Interest rate	Time to pay
5	Bicycle	£200	£50	8%	2 years
6	Motor cycle	£1500	£150	10%	3 years
7	Caravan	£3000	£600	10%	4 years

Example 4

In 1996–97 John Splashout earned £16 465 as a motor engineer. He got the lower personal allowance of £3765 per year and paid tax on his first £3900 at 20% and on the rest of his income at 24%.

How much tax did John pay altogether?

Gross income = £16 465
Allowances = £3 765
Net income = £12 700

Tax on the first £3900 at 20% = 20% of £3900 = £780
Tax on the remainder (£8800) at 24% = 24% of £8800 = £2112

Therefore the total tax John pays = £780 + £2112 = £2892

Exercise 28D

For questions 1–5 find: **a** the yearly tax payable **b** the monthly tax payable.
(**Note** the lower personal allowance is £3765 p.a. The upper personal allowance is £5555 p.a. and this can be claimed by either of the partners in a marriage but not both.)

	Name	Occupation	Annual pay	Personal allowance
1	Bobbie	Electrician	£18 215	Lower
2	Heba	Legal adviser	£15 600	Lower
3	Tony	Truck driver	£12 400	Lower
4	Janet	Office clerk	£11 600	Upper
5	Najwa	Cashier	£13 250	Upper

For questions 6–10 find: **a** the yearly tax payable **b** the weekly tax payable.

	Name	Occupation	Annual pay	Personal allowance
6	Ayo	Milkman	£12 055	Upper
7	Boutheina	Machinist	£13 368	Upper
8	Josiah	Sales assistant	£10 746	Lower
9	Tnisha	Typist	£13 125	Lower
10	Kanika	Waitress	£12 085	Lower

28.3 Household, car and personal insurance

Example 5

Miss Prudence wishes to insure the buildings of her house which is valued at £52 000 and the contents of her house which are worth £15 000. She is quoted a rate of £1.80 per £1000 for the buildings and a rate of £2.60 per £1000 for the contents or £5.40 per £1000 if she wishes to insure the contents for accidental damage.

a How much will she have to pay altogether for the buildings insurance and the standard contents insurance?

b How much more will she have to pay for the enhanced contents insurance?

a Buildings (£52 000) at £1.80 per £1000 is: $52 \times £1.80 = £93.60$.
   Contents (£15 000) at £2.60 per £1000 is: $15 \times £2.60 = £39.00$.
   Therefore the total bill is £93.60 + £39.00 = £132.60.

b Extra for accidental damage is £5.40 – £2.60 or £2.80 per 1000.
   Therefore the extra payable is $15 \times £2.80 = £42$.

Exercise 28E

All the people in questions 1–5 are insured through the Takefullcare Company whose rates are £1.50 per £1000 for buildings, £2.50 per £1000 for contents, and £4.50 per £1000 if the contents are also to be covered for accidental damage. Find for each person:

a the cost of the buildings insurance   **b** the cost of the contents insurance
c the extra cost if the contents are to be insured for accidental damage.

	Name	Value of property	Value of contents
1	Afiya	£50 000	£10 000
2	Martyn	£60 000	£8000
3	Jordan	£48 000	£6000
4	Eshe	£45 000	£12 000
5	Marlon	£56 000	£9000

For questions 6–8 the people are insured with the Coveritall Company where the rates are £2.00 per £1000 for buildings, £2.50 per £1000 for contents and £5.00 per £1000 for accidental damage to contents. Find for each person the same information as for question 1–5.

	Name	Value of property	Value of contents
6	Zoey	£40 000	£12 000
7	Ronnie	£55 000	£8000
8	Charmaine	£50 000	£16 000

Example 6

Mrs Drivit has a good driving record and wants to insure her Ford Escort fully comprehensive. She is quoted a premium of £600 less 10% for being the only driver less 5% for the age of her car (over 5 years) less 50% for 3 years without a claim (a 'no-claims bonus').

a Find how much Mrs Drivit's annual car insurance is going to be.

b In twelve months' time Mrs Drivit will get a 60% discount if she has another accident-free year.
How much will her insurance be then?

c Mrs Drivit can pay monthly but this will cost a 3% surcharge.
How much would the monthly premium be in each case above?

a £600 – 10% of £600 = £600 – £60 = £540
£540 – 5% of £540 = £540 – £27 = £513
£513 – 50% of £513 = £513 – £256.50 = £256.50
Therefore her annual premium with 3 years no-claims bonus is £256.50.

b £513 – 60% of £513 = £513 – £307.80 = £205.20
Annual premium with 4 years no-claims bonus is £205.20.

c £256.50 + 3% of £256.50 = £256.50 + £7.70 = £264.20
Monthly premium with 3 years no-claims bonus = £264.20 ÷ 12 = £22.02
£205.20 + 3% of £205.20 = £205.20 + £6.16 = £211.36
Monthly premium with 4 years no-claims bonus = £211.36 ÷ 12 = £17.61

Exercise 28F

Everyone in this exercise is insured through the Supermotorsafe Company. The company offers a 20% discount for 'owner-driver only cover', a 10% discount for a car which is more than 5 years old, and its no-claims bonuses are 20% for two years, 40% for three years, and 60% for four years or more. All bills can be paid monthly but this involves a 5% surcharge.

Find the amount payable by each of the following if the bill is paid: **a** for the whole year **b** monthly.

	Name	Policy price	Is it an owner-driver only policy?	Is the car more than five years old?	Time without making a claim
1	Marcus	£600	Yes	Yes	3 years
2	Tnisha	£500	Yes	Yes	3 years
3	Josiah	£450	Yes	Yes	3 years
4	Kanika	£550	Yes	Yes	4 years
5	Ronnie	£625	Yes	Yes	4 years
6	Charmaine	£400	No	Yes	4 years

(continued)

28.4 Savings

Example 7

Mrs Savit does not have to pay any tax. She has savings of value £5000 which she can either invest in National Savings paying 7% gross simple interest or with the Friendly Building Society which pays 6% gross but compound interest.

If she wishes to leave her savings untouched for 3 years, which is the more advantageous to her? Would it make any difference if she was able to leave her savings untouched for 7 years?

National Savings: The simple interest of 7% is paid each year.

$$7\% \text{ of } £5000 = \frac{7}{100} \times £5000 = £350$$

So in 3 years the interest would be $3 \times £350 = £1050$.

Her total savings after 3 years would therefore be £6050.

Friendly Building Society: The compound interest of 6% is added to the capital each year and then interest is earned on both the capital and the interest during the next year.

Year 1   £5000 + 6% of £5000 = £5000 + £300 = £5300
Year 2   £5300 + 6% of £5300 = £5300 + £318 = £5618
Year 3   £5618 + 6% of £5618 = £5618 + £337.08 = £5955.08

Her total savings after three years would therefore be £5955.08, so National Savings is the better option over three years.

After 7 years the interest on the National Savings scheme is $7 \times £350 = £2450$, so after 7 years her savings would be £7450.

For the Friendly Building Society: (continuing the above procedure)

Year 4   £5955.08 + 6% of £5955.08 = £5955.08 + £357.30 = £6312.38
Year 5   £6312.38 + 6% of £6312.38 = £6312.38 + £378.74 = £6691.12
Year 6   £6691.12 + 6% of £6691.12 = £6691.12 + £401.47 = £7092.59
Year 7   £7092.59 + 6% of £7092.59 = £7092.59 + £425.56 = £7518.15

Her total savings after seven years would therefore be £7518.15, so the Friendly Building Society is the better option over seven years.

Exercise 28G

For questions 1–6 find the value of the person's savings after the time stated.

1   David invests £6000 at a simple interest rate of 5% for 4 years.
2   Stuart invests £4000 at a simple interest rate of 8% for 4 years.

3 Rebecca invests £9000 at a simple interest rate of 6% for 4 years.

4 Maria invests £12 000 at a simple interest rate of 9% for 3 years.

5 Najwa invests £12 000 at a compound interest rate of 10% for 5 years.

6 Heba invests £10 000 at a compound interest rate of $7\frac{1}{2}$% for 2 years.

For questions 7–10 find the number of years after which the compound interest option becomes the more advantageous.

7 5% compound interest or $5\frac{1}{4}$% simple interest on an investment of £10 000.

8 8% compound interest or $8\frac{1}{4}$% simple interest on an investment of £2500.

9 6% compound interest or $6\frac{1}{8}$% simple interest on an investment of £5000.

10 10% compound interest or $11\frac{1}{2}$% simple interest on an investment of £8000.

Example 8

Mrs Savit is also considering putting her savings into a five-year TESSA.

The Friendly Building Society have a scheme which pays 5% in Year 1, 6% in Year 2, 7% in Year 3, 8% in Year 4 and 9% in Year 5.

The Better Building Society pays a fixed rate of 7% per year. Which is the better investment?

	Friendly Building Society	Better Building Society
Year 1	£5000 + 5% of £5000 = £5250	£5000 + 7% of £5000 = £5350
Year 2	£5250 + 6% of £5250 = £5565	£5350 + 7% of £5350 = £5724.50
Year 3	£5565 + 7% of £5565 = £5954.55	£5724.50 + 7% of £5724.50 = £6125.22
Year 4	£5954.55 + 8% of £5954.55 = £6430.91	£6125.22 + 7% of £6125.22 = £6553.98
Year 5	£6430.91 + 9% of £6430.91 = £7009.70	£6553.98 + 7% of £6553.98 = £7012.76

So the Better Building Society is slightly better over the five-year period.

Exercise 28H

For questions 1–4 find which is the better option over a three-year period.
(All rates are compound interest rates.)

1 £10 000 is to be invested.
Option A: Fixed rate of 5%.
Option B: Year one 4%, Year two 5%, Year three 6%.

3 £2500 is to be invested.
Option A: Fixed rate of 4%.
Option B: Year one 3%, Year two 4%, Year three 5.5%.

2 £5000 is to be invested.
Option A: Fixed rate of 8%.
Option B: Year one 7.5%, Year two 8%, Year three 9%.

4 £7500 is to be invested.
Option A: Fixed rate of 6%.
Option B: Year one 4%, Year two 5%, Year three 8%.

29 INTERPRETING DATA

29.1 Advertisements

Example 1

Smartcars are advertising a new Mini for £6995*. The * refers to the small print which excludes the delivery cost of £450, the number plates at £25 and twelve months' car tax at £140. Mr Steer decides, despite all this, that he will buy a new Mini but discovers that Smartcars only have ones with metallic paint which actually costs another £265.

a What is the actual cost of a new Mini?

b If Mr Steer can obtain a 10% discount, how much more than the originally advertised price will he actually pay?

a £6995 + £450 + £25 + £140 + £265 = £7875

b 10% of £7875 = £787.50

So the car will cost £7875 − £787.50 = £7087.50 or £92.50 more than the originally advertised price.

Exercise 29A

For each of the following find:
a the total price payable before the discount
b the actual amount paid after the discount
c the difference between the actual amount paid and the originally advertised price.

1 Ayo sees a train set advertised at £60, but this does not include a set of rails (£12.50) or a transformer and controller unit (£23.50). He can, however, obtain a 15% discount.

2 Jean sees a bicycle which she wants to use for shopping advertised at £150 but this does not include a basket carrier (£16.50) or a set of lights with a dynamo (£13.50). She can, however, get a 15% discount.

3 Peter sees a television for sale at £255 but this does not include an indoor aerial (£15) or a licence for one year (£90). He can, however, get a 20% discount.

4 Rita sees a portable computer advertised at £150 but this does not include a memory expansion pack (£25) or an interface for storing programs on discs (£75). She is, however, offered a 20% discount.

5 Martyn sees a poster at his local railway station which advertises a trip to a safari park for £25 but this does not include a short coach ride from the station to the park (£2.50) or admission to the park itself (£3.50). He has, however, a Railcard which gives him a 5% discount on everything.

Example 2

It is claimed that on average children aged between nine and thirteen play video games for 1.4 hours a day. 400 children were asked about this and the results are shown on the pie chart.

a Convert the sector angles to percentages.

b Convert the percentages to actual numbers.

c Use the mid-value for each of the time categories to estimate the mean time. Does this agree with the figure stated?

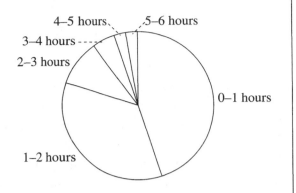

a For 0–1 hours, 162° is equivalent to

$\frac{162°}{340°} \times 100\% = 45\%$. The other angles

can similarly be shown to be equivalent to 35%, 10%, 5%, $2\frac{1}{2}\%$ and $2\frac{1}{2}\%$.

b 45% of 400 = $\frac{45}{100} \times 400 = 180$.

Sector angles

0–1 hours	162°
1–2 hours	126°
2–3 hours	36°
3–4 hours	18°
4–5 hours	9°
5–6 hours	9°

The other figures can similarly be shown to be 140, 40, 20, 10 and 10.

c Using the mid-value for each range, an estimate of the mean is:

$$[0.5 \times 180 + 1.5 \times 140 + 2.5 \times 40 + 3.5 \times 20 + 4.5 \times 10 + 55 \times 10] \div 400 = 1.425.$$

This agrees with the figure stated to 2 significant figures.

Exercise 29B

1 It is said that on average people aged between 20 and 30 do some form of exercise for an average amount of 2 hours per week.

400 such people were asked about this and the results are shown on the pie chart.

a Convert the sector angles to percentages.

b Convert the percentages to actual numbers.

c Estimate the mean time. Does this agree with the figure stated?

2 It is stated that on average people between 30 and 40 spend 3.5 hours per week reading. 400 such people were asked about this and the pie chart shows the results.

a Convert the sector angles to percentages.

b Convert the percentages to actual numbers.

c Estimate the mean time. Does this agree with the time stated?

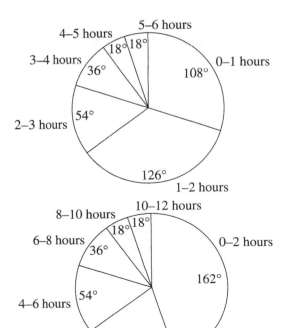

29.2 Special offers and sales promotions

Example 3

A travel agent has a range of special offers to try and attract customers. These are £50 off the total cost of the holiday **or** 15% off the basic cost of the holiday (i.e. excluding insurance) **or** free insurance. If European insurance costs £14.20 per person for one week or £26.20 per person for two weeks, which would be the best discount to take on each of these holidays assuming that two people were travelling together?

a one week in Benidorm (Spain), in a self-catering apartment costing £159 per person

b two weeks in Malta, in a self-catering apartment costing £169 per person

c two weeks with half-board in a hotel in Austria costing £179 per person.

a 15% of £159 = £23.85 per person, i.e. £47.70 for two people.
One week's insurance for two people = 2 × £14.20 = £28.40.
So the £50 discount would be the best offer.

b 15% of £169 = £25.35 per person, i.e. £50.70 for two people.
Two weeks' insurance for two people = 2 × £26.20 = £52.40.
So the free insurance would be the best offer.

c 15% of £179 = £26.85 per person, i.e. £53.70 for two people.
Two weeks' insurance for two people = 2 × £26.20 = £52.40.
So the 15% discount is the best offer.

Exercise 29C

1 The Northern Intercity Railway Company offers three alternative incentives to attract passengers: £6 off the fare, or 5% off the fare, or free travel by tube train from where the passenger lives into London. Which would be the best for each of the following?

  a Josiah, who is travelling to York (£90) and whose tube fare into London is £4

  b Kanika, who is travelling to Newcastle (£130) and whose tube fare into London is £5

  c Zoey, who is travelling to Peterborough (£60) and whose tube fare into London is £6.50.

2 A car dealer offers three alternative incentives to attract business: £500 off the price, or 6% off the price, or free servicing costs for two years.
If servicing costs £75 for every 6000 miles driven, find the best alternative for each of the following:

  a Ronnie, who buys a second-hand car for £5000 and expects to drive 30 000 miles in the first two years

  b Charmaine, who buys a new car for £8500 and expects to drive 24 000 miles in the first two years

  c Marcus, who buys a new car for £9750 and expects to drive 42 000 miles in the first two years.

Example 4

A double-glazing firm has an offer of £1299 for any seven windows, provided that the total area of the windows is not more than 10 square metres.

Mr Draughty has seven windows of the following dimensions:

1.2 m by 2 m, 1.2 m by 1.5 m, 1.2 m by 2.5 m, 0.8 m by 1 m, 0.8 m by 0.6 m, 0.6 m by 0.6 m and 0.6 m by 1.2 m.

Will he qualify for the special offer price of £1299?

The total window area is:
$(1.2 \times 2 + 1.2 \times 1.5 + 1.2 \times 2.5 + 0.8 \times 1 + 0.8 \times 0.6 + 0.6 \times 0.6 + 0.6 \times 1.2)$ square metres
$= 9.56$ square metres

So Mr Draughty will just qualify for the special price offer.

Exercise 29D

1   A fencing contractor has an offer of £500 for up to 35 metres of fencing and an additional charge of £20 per metre after that.
    Find the amount payable by each of the following:
    a Rosalia, who wants four fences, the lengths of which are 14 m, 9.5 m, 6 m and 4.5 m
    b Isabella, who wants four fences, the lengths of which are 12 m, 15 m, 6 m and 4 m.

2   A builder makes an offer for fitting rain gutters of £250 for up to 25 metres of guttering and an additional charge of £12.50 per metre after that.
    Find the amount payable by each of the following:
    a George, who wants four lengths of guttering fitted: one of length 9 m, one of length 5 m, one of length 4 m and one of length 6 m.
    b Bernard, who wants five lengths of guttering fitted: one of length 8 m, one of length 7.5 m, one of length 5.5 m, one of length 4 m and one of length 5 m.

3   A tarmac surfacing company makes an offer of £3000 for up to 70 square metres of surface and a further charge of £50 per square metre after that.
    Find the amount payable by each of the following:
    a Deena, who wants three surfaces covered whose dimensions are 7 m by 4.5 m, 5 m by 1.5 m and 9 m by 4 m
    b Helen, who wants three surfaces covered whose dimensions are 6.5 m by 6 m, 9 m by 2 m and 5 m by 3 m.

4   A carpet dealer makes an offer of £1000 for 100–125 square metres of carpet and a charge of £10 per square metre after that.
    Find the amount payable by each of the following:
    a Eva, who wants seven rooms carpeted: three of dimensions 5.5 m by 3.5 m, two of dimensions 5 m by 4 m, one of dimensions 4.5 m by 3.5 m and one of dimensions 5.5 m by 3 m.
    b Suzanne, who wants seven rooms carpeted: three of dimensions 5 m by 4 m, two of dimensions 4.5 m by 4 m, one of dimensions 6 m by 3 m and one of dimensions 3 m by 3 m.

29.3 Surveys and opinion polls

Example 5

In a sample of 1000 people who were asked about washing powders 600 indicated that they used Sudso, 300 indicated that they used Brighto and 100 indicated that they used Cleano.

a What percentage of the 1000 people used each washing powder?

b If a supermarket intended to stock 200 boxes containing packets of washing powder, how many of each of the three kinds should they order?

a Sudso: $\dfrac{600}{1000} = \dfrac{60}{100} = 60\%$

Brighto: $\dfrac{300}{1000} = \dfrac{30}{100} = 30\%$

Cleano: $\dfrac{100}{1000} = \dfrac{10}{100} = 10\%$

b Sudso: 60% of 200 = 120   Brighto: 30% of 200 = 60
Cleano: 10% of 200 = 20

Exercise 29E

1 1000 people were asked which flavoured crisps they preferred and they answered as follows:
360 preferred Plain   100 preferred Cheese and Onion
240 preferred Salt and Vinegar   300 preferred Smoky Bacon.
a What percentage of the 1000 people preferred each kind?
b If a supermarket intended to stock 200 boxes containing packets of crisps, how many of each kind should they order?

2 1000 housewives were asked which flavoured fruit squash they bought for their children and they answered as follows:
300 bought orange   250 bought lemon   240 bought lime
100 bought raspberry   110 bought blackcurrant.
a What percentage of the 1000 housewives bought each kind?
b If a supermarket intended to stock 200 boxes containing bottles of fruit squash, how many of each kind should they order?

3 500 people were asked which flavour ice-cream they preferred and they answered as follows:
150 preferred vanilla   125 preferred strawberry   50 preferred orange
75 preferred chocolate   100 preferred banana.
a What percentage of the 500 people preferred each kind?
b If a cafe owner is going to make 60 litres of ice cream, how many litres of each kind should he make?

Example 6

a In a large town with four MPs an opinion poll of 2000 voters suggested that 50% would vote Labour, 30% would vote Liberal Democrat and 20% would vote Conservative. How many of the four seats would this suggest that each party should win?

b In the actual election the results from the four separate wards were as follows:

Party	East	South	West	North
Conservative	6500	5600	400	300
Labour	6000	5000	7000	14000
Liberal Democrat	3500	5400	8600	1700

i How many seats did each party actually win?

ii Find the total number of votes cast for each party. How many votes were cast in the four wards altogether? Find the percentage of the total number of votes that each party received.

iii Was the opinion poll an accurate prediction of the result of the election?

a Labour: 50% of 4 is 2. Liberal Democrat: 30% of 4 is 1.2 (i.e. 1 or 2 seats to the nearest whole number). Conservative: 20% of 4 is 0.8 (i.e. 0 or 1 seats to the nearest whole number).

b i Conservative: 2 seats (East and South wards)   Labour: 1 seat (North ward)
Liberal Democrat: 1 seat (West ward)

ii Total number of votes is 64 000.
Conservative 12 800 votes which is $\dfrac{12\,800}{64\,000} = 20\%$.

Labour 32 000 votes which is $\dfrac{32\,000}{64\,000} = 50\%$.

Liberal Democrat 19 200 votes which is $\dfrac{19\,200}{64\,000} = 30\%$.

iii The opinion poll correctly predicted the number of votes cast for each party, but it did not show how these would be distributed across the four wards.

Exercise 29F

1 A national opinion poll suggested that people would vote as follows in a general election: 50% Labour, 30% Conservative and 20% Liberal Democrat.
   a Find the expected number of votes for each party in a town where 15 000 people vote.
   The actual results in the above town were:
   Labour 7200   Conservative 4950   Liberal Democrat 2850.
   b Convert the above figures to percentages.
   c Was the opinion poll accurate?
   Find also:
   d which party or parties did better than expected and by how many votes
   e which party or parties did poorer than expected and by how many votes.

30 DIY IN THE HOME

30.1 Cooking

Example 1

Mrs Cook has a recipe for a rich Madeira cake.

The ingredients consist of:

125 g of butter	$\frac{1}{2}$ teaspoonful of baking powder
125 g of caster sugar	grated rind of $\frac{1}{2}$ a lemon
2 eggs	milk if required
200 g of flour	125 g of raisins

Mrs Cook buys the following quantities at her local supermarket with the prices as shown:
250 g of butter (86p), 500 g of caster sugar (80p), 6 eggs (72p), 1 kg flour (90p), 1 lemon (22p) and 500 g of raisins (£1.60).

a What is the approximate cost of the ingredients used in this cake?

b What is the approximate cost of a cake which is twice this size?

a Butter $\frac{1}{2}$ of 86p = 43p, caster sugar $\frac{1}{4}$ of 80p = 20p, 2 eggs $\frac{1}{3}$ of 72p = 24p, flour $\frac{1}{5}$ of 90p = 18p, 1 lemon = 22p and raisins $\frac{1}{4}$ of £1.60 = 40p. (Baking powder and milk already in stock.) Therefore total cost is 43p + 20p + 24p + 18p + 22p + 40p = £1.67.

b Total cost is £1.67 × 2 − 22p = £3.34 − 22p = £3.12 since only one lemon is used.

Exercise 30A

1 Barbara has a recipe for a trifle.

The ingredients consist of:

100 g of jelly	500 g of fresh cream
one serving of blancmange powder	four trifle sponges

She buys the following quantities:
a 200 g packet of jelly (£1.40), 1 kg (1000 g) of fresh cream (£1.80), four servings of blancmange powder (68p) and a packet of eight trifle sponges (60p).
What is the cost of preparing this trifle?

2 Rita has a recipe for an apple pie.

The ingredients consist of:

250 g of caster sugar	500 g of cooking apples
150 g of margarine	200 g of flour

She buys the following quantities:
$\frac{1}{2}$ kg (500 g) of sugar (84p), 1 kg (1000 g) of cooking apples (96p),
450 g of margarine (£1.20) and 1 kg of flour (90p).
What is the cost of preparing this apple pie?

(continued)

3   Jean has a recipe for a chocolate cake. The ingredients consist of:
150 g of margarine, 150 g of caster sugar, 3 eggs, 125 g of flour, 50 g of cocoa.
She buys the following quantities: 300 g of margarine (90p), 300 g of sugar (60p), 6 eggs (70p),
500 g of flour (48p) and 200 g of cocoa (£1.20).
What is the cost of preparing this cake?

4   Deena has the following recipe for making pancakes for herself and a visitor.
125 g of flour, 1 egg, $\frac{1}{4}$ of a litre of milk, 125 g of sugar and $\frac{1}{2}$ lemon.
She buys the following:
500 g of flour (48p), 6 eggs (72p), 1 litre of milk (£1.08), 500 g of sugar (92p) and 1 lemon (25p).
What is the cost of preparing the above?
What would be the cost of preparing the same for four people?

Example 2

Mrs Sweet grows fruit in her garden and likes to make blackcurrant jam. Her recipe includes
$1\frac{1}{2}$ kg of blackcurrants, 3 kg of sugar and 1 litre of water.

If she picks 6 kg of blackcurrants and wants to use them all, find:

a how much sugar she must buy

b how many half-kilogram jars she will be able to fill, assuming the water evaporates

c how much it will cost to make each jar if sugar costs 78p per kilogram

d how much profit she makes if she sells all of the jars for 50p each.

a 6 kg = 4 × $1\frac{1}{2}$ kg, so she will need 4 × 3 kg or 12 kg of sugar.

b 6 kg + 12 kg = 18 kg so she can make 36 half-kilogram jars of jam.

c 12 kg of sugar will cost 12 × 78p = £9.36.

Therefore each jar of jam will cost £9.36 ÷ 36 or 26p to make.

d Therefore the profit on each jar is 50p − 26p or 24p, which is 36 × 24p or £8.64 in all.

Exercise 30B

1   Najwa grows raspberries in her garden and likes to make raspberry jam. Her recipe includes 2 kg of raspberries, 3 kg of sugar and 1 litre of water.
If she picks 10 kg of raspberries and wants to use all of them for making jam, find each of the following:

  a how many kilograms of sugar she must buy

  b how many half-kilogram jars her jam will fill (assume the water evaporates)

  c how much it will cost to make each jar if sugar costs 70p per kilogram

  d the profit she makes after selling all the jars if her selling price is 60p per jar.

2   Heba grows onions in her garden, and she uses them for making up jars of pickled onions. Her recipe includes $\frac{1}{2}$ lb onions (about 0.2 kg) and 200 ml (0.2 litres) of vinegar. If she picks 6 kg of onions and wants to use them all, find each of the following:

  a how many litres of vinegar she must buy

  b how many half-kilogram jars she will be able to fill (assume that 1 litre of vinegar weighs 1 kg)

  c how much it will cost to make each jar if vinegar costs £1.08 a litre

  d the profit she makes if she sells all of the jars at a market for 45p each.

30.2 Decorating

> **Example 3**
>
> Exterior wall paint comes in 1 litre, 2.5 litre, 5 litre and 10 litre tins. These cost £3.99, £5.99, £8.99 and £14.99 respectively. Each litre of paint covers approximately 2 square metres of wall surface.
>
> **a** Find how much paint will be needed for each of the following areas:
>   **i** a 3 m by 5 m wall   **ii** a 3 m by 15 m wall   **iii** a 6 m by 25 m wall.
> **b** Find the cheapest way of buying the paint for each area in part **a**.
>
> **a** **i** Area is 3×5 square metres = 15 square metres to 7.5 litres of paint are needed.
>   **ii** Area is 3×15 square metres = 45 square metres to 22.5 litres of paint are needed.
>   **iii** Area is 6×25 square metres = 150 square metres to 75 litres of paint are needed.
> **b** **i** a 2.5-litre tin and a 5-litre tin cost £5.99 + £8.99 = £14.98, so for 1p more you could buy a 10-litre tin and have 2.5 litres left over.
>   **ii** Two 10-litre tins and one 2.5-litre tin cost $2 \times$ £14.99 + £5.99 = £35.97, however, to be on the safe side you should buy two 10-litre tins and a 5-litre tin which will cost £38.97.
>   **iii** Seven 10-litre tins and one 5-litre tin cost $7 \times$ £14.99 + £8.99 or £113.92.

Exercise 30C

For all questions below the area of any doors or windows in the walls may be ignored. This ensures that the paint coverage is adequate.

1 Ayo has an outside wall to paint which measures 10 m by 6 m. Find:
   a the area of the wall
   b the amount of paint he requires.
     (1 litre can cover 2 square metres).
The price of the paint is as follows: one 25-litre tin £36, one 10-litre tin £15 and one 6-litre tin £10.
He considers two ways of buying the paint: the first is to buy a 25-litre tin and a 6-litre tin, whereas the second is to buy three 10-litre tins.
Which way do you think is the better for him and why?

10 m

6 m

2 Ronnie wants to paint the outside walls of his bungalow and the dimensions of each of the four walls are shown. Find:
   a the total area that he has to paint
   b the amount of paint he requires.
The price of the paint is as follows: one 20-litre tin £27.50, one 10-litre tin £16 and one 5-litre tin £9. (1 litre can cover 2 square metres.)
He considers two ways of buying the paint, the first is to buy three 20-litre tins, one 10-litre tin and one 5-litre tin, whereas the second is to buy four 0-litre tins. Which way do you think is the better for him and why?

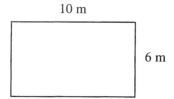

3 m

10 m

15 m

Example 4

A room measures 3 m by 4 m and is 2.5 m high. A roll of wallpaper is approximately 50 cm wide and 11 m in length. A roll of ceiling frieze is approximately 5 cm wide and 5 m in length.

a Find how many rolls of wallpaper are needed to paper this room. (Ignore any doors and windows in your calculation.)

b Find how many rolls of ceiling frieze are needed if the frieze is to go all the way round the room.

c Find the cost of papering this room if the paper costs £7.99 a roll and the frieze costs £3.99 a roll.

a The perimeter of the room is 14 m (i.e. 3 m + 4 m + 3 m + 4 m). This will need 28 drops of paper if each is 50 cm wide. Each roll of 11 m should provide 4 drops of 2.5 m, so 28 ÷ 4 or 7 rolls will be needed altogether.

b As the perimeter is 14 m, three 5-metre rolls of frieze will be needed.

c Wallpaper: 7 rolls at £7.99 each will cost 7 × £7.99 or £55.93.
Frieze: 3 rolls at £3.99 each will cost 3 × £3.99 or £11.97.
Therefore the total cost will be £55.93 + £11.97 or £67.90.

Exercise 30D

For all questions find each of the following:

a the perimeter of the room

b the number of rolls of ceiling frieze required if it is to go right around the room and is sold in 4 metre rolls

c the number of 'drops' of wallpaper required if each drop is 50 cm (0.5 m) wide

d the total length of wallpaper required

e the number of rolls of wallpaper required if it is sold in 15-metre rolls

f the total cost of the decorating if a roll of frieze costs £4 and a roll of wallpaper costs £7.50.

1 Kitchen

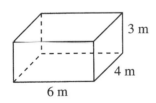

2 Large living room

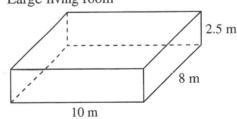

3 Small bedroom

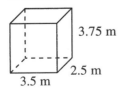

4 Waiting room in a bus station

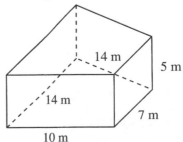

30.3 Landscaping

Example 5

Mr Private wants to put a 6-feet-high fence around his back garden. The two sides are 29 feet long and the back is 40 feet wide. The panels he can buy are priced as follows:

6 ft by 6 ft £13.99, 6 ft by 5 ft £12.79 and 6 ft by 4 ft £12.69.

He needs a fence post at the end of each panel and the posts cost £5.49 each.

How much will the materials for this fence cost altogether?

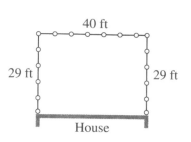

He needs four 6 ft by 6 ft and one 6 ft by 5 ft panel(s) for each side and six 6 ft by 6 ft and one 6 ft by 4 ft panel(s) for the end. He also needs eighteen fence posts. He will require fourteen 6 ft by 6 ft panels together with two 6 ft by 5 ft and one 6 ft by 4 ft panel(s).

6 ft by 6 ft panels: 14 × £13.99 = £195.86
6 ft by 5 ft panels: 2 × £12.79 = £25.58
6 ft by 4 ft panels: 1 × £12.69 = £12.69
Posts: 18 × £5.49 = £98.82

Therefore the total cost of the materials is £332.95.

Exercise 30E

For questions 1–6 find each of the following for the back garden fence illustrated:

a the number of 6 ft by 6 ft panels required　　　　**b** the number of 6 ft by 5 ft panels required
c the number of posts required
d the total cost of the materials for the fence if the prices are:
　6 ft by 6 ft panels £13.50 each, 6 ft by 5 ft panels £12 each and posts £6 each.

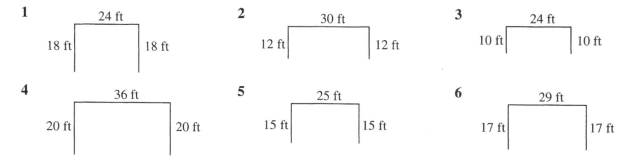

For questions 7 and 8 there are two methods of making the stated fence.
Find the cost of materials for both methods.

7 a straight fence of length 30 ft　　　　　　**8** a straight fence of length 52 ft

Example 6

Mrs Trellis wants a patio which measures 6 ft
by 12 ft at the back of her house. She is
considering one of three designs.
Find the cost of the paving slabs for each design.
(2 ft by 2 ft slabs cost £2.50 each, 2 ft by 1 ft slabs
cost £1.99 each and 1 ft by 1 ft slabs cost £1.79.)

a 18 slabs (2 ft by 2 ft) cost 18 × £2.50 or £45

b 15 slabs (2 ft by 2 ft) cost 15 × £2.50 or
£37.50 and 6 slabs (2 ft by 1 ft) cost 6 × £1.99
or £11.94. So the total cost is £49.44.

c 11 slabs (2 ft by 2 ft) cost 11 × £2.50 or £27.50,
7 slabs (2 ft by 1 ft) cost 7 × £1.99 or £13.93
and 14 slabs (1 ft by 1 ft) cost 14 × £1.79 or
£25.06. So the total cost is £66.49.

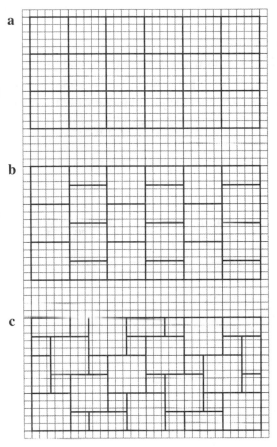

Exercise 30F

For each question two patterns have been given for the same patio. Work out the cost for each if the
prices are £2.50 for a 2 ft by 2 ft slab, £2.00 for a 1½ ft by 1½ ft slab and £2.00 for a 2 ft by 1 ft slab.

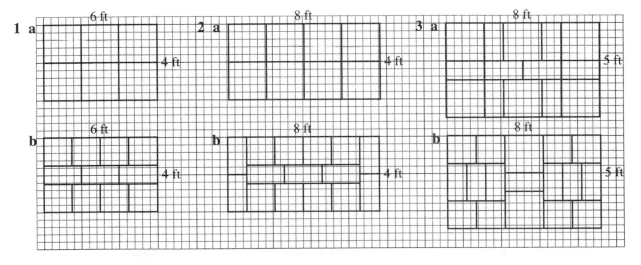

Planning a new bathroom or kitchen

Example 7

Mr and Mrs Kleenit want a new bathroom suite consisting of a bath, a washbasin, a toilet, the taps, the bath panel and tiles for an area of 4 square metres. In a special offer at their local DIY store they find a suite they like which costs £350 but the bath taps cost £65, the basin taps cost £45, the bath panel costs £95 and the tiles cost £15 per square metre.

Is it cheaper to buy this suite or an identical one at another store which has an all-in price including up to 4 square metres of tiles of £599.99?

The cost of the first suite is £350 + £65 + £45 + £95 + 4 × £15 = £615. So the second suite is cheaper by £15.01.

Exercise 30G

In all the questions below the same bathroom suite can be bought at Store A where the sundries are paid for separately or at Store B where the price is all in. For each case find the price at each store and state which is the cheaper and by how much.

	Purchaser	Price of bath, basin and toilet at Store A	Price of sundries at Store A	All-in price at Store B (including 4 square metres of tiles)
1	Mr and Mrs Jones	£320	Bath taps £55 Basin taps £50 Bath panel £75 Tiles: 4 sq m required at £12.50 per sq m	£555
2	Mr and Mrs Patel	£270	Bath taps £50 Basin taps £40 Bath panel £60 Shower unit £150 Tiles: 6 sq m required at £12.50 per sq m	£635
3	Mr and Mrs Jehta	£290	Bath taps £50 Basin taps £45 Bath panel £65 Heater unit £80 Tiles: 4 sq m required at £12.50 per sq m	£560

Exercise 30H

For questions 1 and 2 find each of the following:

a the number of units of each kind required if 800 mm × 800 mm corner units and 1200 mm, 600 mm and 450 mm base units are available

b the total cost of the units required if the prices are as follows: 450 mm units £150 each, 600 mm units £175 each, 1200 mm units £300 each and corner units £250 each

c the length of working surface required (assume its width will cover the whole of the corner unit)

d the cost of the working surface if it can be cut to any length and is charged at £40 per metre

e the total cost of the kitchen, if the cost of fitting is 10% of the cost of the units and working surface.

1

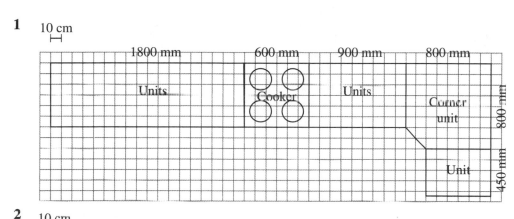

2

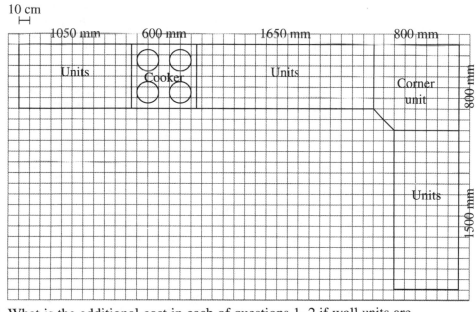

3–4 What is the additional cost in each of questions 1–2 if wall units are placed above each of the base units and the price of each wall unit is the same price of the corresponding base unit and the fitting charge is 5% of the cost?

Answers

Exercise 1A
1	a	two tens and two	b	22	2 a three tens and two	b 32	3 a five tens and two	b 52

1 a two tens and two   **b** 22   **2** a three tens and two   **b** 32   **3** a five tens and two   **b** 52
4 a six tens and two   **b** 62   **5** a four tens and two   **b** 42   **6** a two tens and five   **b** 25
7 a three tens and five   **b** 35   **8** a four tens and five   **b** 45   **9** a four tens and eight   **b** 48
10 a four tens and six   **b** 46   **11** a two tens and seven   **b** 27   **12** a three tens and seven   **b** 37

Exercise 1B
1 300   **2** 330   **3** 332   **4** 220   **5** 228   **6** 500   **7** 510   **8** 515   **9** 700   **10** 790

Exercise 1C
1 a eighteen   **b** thirteen   **c** fifteen   **d** nineteen   **e** twelve
2 a twenty-four   **b** twenty-eight   **c** thirty-four   **d** thirty-eight   **e** forty-five   **f** forty-nine
3 a sixty-eight   **b** sixty-two   **c** seventy-seven   **d** ninety-two   **e** ninety   **f** sixty
4 a five hundred and forty   **b** five hundred and ninety   **c** five hundred and ninety-three
    d seven hundred and fifty   **e** seven hundred and fifty-nine
5 a eight hundred   **b** eight hundred and ten   **c** eight hundred and fifteen
    d eight hundred and three   **e** eight hundred and eight
6 a two hundred and thirty   **b** two hundred and thirty-eight   **c** five hundred and thirty-eight
    d five hundred and eight
7 three hundred and thirty-four   **8** one hundred and eighty-nine

Exercise 1D
1 a 17   **b** 15   **c** 16   **d** 14   **e** 11   **2** a 26   **b** 25   **c** 29   **d** 32   **e** 37
3 a 80   **b** 70   **c** 40
4 357   **5** 365   **6** 736   **7** 792   **8** 650
9 630   **10** 408   **11** 726   **12** 225

Exercise 1E
1 four units; 4   **2** five units; 5   **3** nine units; 9   **4** three units; 3
5 two units; 2   **6** six units; 6   **7** nine tens; 90   **8** three tens; 30
9 six tens; 60   **10** eight units; 8   **11** eight hundreds; 800   **12** nine hundreds; 900
13 five hundreds; 500   **14** eight hundreds; 800   **15** one ten; 10   **16** three tens; 30

Exercise 1F
1 980, 908, 890, 809   **2** 760, 706, 670, 607   **3** 765, 756, 675, 657, 576, 567
4 543, 534, 453, 435, 354, 345   **5** 455, 456, 465, 466   **6** 866, 867, 876, 877
7 223, 232, 233, 322, 323, 332   **8** 889, 898, 899, 988, 989, 998

Exercise 1G
1 852, 825, 582, 528, 285, 258   **2** 743, 734, 473, 437, 374, 347   **3** 975, 957, 795, 759, 597, 579
4 421, 412, 241, 214, 142, 124   **5** 840, 804, 480, 408   **6** 760, 706, 670, 607
7 533, 353, 335   **8** 882, 828, 288   **9** 722, 272, 227
10 770, 707   **11** 239, 293, 329, 392, 923, 932   **12** 368, 386, 638, 683, 836, 863
13 135, 153, 315, 351, 513, 531   **14** 148, 184, 418, 481, 814, 841   **15** 506, 560, 605, 650
16 204, 240, 402, 420   **17** 355, 535, 553   **18** 447, 474, 744
19 116, 161, 611   **20** 404, 440

Exercise 1H
1 24 000   **2** 215 000   **3** 19 000 000   **4** 13 000 000 000
5 forty-nine thousand   **6** nine hundred and seventy-three thousand
7 twelve million   **8** two hundred million
9 fifty-three billion   **10** seven hundred and seventy-seven billion

Exercise 1J
1 a 1000   **b** 100   **c** 100 000   **d** 10 000 000 000
  e 10 000 000   **f** 100 000 000 000
2 a 10^5 **b** 10^7 **c** 10^3 **d** 10^2 **e** 10^{15}

Exercise 1K
1 a two, four, six, eight   **b** 8   **2 a** two, four, six   **b** 6
3 a two, four, six, eight, ten   **b** 10   **4 a** two, four, six, eight, ten, twelve, fourteen   **b** 14
5 a two, four, six, eight, ten, twelve, fourteen, sixteen, eighteen   **b** 18
6 a five, ten, fifteen, twenty   **b** 20   **7 a** five, ten, fifteen   **b** 15
8 a five, ten, fifteen, twenty-five, thirty, thirty-five   **b** 35
9 a ten, twenty, thirty, forty, fifty, sixty   **b** 60
10 a ten, twenty, thirty, forty, fifty   **b** 50

Exercise 1L
1 a eleven; 11   **b** sixteen; 16   **c** nineteen; 19   **d** nine; 9   **e** seven; 7
2 a eighteen; 18   **b** fourteen; 14   **c** eight; 8   **d** six; 6
3 a twenty-five; 25   **b** forty-five; 45   **c** fifteen; 15

Exercise 1M
1 a seven; 7   **b** seventy; 70   **c** seven hundred; 700   **d** seven thousand; 7000
2 a 5   **b** 50   **c** 500   **d** 5000   **3 a** 8   **b** 80   **c** 800   **d** 8000
4 a 1   **b** 10   **c** 100   **d** 1000   **5 a** 4   **b** 40   **c** 400
6 a 6   **b** 60   **c** 600   **7 a** 7   **b** 70   **c** 700
8 a 5   **b** 50   **c** 500   **9 a** 9   **b** 90
10 a 4   **b** 40   **11 a** 2   **b** 20
12 a 6   **b** 60

Exercise 1N
1 50   **2** 20   **3** 40; 400   **4** 90; 900   **5** 80   **6** 40

Exercise 1P
1 400 g   **2** 900 g   **3** 300   **4** 800; 80   **5** 200; 20   **6** 100 g; 10 g
7 50 l; 5 l   **8** 70 kg

Exercise 2A
1 8   **2** 7   **3** 9   **4** 9   **5** 10   **6** 12
7 14   **8** 12   **9** 10   **10** 11   **11** 13   **12** 10

Exercise 2B
1 13   **2** 11   **3** 15   **4** 16   **5** 11   **6** 17   **7** 11   **8** 8   **9** 9   **10** 9
11 9   **12** 15   **13** 12   **14** 14   **15** 16   **16** 17   **17** 14   **18** 17   **19** 16   **20** 19

Exercise 2C
1 78   **2** 89   **3** 77   **4** 96   **5** 79   **6** 98   **7** 87   **8** 69   **9** 88   **10** 96
11 90   **12** 70   **13** 92   **14** 82   **15** 61   **16** 91   **17** 65   **18** 75   **19** 94   **20** 73

Exercise 2D
1 868   **2** 769   **3** 798   **4** 997   **5** 767   **6** 765   **7** 592   **8** 873   **9** 784   **10** 664
11 969   **12** 747   **13** 658   **14** 942   **15** 723   **16** 1134   **17** 1423   **18** 1241   **19** 1550   **20** 1316

Exercise 2E
1 30   **2** 24   **3** 26   **4** 35   **5** 32   **6** 36

Exercise 2F
1 80   **2** 90   **3** 100   **4** 130   **5** 150   **6** 135

348 Basic Mathematics Skills

Exercise 2G
1 117   2 147   3 126   4 174   5 136   6 145
7 162   8 186   9 115   10 177   11 174   12 194

Exercise 2H
1 22   2 21   3 16   4 12   5 12   6 17   7 14   8 15

Exercise 2J
1 47   2 65   3 95   4 58   5 90   6 100

Exercise 2K
1 698   2 898   3 981   4 692   5 775   6 927
7 858   8 649   9 568   10 857   11 842   12 763

Exercise 2L
1 200 km   2 650   3 1350 g   4 340   5 490   6 320 g

Exercise 3A
1 4   2 2   3 5   4 8   5 7   6 9   7 7   8 5   9 3
10 3   11 6   12 4   13 7   14 5   15 2   16 2   17 5   18 10

Exercise 3B
1 4   2 6   3 4   4 7   5 4   6 6   7 4   8 6   9 6
10 8   11 6   12 3   13 6   14 3   15 5   16 5   17 3   18 4

Exercise 3C
1 42   2 33   3 26   4 54   5 45   6 42   7 32   8 63
9 41   10 45   11 23   12 45   13 36   14 54   15 32

Exercise 3D
1 324   2 542   3 263   4 452   5 233   6 424   7 252   8 736   9 556   10 633
11 546   12 345   13 768   14 637   15 748   16 627   17 551   18 635   19 933   20 526

Exercise 3E
1 61   2 31   3 41   4 21   5 41   6 31   7 42   8 32   9 52   10 42
11 71   12 41   13 61   14 71   15 31   16 21   17 51   18 151   19 131   20 171

Exercise 3F
1 51   2 21   3 51   4 21   5 51   6 32   7 22   8 62   9 32   10 12
11 151   12 121   13 171   14 141   15 111   16 102   17 302   18 202   19 401   20 101

Exercise 3G
1 5 years   2 9 years   3 6   4 6   5 7   6 7
7 8   8 8   9 5 tonnes   10 8 cm   11 8 cm   12 6 min

Exercise 3H
1 a 14p   b 64p   2 a 26 cm   b 76 cm
3 53 m   4 £22   5 37 l   6 28   7 25   8 34   9 39   10 27

Exercise 3J
1 135 km   2 115   3 176   4 £175   5 288 years   6 135 m   7 57 cm   8 453 cm

Exercise 4A
1 8   2 10   3 12   4 6   5 9   6 18   7 21   8 16   9 24   10 25

Exercise 4B

1 30	**2** 50	**3** 90	**4** 120	**5** 180	**6** 360	**7** 720
8 500	**9** 100	**10** 300	**11** 700	**12** 800	**13** 300	**14** 100
15 1300	**16** 1900	**17** 2500	**18** 6000	**19** 2000	**20** 9000	**21** 140 mm
22 180 mm	**23** 850 mm	**24** 300 mm	**25** 80 mm	**26** 70 mm	**27** 90 mm	**28** 60 mm
29 500 cm	**30** 200 cm	**31** 400 cm	**32** 900 cm	**33** 3000 cm	**34** 5000 cm	**35** 60 years

Exercise 4C

1 30　　**2** 63　　**3** 36　　**4** 40 cm　　**5** 32 cm　　**6** 24 cm　　**7** 21 g　　**8** 28 kg

Exercise 4D

1 a 76　**b** 72　**c** 72; a　　**2 a** 84　**b** 84　**c** 88; c　　**3 a** 92　**b** 98　**c** 98; a
4 a 96　**b** 94　**c** 96; b　　**5 a** 132　**b** 136　**c** 132; b　　**6 a** 128　**b** 126　**c** 126; a
7 a 108　**b** 104　**c** 108; b　　**8 a** 144　**b** 144　**c** 154; c　　**9 a** 48 cm　**b** 84 cm
10 a 39 kg　**b** 65 kg　**c** 78 kg

Exercise 4E

1 765	**2** 286	**3** 294	**4** 288	**5** 572	**6** 345	**7** 742	**8** 672	**9** 576
10 391	**11** 375	**12** 544	**13** 954	**14** 456	**15** 765	**16** 792	**17** 612	**18** 285

Exercise 4F

1 a 756　　**b** 756　　**c** 736; c　　　**2 a** 682　　**b** 672　　**c** 672; a
3 a 1008　　**b** 1014　　**c** 1008; b　　**4 a** 1344　**b** 1394　**c** 1344; b
5 a 1968　**b** 1938　**c** 1938; a　　**6 a** 2898　**b** 2808　**c** 2898; b
7 a 3528　**b** 3528　**c** 3536; c　　**8 a** 3776　**b** 3876　**c** 3876; a

Exercise 4G

1 a 6552　**b** 6572　**c** 6552; b　　**2 a** 8064　**b** 8052　**c** 8064; b
3 a 4032　**b** 4028　**c** 4032; b　　**4 a** 4394　**b** 4392　**c** 4392; a
5 a 4144　**b** 4144　**c** 4152; c　　**6 a** 3744　**b** 3834　**c** 3744; b
7 a 3850　**b** 3840　**c** 3840; a　　**8 a** 3600　**b** 3400　**c** 3600; b

Exercise 4H

1 37 488　　**2** 36 685　　**3** 74 104　　**4** 69 438　　**5** 63 036
6 a 24 552　**b** 24 576　**c** 24 552; b　　**7 a** 43 776　**b** 43 776　**c** 43 792; c
8 a 50 544　**b** 50 512　**c** 50 512; a　　**9 a** 66 528　**b** 66 608　**c** 66 528; b

Exercise 4J

1 3600	**2** 2100	**3** 1500	**4** 3200	**5** 4200	**6** 2400	**7** 4500	**8** 1400	**9** 1800	**10** 5400
11 1600	**12** 2700	**13** 8000	**14** 6000	**15** 8000	**16** 12 000	**17** 4000	**18** 9000	**19** 12 000	**20** 24 000

Exercise 4K

1 52 cm　　**2** 80 cm　　**3** 161p　　**4** 402 m　　**5** 936 g　　**6** 1340 m　　**7** 3724

Exercise 4L

1 494　　**2** 896 kg　　**3** 2880　　**4** 2184　　**5** 6384 km　　**6** 2760 km

Exercise 5A

1 4	**2** 3	**3** 3	**4** 2	**5** 2	**6** 5
7 4	**8** 4	**9** 7	**10** 3	**11** 2	**12** 3

Exercise 5B

1 8	**2** 6	**3** 9	**4** 3	**5** 5	**6** 15	**7** 45	**8** 18
9 7	**10** 4	**11** 42	**12** 81	**13** 60	**14** 50	**15** 38	

16 a 15　**b** 150

Exercise 5C

1 9	**2** 7	**3** 9	**4** 7	**5** 8	**6** 5	**7** 5	**8** 7	**9** 4
10 6	**11** 6 cm	**12** 6p	**13** 4p	**14** 8p	**15** 3 kg	**16** 8 cm	**17** 9	**18** 9

Exercise 5D

1 a 12	**b** 13	**c** 12; b	**2 a** 23	**b** 23	**c** 24; c	**3 a** 18	**b** 17	**c** 18; b
4 a 14	**b** 15	**c** 14; b	**5 a** 18	**b** 19	**c** 19; a	**6 a** 46	**b** 48	**c** 48; a
7 a 24	**b** 26	**c** 24; b	**8 a** 37	**b** 37	**c** 39; c			

Exercise 5E

1 a 36	**b** 36	**c** 34; c	**2 a** 43	**b** 42	**c** 42; a	**3 a** 21	**b** 22	**c** 21; b
4 a 35	**b** 34	**c** 34; a	**5 a** 24	**b** 24	**c** 26; c	**6 a** 50	**b** 60	**c** 50 ; b
7 a 30	**b** 40	**c** 30; b	**8 a** 50	**b** 40	**c** 50; b			

Exercise 5F

1 9	**2** 8	**3** 5	**4** 8	**5** 9	**6** 7	**7** 9	**8** 8
9 7	**10** 5	**11** 6	**12** 4	**13** 8	**14** 5	**15** 5	

Exercise 5G

1 19	**2** 123	**3** 115	**4** 150 kg

Exercise 5H

1 13; 2	**2** 12; 2	**3** 19; 2	**4** 14; 3	**5** 7; 1p	**6** 5; 5p	**7** 24; 3	**8** 12; 2	**9** 8; 2	**10** 5; 5

Exercise 5J

1 24	**2** 15	**3** 28	**4** 12	**5** 25	**6** 18	**7** 54	**8** 24

Exercise 6A

1 480 m, 28 800 s	**2** 300 m, 18 000 s	**3** 1200 m, 72 000 s	**4** 3000 m, 180 000 s
5 4 hr, 14 440 s	**6** 7 hr, 25 200 s	**7** 9 hr, 540 m	**8** 25 hr, 1500 m

Exercise 6B

1 Thursday	**2** Monday	**3** Tuesday	**4** Thursday	**5** 5th
6 3rd	**7** 11th	**8** 15th	**9** 28th	**10** 29th

Exercise 6C

1 Sunday	**2** as for February 1998 with 29, 30 and 31 added
3 a 4th **b** 13th **c** 22nd	**4** 22nd–28th **5 a** 27th **b** 30th

Exercise 6D

1 2 9 16 23 30		**2** 1 8 15 22 29		**3** – 7 14 21 28	
3 10 17 24 31		2 9 16 23 30		1 8 15 22 29	
4 1 8 15 22 29		**5** – 6 13 20 27		**6** 3 10 17 24 31	
2 9 16 23 30		– 7 14 21 28		4 11 18 25 –	
3 10 17 24 31		1 8 15 22 29		5 12 19 26 –	

Exercise 6E

1 a 3rd	**b** 17th	**c** 24th	**d** Monday 19th	
2 a 6th	**b** 20th	**c** 27th	**d** Wednesday 23rd	
3 a 10th	**b** 3rd	**c** 24th	**d** 31st	**e** Sunday 29th
4 a 8th	**b** 1st	**c** 22nd	**d** 29th	**e** Sunday 28th

Exercise 6F

1 a 10th	**b** 17th	**c** Thursday 24th	**d** Wednesday 30th
2 a 8th	**b** 15th	**c** Saturday 23rd	**d** Friday 29th
3 a 4th	**b** Thursday 17th	**c** Tuesday 29th February	
4 a 7th, 8th	**b** Tuesday 24th	**c** Monday 30th	

Exercise 6G

1 eleven fifteen 2 ten forty 3 nine twenty 4 eight fifteen 5 seventeen thirty
6 twenty-two thirty-five 7 10.15 8 11.40 9 09.25
10 07.45 11 13.20 12 18.45 13 19.40 14 22.30

Exercise 6H

1 a 9.30 b 09.30, 21.30 2 a 10.15 b 10.15, 22.15
3 a 10.45 b 10.45, 22.45 4 a 6.20 b 06.20, 18.20
5 a 5.18 b 05.18, 17.18 6 a 3.42 b 03.42, 15.42
7 8.10 8 9.15 9 7.25 10 1.15 11 4.20 12 8.30

Exercise 6J

1 1 hr 15 min 2 1 hr 25 min 3 5 hr 25 min 4 40 min 5 45 min
6 25 min 7 2 hr 15 min 8 4 hr 15 min 9 25 min 10 1 hr 35 min

Exercise 6K

1 a i 9.15, Head ii 10.30, Head iii 10.15, D/Head
   iv 9.30, D/Head v 9.30, S/T vi 10.15, S/T
  b i Bobbie ii Kate iii Marcus
   iv Naomi v Jordan vi Wendy
  c 9.30, 10.30, 9.15
2 a i 11.30, Charmaine, C&B ii 9.30, Charmaine, C&B
   iii 9.30, Rita, S&S iv 11.00, Rita, S&S
   v 12.00, Zoey, Perm vi 10.30, Zoey, Perm
   vii 10.00, Afiya, Dye viii 11.30, Afiya, Dye
  b i Ms Sherman ii Mrs Patel iii Mrs Vaughan iv Ms Sing
   v Miss Satur vi Mrs O'Brien vii Mrs Hornsby-Smith viii Joanna
  c yes, 9.30

Exercise 6L

1 09.27 2 09.47 3 12.19 4 20 min 5 37 min
6 New Milton to Marryat Road
7 Chatsworth Park to Hazelwood Avenue and Marryat Road to New Milton
8 Yes – no stops and the times are the same, 20 min.

Exercise 6M

2 1 hr 55 min 3 8 hr 35 min 4 11 hr 15 min 5 3 hr 35 min 6 a 18.30 b 10 hr 5 min
7 a Dent b Lazonby 8 30 min 9 1 hr
10 14.15 from Settle and 12.30 from Carlisle

Exercise 7A

1 a 84 b 83 c 83; a 2 a 115 b 115 c 116; c 3 a 58 b 59 c 59; a
4 a 87 b 86 c 86; a 5 a 162 b 168 c 168; a 6 a 936 b 936 c 946; c
7 a 16 b 14 c 14; a 8 a 23 b 24 c 23; b

Exercise 7B

1 £41 2 £35 3 £8 4 £4 5 £750 6 £34

Exercise 7C

1 110; 90 + 20 = 110 2 75; 50 + 30 = 80 3 115; 80 + 40 = 120 4 37; 30 + 10 = 40
5 403; 300 + 100 = 400 6 798; 400 + 400 = 800 7 800; 500 + 300 = 800 8 973; 600 + 400 = 1000
9 39; 100 − 60 = 40 10 49; 70 − 20 = 50 11 59; 90 − 30 = 60 12 28; 70 − 40 = 30
13 269; 500 − 200 = 300 14 277; 600 − 300 = 300 15 389; 900 − 500 = 400 16 193; 400 − 200 = 200

Exercise 7D

1 5658; 80 × 70 = 5600 2 3577; 70 × 50 = 3500 3 2028; 50 × 40 = 2000 4 3024; 60 × 50 = 3000
5 4779; 80 × 60 = 4800 6 2668; 90 × 30 = 2700 7 1989; 50 × 40 = 2000 8 2736; 70 × 40 = 2800
9 4248; 70 × 60 = 4200 10 2014; 50 × 40 = 2000

Exercise 7E

1 2.9; 3 **2** 5.9; 6 **3** 8.9; 9 **4** 8.7; 9 **5** 4.2; 4 **6** 9.2; 9 **7** 12.2; 12 **8** 6.7; 7
9 8.7; 9 **10** 12.6; 13 **11** 14.6; 15 **12** 5.3; 5 **13** 9.3; 9 **14** 2.4; 2 **15** 15.8; 16 **16** 5.4; 5
17 7.5; 8 **18** 4.5; 5 **19** 17.6; 18 **20** 17.5; 18

Exercise 7F

1 23.65; 24 **2** 27.65; 28 **3** 29.65; 30 **4** 21.85; 22 **5** 14.85; 15 **6** 18.85; 19 **7** 42.95; 43
8 13.75; 14 **9** 42.15; 42 **10** 52.15; 52 **11** 76.35; 76 **12** 72.35; 72 **13** 65.45; 65 **14** 26.45; 26
15 14.625; 15 **16** 56.125; 56 **17** 53.375; 53 **18** 62.375; 62 **19** 46.55; 47 **20** 54.55; 55

Exercise 7G

1 238; 240 **2** 648; 650 **3** 567; 570 **4** 216; 220 **5** 817; 820 **6** 536; 540 **7** 741; 740
8 232; 230 **9** 963; 960 **10** 952; 950 **11** 2436; 2440 **12** 5148; 5150 **13** 2208; 2210 **14** 1552; 1550
15 1862; 1860

Exercise 7H

1 2232; 2200 **2** 1634; 1600 **3** 4623; 4600 **4** 5544; 5500 **5** 4896; 4900 **6** 3168; 3200 **7** 6688; 6700
8 1869; 1900 **9** 1728; 1700 **10** 4116; 4100 **11** 2106; 2100 **12** 6024; 6000 **13** 4032; 4000 **14** 4096; 4100
15 3087; 3100

Exercise 7J

1 4160 **2** 5660 **3** 2760 **4** 6570 **5** 3710 **6** 4620 **7** 6540 **8** 9250 **9** 8570 **10** 2940
11 8160 **12** 4960 **13** 3780 **14** 6190 **15** 5650 **16** 5710 **17** 5700 **18** 6500

Exercise 7K

1 580 **2** 280 **3** 680 **4** 380 **5** 580 **6** 650 **7** 970
8 310 **9** 200 **10** 500 **11** 700 **12** 300

Exercise 7L

1 8400 **2** 7400 **3** 3400 **4** 7600 **5** 8700 **6** 6100 **7** 3100
8 4000 **9** 3000 **10** 7000 **11** 7900 **12** 3700

Exercise 7M

1 93p; 7p **2** 240 g; 60 g **3** 17 cm **4** 26 kg **5** 250 m **6** 550 cm

Exercise 7N

1 a 6 **b** 3 **2 a** 4 **b** 3 **3 a** 14 **b** 15 tonnes **4 a** 6 **b** 2 tonnes
5 a 6 **b** 18

Exercise 7P

1 a 4 **b** 3 **2 a** 9 **b** 3 **3 a** 6 **b** 6 **4 a** 6 **b** 4
5 a 4 **b** 9

Exercise 8A

11 1.1 **12** 1.3 **13** 1.6 **14** 1.9 **15** 2.1 **16** 2.3 **17** 2.7 **18** 0.4 **19** 0.7 **20** 2.0

Exercise 8B

11 3.13 **12** 3.21 **13** 3.37 **14** 3.45 **15** 3.56 **16** 3.72 **17** 3.03 **18** 3.06 **19** 3.10 **20** 3.40

Exercise 8C

1 nine units, two tenths **2** seven units, three tenths **3** five units, nine tenths
4 one ten, two units, three tenths **5** one ten, five units, two tenths **6** one ten, eight units, nine tenths
7 one hundred, three tens, five units, two tenths **8** two hundreds, six tens, nine units, three tenths
9 three hundreds, two tens, six units, nine tenths **10** two units, four tenths, six hundredths
11 one unit, three tenths, seven hundredths **12** three units, two tenths, four hundredths
13 one ten, three units, two tenths, six hundredths **14** one ten, four units, three tenths, eight hundredths
15 two tens, one unit, eight tenths, five hundredths **16** two tens, one unit, no tenths, five hundredths
17 three tens, four units, no tenths, eight hundredths **18** one ten, no units, no tenths, nine hundredths

Exercise 8D

1 4.8 cm, 48 mm **2** 8.6 cm, 86 mm **3** 3.4 cm, 34 mm **4** 10.2 cm, 102 mm **5** 12.8 cm, 128 mm

Exercise 8E

1 5 cm 3 mm, 5.3 cm, 53 mm **2** 4 cm 8 mm, 4.8 cm, 48 mm **3** 9 cm 1 mm, 9.1 cm, 91 mm
4 13 cm 6 mm, 13.6 cm, 136 mm **5** 15 cm 4 mm, 15.4 cm, 154 mm **6** 12 cm 9 mm, 12.9 cm, 129 mm
7 20 cm 6 mm, 20.6 cm, 206 mm **8** 21 cm 4 mm, 21.4 cm, 214 mm **9** 31 cm 9 mm, 31.9 cm, 319 mm
10 10 cm 8 mm, 10.8 cm, 108 mm

Exercise 8F

1 1.23 m, 123 cm; 1.40 m, 140cm; 1.03 m, 103 cm **2** 1 m 17 cm, 117 cm; 1 m 2 cm, 102 cm; 1 m 20 cm, 120 cm
3 1 m 18 cm, 1.18 m; 1 m 10 cm, 1.10 m; 1 m 4 cm, 1.04 m
4 1.25 m, 125 cm; 2.40 m, 240 cm; 1 m 95 cm, 195 cm; 2 m 5 cm, 205 cm; 1 m 85 cm, 1.85 m; 5 m 5 cm, 5.05 m

Exercise 8G

1 four tens, three units, six tenths, eight hundredths **2** five tens, seven units, three tenths, two hundredths
3 five tens, six units, four tenths, three hundredths, two thousandths
4 seven tens, eight units, six tenths, nine hundredths, four thousandths
5 two units, seven tenths, three hundredths, four thousandths
6 eight units, two tenths, six hundredths, three thousandths **7** six units, five tenths, seven hundredths
8 four units, nine tenths, three hundredths **9** three tens, five units, eight tenths
10 five tens, three units, four tenths **11** eight units, two tenths **12** two units, nine tenths

Exercise 8H

1 0.56, 0.47, 0.38, 0.29 **2** 0.45, 0.34, 0.23, 0.12 **3** 0.76, 0.67, 0.58, 0.49
4 0.915, 0.824, 0.735, 0.644 **5** 0.912, 0.821, 0.730, 0.640 **6** 0.616, 0.520, 0.437, 0.300
7 0.680, 0.591, 0.400, 0.319 **8** 0.900, 0.850, 0.760, 0.675 **9** 0.730, 0.647, 0.500, 0.450

Exercise 8J

1 8.567, 8.576, 8.657, 8.675, 8.756, 8.765 **2** 4.123, 4.132, 4.213, 4.231, 4.312, 4.321
3 3.045, 3.054, 3.405, 3.450, 3.504, 3.540 **4** 5.067, 5.076, 5.607, 5.670, 5.706, 5.760
5 1.023, 1.032, 1.203, 1.230, 1.302, 1.320 **6** 4.056, 4.065, 4.506, 4.560, 4.605, 4.650
7 8.009, 8.090, 8.099, 8.900, 8.909, 8.990 **8** 6.005, 6.050, 6.055, 6.500, 6.505, 6.550

Exercise 8K

1 7.9 **2** 7.7 **3** 9.4 **4** 10.3 **5** 12.4 **6** 2.5 **7** 5.3 **8** 7.5 **9** 1.4 **10** 2.3

Exercise 8L

1 7.69 **2** 6.58 **3** 9.29 **4** 7.57 **5** 12.49 **6** 3.25 **7** 4.42 **8** 6.72 **9** 2.78 **10** 1.46

Exercise 8M

1 a 4 **b** 40 **2 a** 6 **b** 60 **3 a** 2 **b** 20 **4 a** 7 **b** 70
5 a 5 **b** 50 **6 a** 9 **b** 90 **7 a** 18 **b** 180 **8 a** 16 **b** 160
9 a 15 **b** 150 **10 a** 25 **b** 250 **11 a** 29 **b** 290 **12 a** 23 **b** 230

Exercise 8N

1 4.8 **2** 3.2 **3** 2.1 **4** 5.6 **5** 1.4 **6** 4.5
7 6.3 **8** 0.9 **9** 4.0 **10** 2.0 **11** 2.0 **12** 3.0

Exercise 8P

1 8.6 **2** 6.9 **3** 9.6 **4** 8.4 **5** 6.2 **6** 3.6 **7** 7.2 **8** 7.6 **9** 9.2
10 6.5 **11** 9.6 **12** 6.8 **13** 27.0 **14** 28.0 **15** 28.0 **16** 37.0 **17** 15.9 **18** 12.8

Exercise 8Q

1 a 4.5 **b** 45 **2 a** 3.7 **b** 37 **3 a** 6.1 **b** 61 **4 a** 9.3 **b** 93
5 a 7.2 **b** 72 **6 a** 0.5 **b** 5 **7 a** 0.8 **b** 8 **8 a** 0.3 **b** 3
9 a 30.4 **b** 304 **10 a** 40.6 **b** 406 **11 a** 40.2 **b** 402 **12 a** 50.1 **b** 501
13 a 51.0 **b** 510 **14 a** 73.0 **b** 730 **15 a** 65.0 **b** 650 **16 a** 9.0 **b** 90

Exercise 8R

1 1.26 2 1.48 3 1.89 4 1.55 5 1.64 6 2.48 7 2.16 8 3.55 9 4.27 10 3.45
11 2.80 12 3.40 13 0.35 14 0.54 15 0.40

Exercise 8S

1 6.48 2 6.96 3 8.84 4 3.93 5 9.24 6 7.86 7 9.48 8 6.55 9 13.68 10 17.86
11 30.00 12 16.32 13 25.35 14 30.20 15 18.30

Exercise 8T

1 3.6 2 5.2 3 0.15 4 0.45 5 0.07 6 0.03 7 2.56 8 3.25 9 5.04
10 8.05 11 6.70 12 4.30 13 0.372 14 0.965 15 0.0652 16 0.0846 17 0.075 18 0.026

Exercise 8U

1 2.6 2 9.5 3 8.5 4 7.2 5 4.5 6 5.25 7 7.75 8 3.75 9 6.25 10 9.4
11 7.2 12 8.3 13 9.4 14 5.35 15 4.72 16 8.55 17 4.75 18 7.18 19 6.15 20 8.48

Exercise 8V

1 a £15.10 b £4.90 2 a £5.70 b £4.30 3 a £8.40 b £1.60
4 a 2 m 90 cm b 3 m c 10 cm 5 a 1.80 m b 2 m c 20 cm

Exercise 8W

1 a £7.40 b £2.60 2 a 2.30 m b 3 m c 70 cm
3 a £4.80 b 20p 4 a 1.80 m b 2 m c 20 cm

Exercise 8X

1 a 9p b 52p c 26p d 69p e 34p
2 a 6p b 38p c 51p d 19p e 26p
3 a 2 cm b 13 cm c 15 cm d 4 cm e 9 cm f 20 cm
4 a 8 cm b 46 cm c 61 cm d 23 cm e 68 cm f 30 cm
5 a 1 cm b 5 cm c 6 cm d 2 cm e 3 cm f 7 cm

Exercise 9A

1 5 cm 2 8 cm 3 6 cm 4 7 cm 5 5 cm 6 8 cm 7 6 cm 8 4 cm 9 7 cm 10 3 cm

Exercise 9B

1 4 cm 2 9 cm 3 3 cm

Exercise 9C

1 3 cm 8 mm 2 2 cm 4 mm 3 5 cm 2 mm 4 7 cm 4 mm
5 a 8 cm 4 mm b 2 cm c 5 cm d 1 cm 4 mm

Exercise 9D

1 a 5 cm 2 mm b 52 mm c 5.2 cm 2 a 7 cm 4 mm b 74 mm c 7.4 cm
3 a 8 cm 9 mm b 89 mm c 8.9 cm 4 a 1 cm 5 mm b 15 mm c 1.5 cm
5 a 6 cm 0 mm b 60 mm c 6.0 cm (or 6 cm)

Exercise 9E

1 82 m 2 98 m 3 324 m 4 220 m

Exercise 9F

1 a 24 cm b 36 cm c 60 cm d 96 mm e 260 mm f 360 mm
2 a 24 cm b 18 cm c 60 cm d 135 mm e 216 mm f 288 mm
3 a 72 cm b 108 cm c 150 cm d 252 mm e 450 mm f 360 mm

Exercise 9G

1 a 80 cm b 80 cm c 76 cm; c 2 a 160 cm b 164 cm c 160 cm; b
3 a 192 cm b 192 cm c 184 cm; c 4 a 356 cm b 352 cm c 352 cm; a

5 a 18 cm   **6** 18 cm   **7** 10 cm   **8** 12 cm   **9** 24 cm

Exercise 9H
1 15.7 cm   **2** 12.56 cm   **3** 47.1 cm   **4** 109.9 cm   **5** 14.13 cm   **6** 23.55 cm
7 18.84 cm   **8** 62.8 cm   **9** 157 cm   **10** 141.3 mm   **11** 78.5 mm   **12** 4.71 m

Exercise 9J
1 a 10.99 cm   **b** 21 980 cm (or 219.8 m)   **2** 24.55 cm   **3** 33.97 mm
4 a 62.8 cm   **b** 25   **5 a** 10 cm   **b** 5 m   **6 a** 50 mm   **b** 25 mm

Exercise 9K
1 700, 7000   **2** 1500, 15 000   **3** 21, 21 000   **4** 14, 14 000   **5** 5, 500   **6** 30, 3000

Exercise 9L
1 16.2 cm, 162 mm   **2** 25 cm 2 mm, 252 mm   **3** 28 cm 4 mm, 28.4 cm

Exercise 9M
1 1.36 m, 136 cm   **2** 1.06 m, 106 cm   **3** 1 m 38 cm, 138 cm
4 1 m 30 cm, 130 cm   **5** 1 m 34 cm, 1.34 m   **6** 0 m 86 cm, 0.86 m

Exercise 9N
1 a 3500 cm   **b** 35 000 mm   **2 a** 2300 cm   **b** 23 000 mm   **3 a** 4700 cm   **b** 47 000 mm
4 a 5200 cm   **b** 52 000 mm   **5 a** 490 cm   **b** 4900 mm   **6 a** 360 cm   **b** 3600 mm
7 a 250 cm   **b** 2500 mm   **8 a** 730 cm   **b** 7300 mm   **9 a** 30 cm   **b** 300 mm
10 a 70 cm   **b** 700 mm   **11 a** 25 cm   **b** 250 mm   **12 a** 8 cm   **b** 80 mm

Exercise 9P
1 a 243.9 cm   **b** 2.439 m   **2 a** 526.4 cm   **b** 5.264 m   **3 a** 275 cm   **b** 2.75 m
4 a 250 cm   **b** 2.5 m   **5 a** 72.5 cm   **b** 0.725 m   **6 a** 37.9 cm   **b** 0.379 m
7 a 9.6 cm   **b** 0.096 m   **8 a** 7.8 cm   **b** 0.078 m

Exercise 9Q
1 a 24 ft   **b** 288 in   **2 a** 18 ft   **b** 216 in   **3 a** 9 ft   **b** 108 in
4 a 36 ft   **b** 432 in   **5 a** 45 ft   **b** 540 in   **6 a** 135 ft, 60 ft   **b** 1620 in, 720 in
7 a 3520 yd   **b** 10 560 ft   **8 a** 8800 yd   **b** 26 400 ft   **9 a** 10 560 yd   **b** 31 680 ft
10 a 2640 yd   **b** 7920 ft

Exercise 9R
1 a 9 ft   **b** 3 yd   **2 a** 60 ft   **b** 20 yd   **3 a** 12 ft   **b** 4 yd
4 a 42 ft   **b** 14 yd   **5 a** 27 ft   **b** 9 yd   **6 a** 105 ft, 96 ft   **b** 35 yd, 32 yd

Exercise 9S
1 90 cm   **2** 65 cm   **3** 85 cm   **4** 115 cm   **5** 30 in   **6** 28 in   **7** 48 in   **8** 42 in

Exercise 9T
1 3 m   **2** 15 m   **3** 615 m   **4** 4728 m   **5** 231 ft   **6** 429 ft   **7** 29 205 ft   **8** 1287 ft

Exercise 9U
1 27 m   **2** 675 m   **3** 846 m   **4** 1125 m   **5** 66 yd   **6** 22 yd   **7** 836 yd   **8** 913 yd

Exercise 9V
1 640 km   **2** 296 km   **3** 192 km   **4** 56 km   **5** 575 miles   **6** 175 miles   **7** 535 miles   **8** 925 miles

Exercise 10A
1 a 71.4   **b** 71.5   **c** 71.4; b   **2 a** 18.0   **b** 18.0   **c** 19.0; c   **3 a** 728   **b** 738   **c** 728; b

Exercise 10B
1 a 26.75 b 26.85 c 26.85; a   2 a 266 b 256 c 256; a
3 a 4.61 b 4.51 c 4.61; b   4 a 5.125 b 5.225 c 5.125; b

Exercise 10C
1 a £6.15 b £3.85   2 a £7.25 b £2.75   3 a £9.45 b £10.55   4 a 8.35 m b 1.65 m

Exercise 10D
1 a 81.12 b 87.12 c 87.12; a   2 a 952 b 954 c 954; a   3 a 25.92 b 25.92 c 22.92; c

Exercise 10E
1 a 3 b 3 c 4; c   2 a 3.44 b 3.45 c 3.45; a   3 a 600 b 608 c 608; a

Exercise 10F
1 a £29.75 b £20.25   2 a £22.35 b £27.65   3 a £40.45 b £9.55   4 a £27.95 b £22.05

Exercise 10G
1 £2.64; £2.63; 2 kg   2 £1.23; £1.22; 3 kg   3 £1.13; £1.14; 4 kg   4 £0.24; £0.23; 5   5 £0.28; £0.29; 9

Exercise 10H
1 £1.25; £1.26; 3 kg   2 £0.76; £0.74; 1.5 kg   3 £0.97; £0.98; 2 kg
4 i £0.82 ii £0.80 iii 0.78; iii   5 i £1.08 ii £1.12 iii £1.05; iii

Exercise 10J
1 2.35   2 3.65   3 4.75   4 9.14   5 5.48   6 4.28   7 2.78
8 5.25   9 6.31   10 3.51   11 9.50   12 6.80   13 3.30   14 2.40

Exercise 10K
1 2.6   2 5.9   3 3.8   4 8.2   5 5.3   6 3.5   7 7.6   8 4.7
9 6.2   10 9.1   11 5.1   12 3.0   13 8.0   14 5.0   15 3.0

Exercise 10L
1 3.7   2 6.6   3 7.5   4 5.9   5 8.4   6 6.5   7 5.7   8 4.8
9 9.3   10 4.0   11 3.0   12 6.7   13 7.5   14 4.1   15 4.3

Exercise 10M
1 8.5185, 8.518, 8.52, 8.5   2 4.7373, 4.737, 4.74, 4.7   3 2.9824, 2.982, 2.98, 3.0
4 8.5274, 8.527, 8.53, 8.5   5 2.7362, 2.736, 2.74, 2.7   6 4.6154, 4.615, 4.62, 4.6
7 26.5127, 26.513, 26.51, 26.5   8 37.3246, 37.325, 37.32, 37.3

Exercise 10N
1 0.35   2 0.76   3 0.82   4 0.90   5 0.80   6 0.63   7 0.74
8 0.58   9 0.42   10 0.31   11 0.41   12 0.02   13 0.03   14 0.02

Exercise 10P
1 10.7   2 36   3 10.1   4 12.2   5 8.7   6 12.5
7 20.4   8 32.2   9 5.1   10 0.48   11 0.2   12 0.015

Exercise 10Q
1 3.5   2 4.5   3 12.6   4 2.65   5 3.85   6 2.08
7 12.8   8 2.5   9 4.8   10 4.36   11 3.15   12 10.5

Exercise 11A
1 one third, $\frac{1}{3}$ 2 one fifth, $\frac{1}{5}$ 3 one quarter, $\frac{1}{4}$ 4 one seventh, $\frac{1}{7}$

Exercise 11B
1 two thirds, $\frac{2}{3}$
2 three quarters, $\frac{3}{4}$
3 five twelfths, $\frac{5}{12}$
4 five ninths, $\frac{5}{9}$
5 seven twelfths, $\frac{7}{12}$
6 eight thirteenths, $\frac{8}{13}$

Exercise 11C
1 a $\frac{2}{6}$ b $\frac{3}{9}$ c $\frac{5}{15}$ d $\frac{8}{24}$ e $\frac{10}{30}$
2 a $\frac{3}{36}$ b $\frac{5}{60}$ c $\frac{6}{72}$ d $\frac{9}{108}$ e $\frac{10}{120}$
3 a $\frac{15}{24}$ b $\frac{25}{40}$ c $\frac{30}{48}$ d $\frac{35}{56}$ e $\frac{45}{72}$
4 a $\frac{6}{27}$ b $\frac{10}{45}$ c $\frac{14}{63}$ d $\frac{16}{72}$ e $\frac{20}{90}$
5 $\frac{8}{18} = \frac{20}{45} = \frac{24}{54} = \frac{36}{81} = \frac{40}{90}$
6 $\frac{15}{36} = \frac{20}{48} = \frac{30}{72} = \frac{35}{84} = \frac{40}{96}$

Exercise 11D
1 $\frac{3}{10}$ 2 $\frac{7}{10}$ 3 $\frac{6}{7}$ 4 $\frac{5}{6}$ 5 $\frac{3}{10}$ 6 $\frac{3}{5}$ 7 $\frac{2}{5}$ 8 $\frac{3}{10}$ 9 $\frac{1}{10}$ 10 $\frac{1}{2}$

Exercise 11E
1 $\frac{4}{9}$ 2 $\frac{5}{9}$ 3 $\frac{5}{7}$ 4 $\frac{3}{7}$ 5 $\frac{3}{4}$ 6 $\frac{2}{3}$ 7 $\frac{3}{5}$ 8 $\frac{4}{5}$ 9 $\frac{1}{5}$ 10 $\frac{1}{5}$
11 $\frac{1}{2}$ 12 $\frac{1}{10}$

Exercise 11F
1 a $\frac{2}{3}$ b $\frac{5}{8}$ c $\frac{5}{8}$; a 2 a $\frac{3}{4}$ b $\frac{4}{5}$ c $\frac{3}{4}$; b 3 a $\frac{5}{6}$ b $\frac{7}{8}$ c $\frac{5}{6}$ b
4 a $\frac{2}{5}$ b $\frac{3}{8}$ c $\frac{3}{8}$; a 5 a $\frac{4}{5}$ b $\frac{5}{6}$ c $\frac{4}{5}$; b 6 a $\frac{2}{3}$ b $\frac{2}{3}$ c $\frac{3}{5}$; c

Exercise 11G
1 $\frac{7}{10}$ 2 $\frac{9}{10}$ 3 $\frac{4}{5}$ 4 $\frac{7}{8}$ 5 $\frac{1}{3}$ 6 $\frac{1}{5}$ 7 $\frac{4}{5}$ 8 $\frac{3}{4}$ 9 $\frac{5}{6}$ 10 $\frac{4}{5}$

Exercise 11H
1 $\frac{15}{50}, \frac{18}{60}, \frac{21}{70}, \frac{24}{80}, \frac{27}{90}$ 2 $\frac{35}{50}, \frac{42}{60}, \frac{49}{70}, \frac{56}{80}, \frac{63}{90}$ 3 $\frac{20}{25}, \frac{24}{30}, \frac{28}{35}, \frac{32}{40}, \frac{36}{45}$ 4 $\frac{15}{20}, \frac{18}{24}, \frac{21}{28}, \frac{24}{32}, \frac{27}{36}$ 5 $\frac{25}{30}, \frac{30}{36}, \frac{35}{42}, \frac{40}{48}, \frac{45}{54}$ 6 $\frac{5}{20}, \frac{6}{24}, \frac{7}{28}, \frac{8}{32}, \frac{9}{36}$

Exercise 11J
1 $\frac{30}{48}, \frac{25}{40}, \frac{20}{32}, \frac{15}{24}, \frac{10}{16}, \frac{5}{8}$ 2 $\frac{18}{48}, \frac{15}{40}, \frac{12}{32}, \frac{9}{24}, \frac{6}{16}, \frac{3}{8}$ 3 $\frac{42}{60}, \frac{35}{50}, \frac{28}{40}, \frac{21}{30}, \frac{14}{20}, \frac{7}{10}$ 4 $\frac{12}{18}, \frac{10}{15}, \frac{8}{12}, \frac{6}{9}, \frac{4}{6}, \frac{2}{3}$ 5 $\frac{6}{36}, \frac{5}{30}, \frac{4}{24}, \frac{3}{18}, \frac{2}{12}, \frac{1}{6}$
6 $\frac{6}{24}, \frac{5}{20}, \frac{4}{16}, \frac{3}{12}, \frac{2}{8}, \frac{1}{4}$

Exercise 11K
1 $\frac{3}{5}, \frac{9}{15}, \frac{12}{20}$ 2 $\frac{3}{8}, \frac{9}{24}, \frac{12}{32}$ 3 $\frac{5}{6}, \frac{15}{18}, \frac{20}{24}$ 4 $\frac{5}{6}, \frac{10}{12}, \frac{20}{24}$ 5 $\frac{7}{8}, \frac{14}{16}, \frac{28}{32}$
6 $\frac{1}{10}, \frac{2}{20}, \frac{4}{40}$ 7 $\frac{3}{5}, \frac{6}{10}, \frac{9}{15}$ 8 $\frac{5}{7}, \frac{10}{14}, \frac{15}{21}$ 9 $\frac{3}{4}, \frac{6}{8}, \frac{9}{12}$ 10 $\frac{5}{6}, \frac{10}{12}, \frac{15}{18}$

Exercise 11L
1 $\frac{13}{20}$ 2 $\frac{17}{20}$ 3 $\frac{17}{20}$ 4 $\frac{13}{25}$ 5 $\frac{18}{25}$ 6 $\frac{21}{25}$

Exercise 11M
1 $\frac{13}{15}$ 2 $\frac{14}{15}$ 3 $\frac{7}{9}$ 4 $\frac{8}{9}$ 5 $\frac{9}{20}$ 6 $\frac{17}{20}$
7 $\frac{9}{10}$ 8 $\frac{3}{10}$ 9 $\frac{5}{8}$ 10 $\frac{7}{8}$ 11 $\frac{5}{12}$ 12 $\frac{14}{15}$

Exercise 11N
1 $\frac{7}{20}$ 2 $\frac{3}{20}$ 3 $\frac{3}{20}$ 4 $\frac{2}{25}$ 5 $\frac{17}{25}$ 6 $\frac{9}{25}$

Exercise 11P
1 $\frac{17}{20}$ 2 $\frac{3}{20}$ 3 $\frac{3}{10}$ 4 $\frac{1}{10}$ 5 $\frac{1}{8}$ 6 $\frac{3}{8}$
7 $\frac{1}{12}$ 8 $\frac{4}{15}$ 9 $\frac{2}{9}$ 10 $\frac{1}{9}$ 11 $\frac{1}{15}$ 12 $\frac{2}{15}$

Exercise 11Q
1 $\frac{5}{6}$ 2 $\frac{5}{6}$ 3 $\frac{2}{9}$ 4 $\frac{8}{9}$ 5 $\frac{3}{5}$ 6 $\frac{4}{5}$
7 $\frac{3}{4}$ 8 $\frac{3}{5}$ 9 $\frac{3}{4}$ 10 $\frac{3}{4}$ 11 $\frac{2}{3}$ 12 $\frac{1}{2}$

Exercise 11R
1 $\frac{1}{6}$ 2 $\frac{1}{6}$ 3 $\frac{1}{5}$ 4 $\frac{3}{5}$ 5 $\frac{1}{5}$ 6 $\frac{1}{4}$
7 $\frac{2}{5}$ 8 $\frac{1}{5}$ 9 $\frac{1}{4}$ 10 $\frac{1}{4}$ 11 $\frac{1}{3}$ 12 $\frac{1}{2}$

Exercise 11S

1 $\frac{29}{40}$ 2 $\frac{17}{24}$ 3 $\frac{11}{20}$ 4 $\frac{5}{12}$ 5 $\frac{13}{15}$ 6 $\frac{4}{15}$

7 $\frac{1}{40}$ 8 $\frac{13}{24}$ 9 $\frac{1}{24}$ 10 $\frac{7}{12}$ 11 $\frac{1}{15}$ 12 $\frac{11}{15}$

Exercise 11T

1 **a** 315 km   **b** 210 km   **c** 126 km   **d** 105 km   **e** 90 km   **f** 70 km   **g** 63 km   **h** 42 km

2 **a** 480 m   **b** 320 m   **c** 240 m   **d** 192 m   **e** 160 m   **f** 120 m   **g** 96 m   **h** 80 m

   i 64 m   **j** 60 km   **k** 48 m

Exercise 11U

1 **a** 378 km   **b** 294 km   **c** 126 km   **d** 336 km   **e** 252 km   **f** 168 km   **g** 350 km   **h** 280 km   **i** 315 km

2 **a** 210 km   **b** 150 km   **c** 90 km   **d** 100 km   **e** 140 km   **f** 220 km   **g** 200 km   **h** 180 km   **i** 160 km

Exercise 11V

1 **a** £6.24   **b** £6.24   **c** £6.44; c   2 **a** £16.92   **b** £16.32   **c** £16.32; a

3 **a** £5.85   **b** £5.25   **c** £5.25; a   4 **a** £8.75   **b** £8.25   **c** £8.75; b

5 **a** 112 m   **b** 117 m   **c** 112 m; b   6 **a** 91 m   **b** 99 m   **c** 91 m; b

7 **a** 10.08 m   **b** 10.08 m   **c** 10.88 m; c   8 **a** £2.55   **b** £2.45   **c** £2.55; b

9 **a** £3.15   **b** £3.12   **c** £3.12; a

Exercise 11W

1 **a** $\frac{1}{5}$ **b** $\frac{3}{20}$ **c** $\frac{3}{20}$; a   2 **a** $\frac{3}{10}$ **b** $\frac{1}{4}$ **c** $\frac{1}{4}$; a

3 **a** $\frac{3}{5}$ **b** $\frac{13}{20}$ **c** $\frac{3}{5}$; b   4 **a** $\frac{1}{16}$ **b** $\frac{1}{16}$ **c** $\frac{3}{40}$; c

5 **a** $\frac{7}{40}$ **b** $\frac{9}{50}$ **c** $\frac{7}{40}$; b   6 **a** $\frac{1}{2}$ **b** $\frac{9}{20}$ **c** $\frac{9}{20}$; a

Exercise 11X

1 $\frac{2}{5}$ 2 $\frac{3}{5}$ 3 $\frac{9}{10}$ 4 $\frac{2}{5}$ 5 $\frac{4}{5}$ 6 $\frac{1}{4}$ 7 $\frac{3}{5}$; $\frac{3}{10}$; $\frac{1}{10}$ 8 $\frac{2}{5}$; $\frac{7}{20}$; $\frac{1}{4}$

Exercise 11Y

1 0.775   2 0.1875   3 0.625   4 0.125   5 0.58   6 0.3

7 0.8   8 0.064   9 0.012   10 0.045   11 0.0016   12 0.02

Exercise 11Z

1 **a** 0.875   **b** 0.85   **c** 0.85; a   2 **a** 0.75   **b** 0.84   **c** 0.75; b

3 **a** 0.7   **b** 0.68   **c** 0.68; a   4 **a** 0.32   **b** 0.325   **c** 0.325; a

Exercise 11AA

1 $\frac{27}{50}$ 2 $\frac{19}{50}$ 3 $\frac{47}{50}$ 4 $\frac{7}{50}$ 5 $\frac{23}{25}$ 6 $\frac{19}{40}$ 7 $\frac{23}{40}$

8 $\frac{21}{40}$ 9 $\frac{37}{40}$ 10 $\frac{7}{500}$ 11 $\frac{9}{500}$ 12 $\frac{3}{125}$ 13 $\frac{4}{125}$ 14 $\frac{1}{500}$

Exercise 11BB

1 $\frac{57}{100}$ 2 $\frac{63}{100}$ 3 $\frac{12}{25}$ 4 $\frac{18}{25}$ 5 $\frac{51}{100}$ 6 $\frac{5}{8}$ 7 $\frac{39}{40}$ 8 $\frac{13}{40}$ 9 $\frac{9}{200}$ 10 $\frac{17}{200}$

Exercise 11CC

1 125, 75, 50   2 96, 84, 60   3 24, 18, 15, 3   4 420, 378, 252, 210

Exercise 11DD

1 20   2 165 cm   3 £96   4 £315   5 £12 480   6 297 m

Exercise 11EE

1 28 l   2 8 l   3 84   4 200 cm   5 £68   6 4230

Exercise 11FF

1 $\frac{1}{4}$ 2 $\frac{2}{5}$ 3 $\frac{1}{20}$ 4 $\frac{4}{25}$ 5 $\frac{2}{5}$ 6 $\frac{1}{20}$ 7 $\frac{1}{15}$ 8 $\frac{1}{25}$ 9 $\frac{3}{20}$ 10 $\frac{1}{16}$

Exercise 12A

1 35%   2 15%   3 25%   4 30%   5 20%   6 10%

Exercise 12B

1 a 97%   b 77%   c 57%   d 49%   e 17%   f 3%

2 a $\frac{93}{100}$ b $\frac{73}{100}$ c $\frac{47}{100}$ d $\frac{31}{100}$ e $\frac{23}{100}$ f $\frac{7}{100}$

3 a $\frac{81}{100}$ b 81%   c $\frac{19}{100}$ d 19%   4 a $\frac{87}{100}$ b 87%   c $\frac{13}{100}$ d 13%

Exercise 12C

1 8   2 21   3 a 45   b 27   c 18

Exercise 12D

1 £56   2 £45   3 £32   4 £35   5 18 m   6 21 m   7 32 m   8 12 m

Exercise 12E

1 £3.20   2 £1.50   3 £1.80   4 £5.60   5 £0.60

6 2.4 m or 2 m 40 cm   7 5.6 m or 5 m 60 cm   8 3.6 m or 3 m 60 cm

Exercise 12F

1 a £75   b £70   c £75; b   2 a £78   b £80   c £78; b   3 a £12   b £12   c £14; c

4 a £15.96 b £12.96 c £12.96; a   5 a £60.80 b £59.80 c £60.80; b   6 a 36 mm b 36 mm c 35 mm; c

Exercise 12G

1 a 15%   b 15%   c 16%; c   2 a 24%   b 25%   c 25%; a

3 a 35%   b 32%   c 35%; a   4 a 48%   b 45%   c 45%; a

5 a 54%   b 55%   c 55%; a   6 a 5%   b 5%   c 6%; c

Exercise 12H

1 40%, 32%, 28%   2 50%, 30%, 20%   3 20%, 30%, 35%, 15%   4 20%, 30%, 35%, 15%

Exercise 12J

1 0.28   2 0.37   3 0.42   4 0.53   5 0.94   6 0.16

7 0.4   8 0.1   9 0.02   10 0.05   11 0.125   12 0.725

Exercise 12K

1 29%   2 38%   3 47%   4 58%   5 63%   6 81%   7 17%

8 80%   9 20%   10 3%   11 7%   12 40.5%   13 9.5%   14 1.5%

Exercise 12L

1 21, 15, 18, 6   2 36, 24, 60, 48, 72   3 264, 180, 108, 48   4 525, 375, 360, 240

Exercise 12M

1 a £15   b £265   2 a 3p   b 78p   3 a 6   b 56   4 a 90   b 240

Exercise 12N

1 a £2000 b £48 000   2 a 30   b 220   3 a 48   b 192   4 a £162 b £198

Exercise 12P

1 30%   2 50%   3 6%   4 20%   5 12%   6 20%

Exercise 12Q

1 a i $\frac{1}{4}$ ii 25%   iii 0.25   2 a $\frac{1}{3}$ b $33\frac{1}{3}$%   c 0.333…

   b i $\frac{3}{4}$ ii 75%   iii 0.75   3 a 0.23, 23%   b $\frac{87}{100}$, 87%

   c i $\frac{2}{5}$ ii 40%   iii 0.40   c $\frac{7}{20}$, 0.35   d 0.3, 30%

   d i $\frac{1}{2}$ ii 50%   iii 0.50   e $\frac{4}{5}$, 80%   f $\frac{2}{5}$, 0.4

Exercise 12R

1 5%, 4%; 5%   2 4%, 5%; 5%   3 25%, 30%; 30%   4 40%, 35%; 40%

5 30%, 25%; 30%   6 12.5%, 10%; 12.5%   7 10%, 7.5%; 10%   8 20%, 17.5%; 20%

Exercise 12S

1 £60, £72; £12 2 £150, £135; £15 3 £30, £24; £6 4 £25, £30; £5
5 £30, £36; £6 6 £75, £60; £15 7 £50, £45; £5 8 £20, £15; £5

Exercise 12T

1 a £49 b £329 2 a £56 b £376 3 a £18.90 b £126.90
4 a £437.50 b £2937.50 5 a £9.80 b £65.80 6 a £4.34 b £29.14
7 a £180 b £31.50 8 a £108 b £18.90 9 a £35.20 b £6.16
10 a £12.80 b £2.24 11 a £360 b £63 12 a £400 b £70

Exercise 12U

1 a £60 b £180 c £580 2 a £24 b £48 c £198 3 a £75 b £300 c £1050
4 a £60 b £90 c £390 5 a £108 b £270 c £1170 6 a £4.80 b £14.40 c £74.40
7 a £8.40 b £33.60 c £173.60 8 a £15.30 b £61.20 c £265.20 9 a £32.40 b £64.80 c £784.80
10 a £16.80 b £25.20 c £445.20

Exercise 13A

1 210 g 2 250 g 3 45 g 4 66 5 540

Exercise 13B

1 15 2 65 3 16 4 36 5 13

Exercise 13C

1 a 20 g b 15 g c 25 g d 17.5 g e 7.5 g
2 a 5 g b 7 g c 3.75 g d 2.5 g e 0.75 g
3 a 0.15 kg or 150 g b 120 g c 100 g d 80 g e 30 g
4 a 8 g b 5 g c 3.5 g d 1.5 g e 5.5g

Exercise 13D

1 1:4 = 4:16 = 6:24 = 8:32 = 9:36 2 1:9 = 4:36 = 6:54 = 8:72 = 9:81 3 1:20 = 2:40 = 3:60 = 5:100 = 7:140
4 1:3 = 2:6 = 3:9 = 10:30 = 12:36 5 1:8 = 10:80 = 4:32 = 6:48 = 8:64 6 1:7 = 4:28 = 8:56 = 9:63 = 10:70

Exercise 13E

1 12:15 = 4:5 2 9:15 = 3:5 3 8:12 = 2:3 4 15:20 = 3:4
5 15:35 = 3:7 6 12:18 = 2:3 7 42:48 = 7:8 8 32:40 = 4:5

Exercise 13F

1 £12, £30 2 24 kg, 108 kg 3 180 g, 300 g 4 45 cm, 150 cm 5 56 g, 98 g
6 2 m, 4.5 m 7 25, 35 8 25 m, 60 m 9 150 kg, 750 kg 10 24 ml, 96 ml

Exercise 13G

1 a 2 km b 8 km c 10 km d 16 km e 18 km f 22 km g 30 km
2 a 50 kg b 75 kg c 125 kg d 225 kg e 300 kg f 350 kg g 375 kg
3 a 48p b 72p c £1.92 d £2.16 e £2.88 f £3.60 g £3.84 h £6.00
4 a 75 g b 125 g c 150 g d 300 g e 375 g f 450 g g 500 g
5 a 4.5 l b 7.5 l c 10.5 l d 13.5 l e 18 l f 27 l g 22.5 l h 31.5 l
6 a 16 min b 24 min c 36 min d 48 min e 56 min f 60 min g 72 min

Exercise 13H

1 a 2.5 cm, 25 000 cm, 250 m b 2 cm, 20 000 cm, 200 m c 4 cm, 40 000 cm, 400 m
 d 5 cm, 50 000 cm, 500 m e 1.5 cm, 15 000 cm, 150 m f 3.5 cm, 35 000 cm, 350 m
 g 3 cm, 30 000 cm, 300 m
2 a 6 cm, 30 000 cm, 300 m b 10 cm, 50 000 cm, 500 m c 7 cm, 35 000 cm, 350 m
 d 8 cm, 40 000 cm, 400 m e 8 cm, 40 000 cm, 400 m f 7 cm, 35 000 cm, 350 m
 g 4 cm, 20 000 cm, 200 m

3 a 7 cm, 35 000 cm, 350 m   **b** 7 cm, 35 000 cm, 350 m   **c** 5 cm, 25 000 cm, 250 m
   d 4 cm, 20 000 cm, 200 m   **e** 10 cm, 50 000 cm, 500 m   **f** 5 cm, 25 000 cm, 250 m
   g 3 cm, 15 000 cm, 150 m

Exercise 13J
1 0.25 m   **2** 0.4 m   **3** 0.24 m, 0.2 m   **4** 20 cm, 45 cm, 25 cm

Exercise 13K
1 1500 cm (or 15 m)   **2** 90 m   **3** 3 m, 1 m   **4** 27 m, 18 m
5 160 cm, 144 cm, 112 cm

Exercise 13L
1 1:3   **2** 1:4   **3** 1:20   **4** 1:400   **5** 1:5000

Exercise 14A
1 40 °C, 30 °C, 10 °C, –10 °C, –20 °C, –50 °C   **2** 50 °C, 40 °C, 30 °C, –10 °C, –20 °C, –50 °C
3 50 °C, 30 °C, 10 °C, –20 °C, –30 °C, –40 °C   **4** 50 °C, 20 °C, 10 °C, –10 °C, –30 °C, –40 °C
5 –40 °C, –30 °C, –20 °C, 10 °C, 20 °C, 50 °C   **6** –40 °C, –30 °C, –20 °C, 10 °C, 40 °C, 50 °C
7 –40 °C, –20 °C, –10 °C, 10 °C, 30 °C, 50 °C   **8** –40 °C, –20 °C, –10 °C, 30 °C, 40 °C, 50 °C

Exercise 14B
1 10 °C, 11 °C, 5 °C, 3 °C, 4 °C   **2** –2 °C, –3 °C, –2 °C, –4 °C, –3 °C
3 2 °C, 1 °C, 2 °C, 2 °C, 1 °C   **4** –3 °C, 5 °C, –7 °C, –6 °C, –7 °C

Exercise 14C
1 8 °C, 10 °C, 9 °C, 11 °C, 10 °C   **2** 4 °C, 5 °C, 3 °C, 2 °C, 4 °C

Exercise 14D
1 Monday: 12 °C, 10 °C, 2 °C; Tuesday: 13 °C, 11 °C, 2 °C; Wednesday: 11 °C, 9 °C, 2 °C; Thursday: 10 °C, 6 °C, 4 °C;
Friday: 12 °C, 6 °C, 6 °C

Exercise 14E
1 131 °F   **2** 167 °F   **3** 95 °F   **4** 203 °F   **5** 41 °F   **6** 54.5 °F
7 65.3 °F   **8** 72.5 °F   **9** 23 °F   **10** 5 °F   **11** 27.5 °F   **12** 13.1 °F

Exercise 14F
1 15 °C   **2** 65 °C   **3** 85 °C   **4** 45 °C   **5** 105 °C   **6** 10.5 °C
7 16.5 °C   **8** 13.5 °C   **9** –10 °C   **10** –24.7 °C   **11** –21.9 °C   **12** –20.3 °C

Exercise 14G
1 20 °C   **2** 70 °C   **3** 60 °C   **4** 90 °C   **5** 86 °F   **6** 122 °F   **7** 176 °F   **8** 14 °F

Exercise 15A
1 £300 (c), £250 (c), £200, £100, £50 (o), –£150, –£200, £250 (o)
2 £300 (c), £200, £150 (c), £100, –£100, £150 (o), –£200, £250 (o)
3 £300, £250, £150 (c), £50 (c), £50 (o), £150 (o), –£200, –£250
4 £300, £250 (c), £150, £100 (c), –£50, £200 (o), £250 (o), –£300
5 £300, £250 (c), £200 (c), £50, £50 (o), £100 (o), –£150, –£200
6 £250, £150, £100 (c), £50 (c), –£100, £150 (o), £200 (o), –£300

Exercise 15B
1 £10 (c)   **2** £45 (c)   **3** £20 (c)   **4** £20 (o)   **5** £20 (o)   **6** £40 (o)
7 £25 (c)   **8** £50 (c)   **9** £5 (c)   **10** £30 (o)   **11** £20 (o)   **12** £10 (o)

Exercise 15C
1 £175   **2** £125   **3** £200   **4** £250   **5** £150   **6** £75   **7** £25   **8** £100   **9** £75   **10** £100
11 £50, £60, £110   **12** £35, £75, £110   **13** £50, £40, £90   **14** £15, £55, £70   **15** £65, £50, £115

Exercise 15D
1 a 3   **b** 6   **c** −7   **d** −6   **2 a** −7   **b** −12   **c** −10   **d** −9
3 a 10   **b** 9   **c** 14   **d** 14   **4 a** 3   **b** 3   **c** −4   **d** −5
5 a £35 (c)   **b** £25 (c)   **c** £45 (c)   **6 a** £25 (o)   **b** £45 (o)   **c** £15 (o)

Exercise 15E
1 7   **2** 5   **3** 9   **4** 2   **5** 10   **6** 20
7 30   **8** 50   **9** 70   **10** 80   **11** 100   **12** 300

Exercise 15F
1 13   **2** 15   **3** 14   **4** 25   **5** 42   **6** 44
7 2.6   **8** 2.7   **9** 3.6   **10** 3.9   **11** 0.9   **12** 0.2

Exercise 15G
1 a 24   **b** 21   **c** 24; b   **2 a** 54   **b** 54   **c** 56; c
3 a 15   **b** 18   **c** 18; a   **4** 9, 5, 6   **5** 12, 14, 6, 8
6 12 years, 4.5 years, 13.5 years,   **7** 20, 30, 40, 35   **8** 120, 90, 150, 105, 135

Exercise 15H
1 230   **2** 280   **3** 177   **4** £145   **5** £189   **6** £168   **7** 129 m
8 a £63   **b** £81   **c** £795   **d** £7540   **9 a** £141   **b** £517   **c** £329   **d** £846
10 162, 168

Exercise 15J
1 a 70%   **b** 75%   **c** 75%; a   **2 a** 35%   **b** 35%   **c** 36%; c
3 a 17.5%   **b** 22.5%   **c** 22.5%; a   **4 a** 7.5%   **b** 7.5%   **c** 4.5%; c
5 45%, 30%, 25%   **6** 56%, 24%, 20%   **7** 36%, 52%, 12%

Exercise 15K
1 137   **2** 300   **3** 168   **4** £240   **5 a** 500p   **b** £5.00
6 600 kg   **7** 90   **8** 250   **9 a** 600p   **b** £6.00   **10** 840
11 21   **12** 84   **13** 240   **14** 40 kg   **15** 30 g

Exercise 15L
1 £55.40   **2** £85.80   **3** £50   **4** £65

Exercise 15M
1 a £420   **b** £33.60   **c** £386.40   **2 a** £32.80   **b** £1.64   **c** £31.16
3 a £1100   **b** £132   **c** £968   **4 a** £22.75   **b** £1.82   **c** £20.93
5 a £49.25   **b** £1.97   **c** £47.28

Exercise 16A
1 12 cm^2 **2** 10 cm^2 **3** 16 cm^2 **4** 7 cm^2 **5** 14 cm^2 **6** 11 cm^2 **7** 9 cm^2 **8** 10 cm^2

Exercise 16B
1 18 cm^2 **2** 9 cm^2 **3** 14 cm^2 **4** 8 cm^2 **5** 16 cm^2 **6** 32 cm^2

Exercise 16C
1 15 m^2 **2** 25 m^2 **3** 24 m^2 **4** 80 mm^2 **5** 300 mm^2

Exercise 16D
1 6 sq ft   **2** 28 sq ft   **3** 48 sq in   **4** 60 sq in   **5** 160 sq in   **6** 30 sq yd

Exercise 16E
1 80 000 m^2 = 8 hectares   **2** 200 000 m^2 = 20 ha   **3** 120 000 m^2 = 12 ha   **4** 7260 sq yd = 1.5 acres
5 9680 sq yd = 2 acres

Exercise 16F
1 a 216 cm^2 b 216 cm^2 c 224 cm^2; c   2 a 315 cm^2 b 325 cm^2 c 315 cm^2; b
3 a 15.2 m^2 b 14.4 m^2 c 14.4 m^2; a
4 9000 cm^2 5 16 200 cm^2 6 360 m^2 7 0.7 m^2 8 560 mm^2

Exercise 16G
1 180 cm^2 2 350 cm^2 3 210 cm^2 4 2940 mm^2 5 880 mm^2
6 1200 mm^2 7 63 m^2 8 240 cm^2 9 56 cm^2 10 9.375 m^2, 10.935 m^2

Exercise 16H
1 12.56 cm^2 2 200.96 cm^2 3 706.50 cm^2 4 19.625 m^2 5 63.585 m^2
6 153.86 mm^2 7 50.24 mm^2 8 452.16 cm^2 9 615.44 cm^2 10 3.461 85 m^2
11 50.24 cm^2 12 254.34 cm^2 13 1962.5 m^2 14 38.465 m^2 15 176.625 mm^2

Exercise 16J
1 1050 cm^2 2 12 m^2 3 664 m^2 4 24 m^2 5 240 m^2
6 85 m^2 7 30 000 cm^2 (or 3 m^2)   8 15 000 cm^2 9 2228 cm^2 10 2.3925 cm^2

Exercise 16K

	Area (m^2)	Area (cm^2)	Area (mm^2)
1	5	50 000	5 000 000
2	1.5	15 000	1 500 000
3	13.5	135 000	13 500 000
4	0.98	9800	980 000
5	9.5	95 000	9 500 000
6	0.128	1280	128 000

Exercise 16L

	Area (yd^2)	Area (ft^2)	Area (in^2)
1	5	45	6480
2	10.5	94.5	13 608
3	3	27	3888
4	6.5	58.5	8424
5	2.5	22.5	3240
6	13.5	121.5	17 496

Exercise 16M
1 a 25.8 cm^2 b 116.1 cm^2 c 15.48 cm^2 2 a 6.2 in^2 b 8.37 in^2 c 5.642 in^2
3 a 4650 cm^2 b 3255 cm^2 c 558 cm^2 4 a 7.04 ft^2 b 10.12 ft^2 c 24.75 ft^2
5 a 12.615 m^2 b 6.728 m^2 c 1.1774 m^2 6 a 8.33 yd^2 b 3.57 yd^2 c 9.044 yd^2
7 a 3.663 ha   b 5.698 ha   c 3.9072 ha   d 2.6455 ha
8 a 36.9 acres   b 86.1 acres   c 30.75 acres   d 11.07 acres

Exercise 17A
1 24 cm^3 2 12 cm^3 3 32 cm^3 4 30 cm^3 5 10 cm^3
6 14 cm^3 7 16 cm^3 8 14 cm^3 9 12 cm^3 10 7 cm^3

Exercise 17B
1 8 m^3 2 6 m^3 3 9 m^3 4 14 mm^3 5 8 mm^3 6 20 mm^3

Exercise 17C
1 9 in^3 2 9 in^3 3 12 in^3 4 16 in^3 5 8 ft^3 6 9 yd^3

Exercise 17D

1	4 l	2	4 l	3	9 l	4	8 l	5	20 l	6	16 l

Exercise 17E

1 45 ml   2 10 ml   3 16 ml

Exercise 17F

1 12 cm^3 2 40 cm^3 3 210 cm^3 4 190 mm^3 5 13 000 mm^3 6 30 m^3

Exercise 17G

1 512 cm^3 2 343 cm^3 3 1728 cm^3 4 1331 cm^3 5 64 000 mm^3 6 125 000 mm^3
7 15 625 mm^3 8 3375 m^3

Exercise 17H

1 **a** 286 cm^3 **b** 288 cm^3 **c** 288 cm^3; a   2 **a** 432 cm^3 **b** 420 cm^3 **c** 432 cm^3; b
3 **a** 840 mm^3 **b** 840 mm^3 **c** 810 mm^3; c   4 **a** 2.4 m^3 **b** 2.8 m^3 **c** 2.4 m^3; b
5 **a** 3.5 m^3 **b** 3.6 m^3 **c** 3.6 m^3; a   6 **a** 1020.6 m   **b** 1021.02 m   **c** 1020.6 m; b
7 18 000 mm^3 8 2625 cm^3 9 14 400 cm^3

Exercise 17J

1 135 cm^3 2 425 cm^3 3 1080 cm^3 4 2560 cm^3

Exercise 17K

1 942 cm^3 2 141.3 cm^3 3 847.8 cm^3 4 12 717 mm^3 5 58 875 mm^3
6 43 960 mm^3 7 628 cm^3 8 19 625 cm^3 9 9420 m^3 10 16 956 m^3

Exercise 17L

1 5 000 000 cm^3, 5 000 000 000 mm^3 2 12 000 000 cm^3, 12 000 000 000 mm^3 3 1 500 000 cm^3, 1 500 000 000 mm^3
4 7 500 000 cm^3, 7 500 000 000 mm^3 5 4 m^3, 4 000 000 000 mm^3 6 7 m^3, 7 000 000 000 mm^3
7 2.5 m^3, 2 500 000 000 mm^3 8 6 m^3, 6 000 000 cm^3 9 13 m^3, 13 000 000 cm^3 10 4.5 m^3, 4 500 000 cm^3

Exercise 17M

1 1620 ft^3, 2 799 360 in^3 2 405 ft^3, 699 840 in^3 3 216 ft^3, 373 248 in^3 4 30 yd^3, 1 399 680 in^3
5 75 yd^3, 3 499 200 in^3 6 4 yd^3, 186 624 in^3 7 3 yd^3, 139 968 in^3 8 25 yd^3, 675 ft^3
9 16 yd^3, 432 ft^3 10 13 yd^3, 351 ft^3

Exercise 17N

1 9000 ml   2 5000 ml   3 1600 ml   4 2100 ml   5 3600 ml
6 7 l   7 4 l   8 1.8 l   9 2.4 l   10 3.2 l

Exercise 17P

1 20 quarts, 40 pints   2 32 quarts, 64 pints   3 60 quarts, 120 pints   4 10 quarts, 20 pints
5 4 gallons, 16 quarts   6 16.5 gallons, 66 quarts   7 10.5 gallons, 42 quarts   8 6 gallons, 48 pints
9 4 gallons, 32 pints   10 8.5 gallons, 68 pints

Exercise 17Q

1 0.48 l, 0.9 l, 1.5 l, 2.4 l   2 0.24 l, 0.36 l, 0.84 l, 1.44 l   3 0.54 l, 0.96 l, 1.56 l, 1.92 l
4 1.4 pt, 2.1 pt, 3.5 pt, 4.9 pt   5 0.7 pt, 1.05 pt, 2.45 pt, 3.15 pt   6 0.35 pt, 0.875 pt, 2.625 pt, 4.375 pt

Exercise 17R

1 18 l, 45 l, 27 l, 36 l, 54 l, 9 l   2 3.3 gallons, 4.4 gallons, 7.7 gallons, 11 gallons, 13.2 gallons, 9.9 gallons

Exercise 17S

1 **a** 9.1 yd^3 **b** 245.7 ft^3 2 **a** 39 yd^3 **b** 1053 ft^3
3 **a** 52 000 yd^3 **b** 1 404 000 ft^3 4 **a** 936 yd^3 **b** 25 272 ft^3 **c** 157 950 gallons
5 **i** **a** 260 yd^3 **b** 7020 ft^3 **c** 43 875 gallons   **ii** **a** 83.2 yd^3 **b** 2246.4 ft^3 **c** 14 040 gallons
6 **a** 310 yd^3 **b** 238.7 m^3 7 **a** 2050 yd^3 **b** 1578.5 m^3

8 a 0.25 yd^3 **b** 0.1925 m^3
9 a 2700 ft^3 **b** 100 yd^3 **c** 77 m^3 **d** 77 000 l
10 i a 129.6 ft^3 **b** 4.8 yd^3 **c** 3.696 m^3 **d** 3696 l
ii a 6.48 ft^3 **b** 0.24 yd^3 **c** 0.1848 m^3 **d** 184.8 l

Exercise 18A
1 78.2 kg **2** 42.8 kg **3** 15.4 kg **4** 54 kg **5** 82 kg
6 a 320 g **b** 540 g **c** 780 g

Exercise 18B
1 15 000 kg, 15 000 000 g **2** 2000 kg, 2 000 000 g **3** 9000 kg, 9 000 000 g **4** 20 000 kg, 20 000 000 g
5 14 tonnes, 14 000 000 g **6** 26 tonnes, 26 000 000 g (or 26 million g) **7** 6 tonnes, 6 000 000 g
8 16 tonnes, 16 000 kg **9** 25 tonnes, 25 000 kg **10** 7 tonnes, 7000 kg

Exercise 18C
1 8000 ml, 8 kg, 8000 g **2** 14 000 ml, 14 kg, 14 000 g **3** 4 l, 4 kg, 4000 g **4** 13 l, 13 kg, 13 000 g
5 23 l, 23 000 ml, 23 000 g **6** 30 l, 30 000 ml, 30 000 g **7** 19 l, 19 000 ml, 19 kg **8** 42 l, 42 000 ml, 42 kg

Exercise 18D
1 60 cwt, 480 stone, 6720 lb, 107 520 oz **2** 4 tons, 640 stone, 8960 lb, 143 360 oz
3 7 tons, 140 cwt, 15 680 lb, 250 880 oz **4** 2 tons, 40 cwt, 320 stone, 71 680 oz
5 0,5 tons, 10 cwt, 80 stone, 1120 lb

Exercise 18E
1 56 g **2** 280 g **3** 336 g **4** 504 g **5** 588 g **6** 840 g **7** 5 oz **8** 7 oz
9 11 oz **10** 9 oz **11** 14 oz **12** 20 oz

Exercise 18F
1 36 kg **2** 18 kg **3** 72 kg **4** 54 kg **5** 81 kg **6** 27 kg **7** 33 lb **8** 11 lb
9 165 lb **10** 77 lb **11** 154 lb **12** 198 lb

Exercise 19A
1 180° **2** 90° **3** 135° **4** 270° **5** 45° **6** 135° **7** 180° **8** 225°

Exercise 19B
1 90° **2** 30° **3** 120° **4** 60° **5** 60° **6** 180° **7** 150° **8** 150°

Exercise 19C
1 60°, acute angle **2** 30°, acute angle **3** 90°, right angle **4** 120°, obtuse angle **5** 180°, straight angle
6 90°, right angle **7** 120°, obtuse angle **8** 150°, obtuse angle **9** 180°, straight angle

Exercise 19D
1 80° **2** 60° **3** 55° **4** 78° **5** 54° **6** 18° **7** 24° **8** 62.5°
9 150° **10** 140° **11** 90° **12** 10° **13** 175° **14** 165° **15** 25° **16** 82.5°

Exercise 19E
1 YX̂Q **2** PQ̂R, QP̂R, PR̂S **3** XÊH, FX̂G, XĤE
4 LK̂M, KL̂M, KM̂N, KN̂M **5** SP̂X, PQ̂X, QR̂X, RX̂Q **6** TŜW, WT̂U, TŴU, WÛV
7 QL̂X, KÔP **8** reflex PĈQ, PR̂Q

Exercise 19F
1 a 20° **b** 30° **c** 120° **d** 15° **e** 105° **f** 115° **g** 60° **h** 150° **i** 160°
j 65° **k** 75° **l** 165°
2 a 31° **b** 69° **c** 74° **d** 109° **e** 135° **f** 163° **g** 45° **h** 71° **i** 106°
j 111° **k** 149°

Exercise 19G

1 25°	**2** 40°	**3** 80°	**4** 60°	**5** 105°
6 90°	**7** 120°	**8** 270°	**9** 225°	**10** 240°

Exercise 19J

1 80° **2** 30° **3** 60° **4** 100° **5** 30° **6** 50°

Exercise 20A

1 quadrilateral **2** triangle **3** pentagon **4** hexagon **5** quadrilateral
6 hexagon (none of these shapes are regular)

Exercise 20B

1 a 7 cm, 4 cm, 8 cm, 4 cm, 4 cm, 4 cm **b** 30°, 60°, 90°, 30°, 120°, 60°, 60°
   c right-angled scalene, obtuse-angled isosceles, equilateral
2 a 7 cm, 5 cm, 5 cm, 5.3 cm, 7 cm, 2 cm **b** right-angled isosceles, right-angled scalene, acute-angled isosceles

Exercise 20C

1 a square **b** rectangle **c** parallelogram **d** trapezium **e** isosceles trapezium
   f isosceles trapezium
2 a square **b** rectangle **c** rectangle **d** kite **e** arrowhead/kite
   f trapezium **g** trapezium

Exercise 20D

1 2 lines, order 2 **2** 2 lines, order 2 **3** 3 lines, order 3 **4** 4 lines, order 4 **5** 6 lines, order 6
6 5 lines, order 5

Exercise 20E

1 2 lines, order 2 **2** 2 lines, order 2 **3** 4 lines, order 4 **4** 1 line **5** 1 line
6 1 line **7** no lines, order 2

Exercise 20F

1 rhombus **2** square, parallelogram **3** rectangle, kite, 2 parallelograms
4 2 trapeziums, 2 irregular quadrilaterals **5** parallelogram **6** rectangle, parallelogram, square

Exercise 20H

1 acute-angled scalene **2** acute-angled isosceles **3** right-angled scalene **4** obtuse-angled isosceles

Exercise 20S

1 17 cm **2** 29 cm **3** 41 cm **4** 74 cm **5 a** 7.5 cm **b** 65 cm **6** 15 cm, 25.5 cm

Exercise 20T

1 12 cm **2** 30 cm **3** 45 cm **4** 10 m **5** 26 cm **6** 23 mm **7** 22 mm **8** 3.3 m **9** 12 cm **10** 1.5 m

Exercise 21A

1 Dark – 10, Blonde – 8, Ginger – 6; Football – 9, Rugby – 8, Cross-country – 7; Walks – 11, Cycles – 5, Bus – 6, Train – 2
2 Dark – 7, Blue – 8, Green – 5; Netball – 9, Hockey – 6, Lacrosse – 5; Walks – 8, Cycles – 5, Bus – 4, Train – 3
3 Cheese – 4, Ham – 3, Egg – 6, Tomato – 2; Plain – 5, Bovril – 2, Salt and vinegar – 1, Cheese and onion – 7; Tea – 1,
   Coffee – 6, Lemonade – 5, Orange squash – 3

Exercise 21B

1 a 1, 3, 6, 8, 9, 11, 11, 12, 13, 13, 14, 15, 16, 18, 19, 21, 23, 25
   b 0–4: 2, 5–9: 3, 10–14: 6, 15–19: 4, 20–24: 2, 25–29: 1
2 a 38, 39, 42, 44, 45, 47, 48, 52, 55, 56, 63, 65 **b** 30–39: 2, 40–49: 5, 50–59: 3, 60–69: 2
3 a 5, 8, 15, 18, 21, 24, 27, 28, 32, 35, 36, 42 **b** 0–9: 2, 10–19: 2, 20–29: 4, 30–39: 3, 40–49: 1
   c 6, 12, 15, 16, 20, 20, 22, 25, 26, 27, 35, 41 **d** 0–9: 1, 10–19: 3, 20–29: 6, 30–39: 1, 40–49: 1

Exercise 21C

1   Beef – 2, Cheese – 4, Egg – 3, Ham – 3, Tomato – 3
2   Dance – 4, Drama – 2, Electronics – 3, Metalwork – 5, Needlework – 5, Woodwork – 6
3   Brighton – 5, London – 2, North Downs – 3, Portsmouth – 4, Thorpe Park – 6

Exercise 21D

1   **a** Cashier – 2, Cleaner – 3, Cook – 3, Dish washer – 3, Waitress – 4
   b Monday – 4, Tuesday – 4, Wednesday – 2, Thursday – 2, Friday – 1, Saturday – 1, Sunday – 1
2   **a** Bournemouth – 4, Brighton – 5, Hastings – 3, Southend – 4   **b** 45: 3, 50: 6, 55: 4, 60: 3

Exercise 21E

1   20–29: 2, 30–39: 6, 40–49: 8, 50–59: 8, 60–69: 1
2   10–19: 1, 20–29: 2, 30–39: 3, 40–49: 4, 50–59: 6, 60–69: 5, 70–79: 3, 80–89: 1

Exercise 22A

1 **a** 30, 50, 40, 10, 20	**b** 150	**c** £90		
2 **a** 25, 10, 15, 20, 5	**b** 75	**c** £30		
3 **a** 250, 400, 350, 500, 300	**b** 1800	**c** £1350	**d** 4	
4 **a** 100, 150, 250, 200, 125, 75	**b** 900	**c** £180		
5 **a** 15, 25, 20, 30, 35, 10	**b** 135	**c** 540 minutes	**d** 9 hours	
6 **a** 100, 120, 140, 80, 100	**b** 540	**c** £4050	**d** 9	

Exercise 22B

1   **a** Rover, 4   **b** Volvo, 1   2 **a** 140–149 cm, 5   **b** 130–139 cm, 1
3   **a** Canal Bridge, 7   **b** Railway Station, 3   **c** Paid for a ticket, 8
   d Used an OAP pass, 2   **e** Fairmile Estate   **f** 20
4   **a** 20–29, 5   **b** 0–9, 1   **c** 300–399, 6   **d** 400–499, 1
   e 16   **f** Yes, there are far more than 5 second-class passengers for each first-class passenger.

Exercise 22C

1   **b** 12 noon–1 p.m. and 6 p.m.–7 p.m.   **c** By then the film was over half way through.
   d 1100   **e** $700 \times £2.50 + 400 \times £3.00 = £2950$
2   **b** 1 p.m.–2 p.m.
   c **i** leaving London   **ii** arriving in Glasgow   **iii** stopped for lunch   **iv** stopped for tea or people going home
      v school traffic
   d 660 km   **e** 60 kilometres per hour

Exercise 22D

1   **a** 0–1: 2, 1–2: 4, 2–3: 5, 3–4: 7, 4–5: 6, 5–6: 3, 6–7: 2, 7–8: 1   **b** 30   **c** June
2   **a** 10–15 min: 6, 15–20: 7, 20–25: 4, 25–30: 3   **b** 20
   c April, June, September and November each have 30 days.
3   **a** 40–45: 2, 45–50: 5, 50–55: 6, 55–60: 5, 60–65: 2   **b** 20   **c** 52.5 kg

Exercise 22E

1 **a** **i**

Class interval (kg)	29.5–39.5	39.5–49.5	49.5–59.5	59.5–69.5
Frequency	3	10	9	3

     ii

Class interval (kg)	29.5–34.5	34.5–39.5	39.5–44.5	44.5–49.5
Frequency	1	2	4	6

Class interval (kg)	49.5–54.5	54.5–59.5	59.5–64.5	64.5–69.5
Frequency	6	3	2	1

2 **a** **i**

Class interval (°C)	0–9	10–19	20–29
Frequency	11	15	4

ii

Class interval (°C)	0–4	5–9	10–14	15–19	20–24	25–29
Frequency	5	6	8	7	3	1

c March or October, due to mix of low and high temperatures

3 a i

Class interval (km)	89.5–99.5	99.5–109.5	109.5–119.5	119.5–129.5
Frequency	3	9	9	3

ii

Class interval (km)	89.5–94.5	94.5–99.5	99.5–104.5	104.5–109.5
Frequency	1	2	4	5

Class interval (km)	109.5–114.5	114.5–119.5	119.5–124.5	124.5–129.5
Frequency	5	4	2	1

c The diagrams are symmetrical about a central vertical line.

Exercise 22F

1 c i 10 kg ii 25 kg iii 35 kg iv 45 kg

2 a

Time	8 a.m.	9 a.m.	10 a.m.	11 a.m.	12 noon	1 p.m.	2 p.m.	3 p.m.	4 p.m.	5 p.m.
Temperature (°C)	10	30	40	50	45	50	45	50	30	20

c i 20 °C ii 35 °C iii 45 °C iv 40 °C v 25 °C

d Having reached the required temperature the thermostat switches the heater off, and so the water cools down. The heater is then switched back on again.

3 b i 20 cm ii 140 cm iii 120 cm iv 40 cm c i 45 m ii 130 m

Exercise 22G

1 (1,2), (1,3), (1,4), (1,8), (2,1), (2,3), (2,4), (2,5), (2,8), (3,1), (3,2), (3,3), (3,6), (3,7), (4,1), (4,3), (4,4), (4,5), (4,8), (6,5), (4,0), (5,1), (5,2), (5,7), (5,8), (5,0)

2 a (1,2), (1,10), (9,10), (9,2) b (1,12), (1,18), (7,18), (7,12) c (12,2), (12,12), (18,12), (18,2)
d (9,14), (9,18), (18,18), (18,14)

3 a (5,1), (2,5), (6,8), (9,4) b (6,10), (2,13), (5,17), (9,14) c (14,10), (11,14), (15,17), (18,13)
d (15,1), (11,4), (14,8), (18,5)

4 (2,9), (6,12), (9,16), (12,12), (16,9), (12,6), (9,2), (6,6)

Exercise 22H

2 a square b square c rectangle d rectangle
3 hexagon (6 sides) 4 octagon (8 sides) 5 octagon (8 sides)

Exercise 22J

2 b i 10p ii 14p iii 18p 3 b i £6 ii £8 iii £12 iv £16
4 b i 6 cm ii 7 cm iii 9 cm 5 b i 8 kg ii 10 kg iii 12 kg

Exercise 22L

1 $0 \to 3, 1 \to 4, 2 \to 5, 3 \to 6, 4 \to 7, 5 \to 8$
2 $0 \to 5, 1 \to 6, 2 \to 7, 3 \to 8, 4 \to 9, 5 \to 10$
3 $0 \to 2, 1 \to 3, 2 \to 4, 3 \to 5, 4 \to 6, 5 \to 7$
4 $0 \to 4, 1 \to 5, 2 \to 6, 3 \to 7, 4 \to 8, 5 \to 9$
5 $5 \to -1, 1 \to 0, 2 \to 1, 3 \to 2, 4 \to 3, 5 \to 4$
6 $0 \to -2, 1 \to -1, 2 \to 0, 3 \to 1, 4 \to 2, 5 \to 3$
7 $0 \to -4, 1 \to -3, 2 \to -2, 3 \to -1, 4 \to 0, 5 \to 1$
8 $0 \to -3, 1 \to -2, 2 \to -1, 3 \to 0, 4 \to 1, 5 \to 2$

Exercise 22P

1 Football – 72, Rugby – 40, Hockey – 30, Cross-country – 20, Squash – 18
2 Netball – 90, Hockey – 60, Lacrosse – 40, Squash – 30, Ice-skating – 20
3 Plain – 60, Cheese and onion – 45, Salt and vinegar – 30, Smokey bacon – 15
4 Coffee – 90, Tea – 60, Cocoa – 30, Bovril – 20
5 Thursday – 36, Friday – 16, Monday – 12, Tuesday – 8, Wednesday – 8

Exercise 22Q
1 North – 144°, South – 90°, East – 72°, West – 54°   2   Train – 126°, Car – 90°, Coach – 108°, Aeroplane – 36°
3 Chunnel – 144°, Air – 54°, Boat – 126°, Hovercraft – 36°
4 Long distance – 108°, Short distance – 90°, Freight – 72°, Mail – 54°, Car – 36°
5 Black – 144°, Green – 36°, White – 90°, Blue – 36°, Red – 54°

Exercise 22R
1 Tennis – 120°, Swimming – 90°, Rounders – 90°, Athletics – 60°
2 Cricket – 120°, Tennis – 60°, Athletics – 90°, Golf – 30°, Swimming – 60°
3 Manchester – 60°, Leeds – 40°, Liverpool – 60°, Newcastle – 40°, Birmingham – 40°, London – 120°
4 Services – 72°, Transport – 45°, Education – 72°, Landscape – 36°, Police – 60°, Investments – 30°, Roads – 45°
5 Bristol – 126°, Cardiff – 72°, Swansea – 54°, Newport – 45°, Plymouth – 45°, Exeter – 18°

Exercise 23A
1   8 cm   2   11   3   8p   4   5   5   46 kg   6   0.8 sec   7   £650   8   4 min, 8 min

Exercise 23B
1 a 1   b 2   c 4   2 a 1   b 3   c 5   3 a 0   b 2   c 9
4 a 6   b 6.5   c 6.7   5 a 0   b 10   c 22   6 a 5   b 8   c 11
7 a 5   b 3   c 2.5   8 a £68 000   b £125 000   c £137 463

Exercise 23C
1   18   2   33 min   3   5   4   1 min   5   4   6   18 kg   7   poplar   8   cheese

Exercise 23D
1   24   2   19   3   48 kg   4   136 cm   5   3   6   700 m   7   £1.75   8   26.7 sec
9   11 °C 10 7   11 117 cm   12 35.5 kg

Exercise 23E
1   17 min   2   326 g   3   20 940   4   51.4 g   5   9 hours   6   38 °C   7   60 sec
8   9.9 metres per second squared
9   4 °C, 7 °C, 4 °C, 10 °C; 4 °C, 9 °C; 4 °C, 2 °C. The mean temperature is the same for each week but there was a much greater variation in temperature during the first three weeks.
10 11, 5; 11, 14; 11, 11. The mean number of wet days in each month was the same for each year but the variation in the number of wet days in each month was far greater in 1994 and 1995 than in 1993.

Exercise 23F
1   8, 7, 7   2   3 °C, 4 °C, 4 °C   3   3, 2.5, 3   4   2, 1.5, 1.4375

Exercise 23G
1   between 6 m and 7 m   2   between 40 000 and 60 000   3   between 30 m and 35 m
4   between 6 °C and 3 °C

Exercise 24A
1 a 395 mph   b 285 mph   c 430 mph   d 430 mph   e 385 mph
2 a 90 mph   b 50 mph   c 64 mph   d 72 mph   e 68 mph
3 a 36 mph   b 35 mph   c 33 mph   d 39 mph   e 40 mph
4 a 40 mph   b 50 mph   c 44 mph   5 a 90 kph   b 63 kph   c 81 kph

Exercise 24B
1 a 240 miles   b 315 miles   c 170 miles   d 200 miles   e 56 miles   f 44 miles   g 162 miles   h 80 miles
2 192 km   3 231 km   4 80 km   5 36 km
6 a 4 hr   b 8 hr   c 7 hr   d 1.5 hr   e 1.25 hr or 1 hr 15 min   f 1.75 hr or 1 hr 45 min
7 4.5 hr   8 2.5 hr   9 1.75 hr   10 1.75 hr

Exercise 24C

1 **a** 5 mps, 18 kph **b i** 20 m **ii** 50 m **iii** 70 m **iv** 90 m **c i** 8 s **ii** 12 s **iii** 22 s
2 **a** 5 mps, 18 kph **b i** 200 m **ii** 500 m **iii** 350 m **iv** 750 m **c i** 60 s **ii** 130 s **iii** 10 s
3 0.8 hr, 1.6 hr; 100 kph   4 0 hr, 0.5 hr, 1.5 hr, 3.5 hr, 4.5 hr; 600 kph

Exercise 24D

1 40 mph, 20 mph, 25 mph   2 40 mph, 60 mph, 45 mph   3 20 mph, 28 mph, 25 mph
4 **i** 0.8 mph **ii** 2 mph **iii** 1.25 mph

Exercise 24E

1 **a** 45 mpg, 10 mpl   **b** 36 mpg, 8 mpl   **c** 22.5 mpg, 5 mpl
2 **a** 0.4 kpl, 0.25 mpl   **b** 9.2 kpl, 5.75 mpl   **c** 7.2 kpl, 4.5 mpl

Exercise 24F

1 **a** 144 miles **b** 324 miles **c** 54 miles **2 a** 100 miles **b** 160 miles **c** 50 miles
3 **a** 96 km **b** 150 km **c** 54 km **4 a** 36 km **b** 90 km **c** 162 km
5 **a** 5 gallons **b** 7 gallons **c** 4.5 gallons **6 a** 6 gallons **b** 3.5 gallons **c** 12.5 gallons
7 **a** 7 l **b** 3 l **c** 2.5 l **8 a** 1500 l **b** 1125 l **c** 375 l

Exercise 25A

1 £7.60, £12.40   2 £12.50, £7.50   3 £10.00, £40.00   4 £14.50, £35.50
5 £9.25, £40.75   6 £8.50, £41.50

Exercise 25B

1 £0.45, £0.48, £0.47; 3 lb is the best buy   2 £0.42, £0.45, £0.41; 5 lb is the best buy
3 £0.63, £0.64, £0.62; 6 lb is the best buy   4 £0.37, £0.38, £0.36; 1.5 lb is the best buy
5 £1.40, £1.44, £1.42; 2.5 lb is the best buy 6 the 680 g packet 7 the 120 g jar 8 the 405 g bag
9 the 1650 ml bottle 10 100 bags

Exercise 25C

1 £6.91   2 £9.63   3 £6.43   4 £64.69   5 £44.99

Exercise 25D

1 £38.14   2 £40.84   3 £79.00   4 £73.32

Exercise 25E

1 **a** £6.11 **b** £3.18 **2 a** £6.67 **b** £2.91

Exercise 25F

1 **a** £20.05 **b** £8.55 **c** £13.60 **2 a** £13.75 **b** £7.30 **c** £11.00
3 £4.90 + £1.90 = £6.80; £3.35 × 2 = £6.70; separately, 10p
4 £7.30 + £3.15 = £10.45; £4.90 + £5.50 = £10.40; separately, 5p
5 £225.10

Exercise 25G

1 £60.90, £408.90 2 £31.50, £211.50 3 £42.70, £286.70 4 £4.48, £30.08 5 £11.06, £74.26
6 £21.91, £147.11 7 £28.49, £191.29 8 £61.60, £413.60 9 £13.60, £183.60 10 £12.62, £170.37

Exercise 25H

1 £145.23 2 £14.10 3 £216.20 4 £253.80 5 £49.82
6 £89.30 7 £274.95 8 £131.60 9 £119.85 10 £324.30

Exercise 26A

1 $9 \times £42 + 1 \times £48$ 2 $9 \times £56 + 1 \times £64$ 3 $9 \times £78 + 1 \times £79$
4 $9 \times £92 + 1 \times £95$ 5 $9 \times £106 + 1 \times £111$ 6 £213
7 £284   8 £355   9 £355

Exercise 26B

1 £319.50   2 £372.75   3 £479.25   4 £284   5 £390.50   6 £461.50

Exercise 26C

1 390, £58.50, £67.50, £72.90   2 420, £63.00, £72.00, £77.76   3 450, £67.50, £76.50, £82.62
4 610, £91.50, £100.50, £108.54   5 580, £87.00, £96.00, £103.68   6 550, £82.50, £91.50, £98.82
7 730, £109.50, £118.50, £127.98   8 810, £121.50, £130.50, £140.94

Exercise 26D

1 a £11.50, £12.42   b £16.00, £17.28   c £8.00, £8.64   d £12.50, £13.50   e £9.00, £9.72
2 250, 50, £26.00, £28.08   3 950, 125, £94.25, £101.79   4 525, 250, £64.75, £69.93
5 675, 75, £66.00, £71.28   6 450, 325, £63.25, £68.31   7 725, 175, £77.50, £83.70
8 375, 150, £44.25, £47.79

Exercise 26E

1 £16.57   2 £13.28   3 £17.04   4 £11.87   5 £21.27   6 £22.21   7 £19.86   8 £7.17
9 £13.75   10 £9.99

Exercise 26F

1 a 28p   b 35p   c 24.5p   d 5p   e 5p   f 5p   g 5p
2 a 15p   b 20p   c 37.5p   d 22.5p   e 6p   f 6p   g 6p
3 a 32p   b 48p   c 60p   d 10p   e 10p   f 10p   g 10p
4 a 8p   b 16p   c 26p   d 32p
5 £11.40   6 £12.40

Exercise 26G

1 a £402.42   b $2 \times £211.80$ c $7 \times £52 + 1 \times £59.60$
2 a £376.58   b $2 \times £198.20$ c $7 \times £49 + 1 \times £53.40$
3 a £430.16   b $2 \times £226.40$ c $7 \times £56 + 1 \times £60.80$
4 a £519.46   b $2 \times £273.40$ c $7 \times £68 + 1 \times £70.80$
5 a £482.22   b $2 \times £253.80$ c $7 \times £63 + 1 \times £66.60$
6 a £477.67   b $4 \times £129.10$ c $9 \times £51 + 1 \times £57.40$
7 a £400.34   b $4 \times £108.20$ c $9 \times £43 + 1 \times £45.80$
8 a £498.76   b $4 \times £134.80$ c $9 \times £53 + 1 \times £62.20$
9 a £456.58   b $4 \times £123.40$ c $9 \times £49 + 1 \times £52.60$
10 a £538.72   b $4 \times £145.60$ c $9 \times £58 + 1 \times £60.40$

Exercise 26H

1 £59.20, 76 m^3, £60.80, £152.00   2 £48.10, 61.75 m^3, £49.40, £129.50
3 £70.30, 90.25 m^3, £72.20, £174.50   4 £51.80, 66.50 m^3, £53.20, £137.00
5 £61.20, 85.50 m^3, £59.85, £157.05   6 £40.80, 57 m^3, £39.90, £116.70
7 £54.40, 76 m^3, £53.20, £143.60   8 £60.00, 95 m^3, £71.25, £166.25
9 £72.00, 114 m^3, £85.50, £192.50   10 £48.00, 76 m^3, £57.00, £140.00

Exercise 27A

1 a £32.50   b £17.50   2 a £16.40   b £3.60   3 a £18.80   b £1.20
4 a £25.40   b £24.60   5 a £22.50   b £27.50   6 a £39.40   b £10.60

Exercise 27B

1 £10.34   2 £15.51   3 £25.85   4 £20.68   5 £21.62   6 £32.43   7 £29.61   8 £19.74

Exercise 27C

1 a i Newquay, 0.06″   ii Torquay, 0.01″   b i Penzance, 12 °C   ii Minehead, 9 °C
   c i Exmouth and Newquay, 3.6 hours   ii Penzance and Minehead, 3 °C; 51.2 °F, 10.6 °C
2 a i Scarborough, 0.08″   ii Seaburn, 0.01″   b i Bamburgh, 9 °C   ii Redcar, 6 °C
   c i Scarborough and Whitley Bay, 2.4 hours   ii Bamburgh and Redcar, 3 °C; 2.88 hours, 2 hours 53 minutes

Exercise 27D

1 July   2 February   3 May   4 October   5 26.5 °C   6 13.2 °C   7 2.2″   8 1.6″

Exercise 27E

1 a i £280   ii £400   iii £380   b i £380   ii £420   iii £400
   c i £200   ii £190   iii £210
   d £15 per day each   e 17.6 and 30.6, £220   f 17.7 and 31.7, £155
2 a £1061.50   b £1336.50   c £649   d £924

Exercise 27F

1 Shani: FF2430, FF3280; FF5710   2 Shani a FF114.20   b FF5595.80
   Zoey: DM805, DM480; DM1285   Zoey a DM25.70   b DM1259.30
   Janet: BF11 760, BF15 000; BF26 760   Janet a BF535.20   b BF26 224.80
   Afiya: G1300, G675; G1975   Afiya a G49.375   b G1925.625
   Rita: $525, $896; $1421   Rita a $35.525   b $1385.475

Exercise 28A

1 £8280   2 £690   3 £160

Exercise 28B

1 a April to November, £701; December to January, £670; February to March, £625
   b £149, £180, £225
2 a April to November, £751; December to January, £724; February to March, £681
   b £199, £226, £269

Exercise 28C

	a	b	c	d
1	£43.20	£129.60	£489.60	£13.60
2	£59.40	£178.20	£574.20	£15.95
3	£37.80	£75.60	£327.60	£13.65
4	£50.40	£100.80	£580.80	£24.20
5	£12	£24	£174 + £50	£7.25
6	£135	£405	£1755 + £150	£48.75
7	£240	£960	£3360 + £600	£70

Exercise 28D

1 a £3312   b £276   2 a £2684.40   b £223.70   3 a £1916.40   b £159.70
4 a £1294.80   b £107.90   5 a £1690.80   b £140.90   6 a £1404   b £27
7 a £1719.12   b £33.06   8 a £1519.44   b £29.22   9 a £2090.40   b £40.20
10 a £1840.80   b £35.40

Exercise 28E

1 a £75   b £25   c £20   2 a £90   b £20   c £16   3 a £72   b £15   c £12
4 a £67.50   b £30   c £24   5 a £84   b £22.50   c £18   6 a £80   b £30   c £30
7 a £110   b £20   c £20   8 a £100   b £40   c £40

Exercise 28F

1 a £259.20   b £22.68   2 a £216   b £18.90   3 a £194.40   b £17.01
4 a £158.40   b £13.86   5 a £180   b £15.75   6 a £144   b £12.60

Exercise 28G

1 £7200   2 £5280   3 £11 160   4 £15 240   5 £19 326.12
6 £11 556.25   7 3 years   8 2 years   9 2 years   10 4 years

Exercise 28H

1 A   2 B   3 B   4 A

Exercise 29A
1 a £96   b £81.60 c £21.60   2 a £180   b £153   c £3   3 a £360   b £288   c £33
4 a £250   b £200   c £50   5 a £31   b £29.45 c £4.45

Exercise 29B
1 a 30%, 35%, 15%, 10%, 5%, 5%   b 120, 140, 60, 40, 20, 20
   c $\frac{760}{400}$ = 1.9; yes, 1.9 hours, which is nearly 2 hours
2 a 45%, 20%, 15%, 10%, 5%, 5%   b 180, 80, 60, 40, 20, 20
   c $\frac{1400}{400}$ = 3.5; yes, 3.5 hours, which agrees with the survey result of 3.5 hours

Exercise 29C
1 a £6 off   b 5% of £130 = £6.50   c the tube fare £6.50
2 a £500 off b 6% of £8500 = £510   c free servicing worth £525

Exercise 29D
1 a £500   b £540   2 a £250   b £312.50   3 a £3250   b £3100
4 a £1050   b £1000

Exercise 29E
1 a 36%, 10%, 24%, 30%   b 72, 20, 48, 60
2 a 30%, 25%, 24%, 10%, 11%   b 60, 50, 48, 20, 22
3 a 30%, 25%, 10%, 15%, 20%   b 18 l, 15 l, 6 l, 9 l, 12 l

Exercise 29F
1 a Lab–7500, Con–4500, Lib–3000   b Lab–48%, Con–33%, Lib–19%
   c The opinion poll is accurate to within 3%.   d Con–450   e Lab–300, Lib–150

Exercise 30A
1 £2.07   2 £1.48   3 £1.52   4 £0.99, £1.73

Exercise 30B
1 a 15 kg   b 50   c 21p   d £19.50
2 a 6 l   b 24   c 27p   d £4.32

Exercise 30C
1 a 60 m²   b 30 l; £46, £45; three 10-litre tins
2 a 150 m²   b 75 l; £107.50, £110: the first as it is cheaper by £2.50

Exercise 30D
1 a 20 m   b 5   c 40   d 120 m   e 8   f £80
2 a 36 m   b 9   c 72   d 180 m   e 12   f £126
3 a 12 m   b 3   c 24   d 90 m   e 6   f £57
4 a 45 m   b 12   c 90   d 450 m   e 30   f £273

Exercise 30E
1 a 10   b 0   c 11   d £201
2 a 9   b 0   c 10   d £181.50
3 a 4   b 4   c 9   d £156
4 a 6   b 8   c 15   d £267
5 a 0   b 11   c 12   d £204
6 a 8   b 3   c 12   d £216
7 five 6 × 6 panels + six posts, £103.50; six 6 × 5 panels + seven posts, £114
8 seven 6 × 6 panels + two 6 × 5 panels + ten posts, £178.50; two 6 × 6 panels + eight 6 × 5 panels + eleven posts, £189

Exercise 30F
1 a £15   b £24   2 a £20   b £32   3 a £31   b £37

Exercise 30G

1 £550, £555, Store A by £5   **2** £645, £660, Store A by £15   **3** £580, £560, Store B by £20

Exercise 30H

1 a 1 × 1200 mm, 2 × 600 mm, 1 × 450 mm, 1 corner unit
  b £1050   **c** 3650 mm (3.65 m)   **d** £146   **e** £1315.60
2 a 1 × 1200 mm, 2 × 600 mm, 4 × 450 mm, 1 corner unit
  b £1500   **c** 5000 mm (5.0 m)   **d** £200   **e** £1870
3 £1102.50   **4** £1575

Index